SENSORY EXPERIENCE

R. J. CHRISTMAN

Utica College of Syracuse University

INTEXT EDUCATIONAL PUBLISHERS

College Division

Scranton   Toronto   London

The **Intext** Series in

PSYCHOLOGY

Consulting Editor

HAROLD J. VETTER

Florida State University

ISBN 0-7002-2379-7 (cloth)
ISBN 0-7002-2356-8 (paper)

Library of Congress Catalog Card Number: 70-143621

PREFACE

The content and organization of *Sensory Experience* are predicated upon a clearly felt need for a textbook that would meet several overlapping requirements. Indeed, it arose from the author's experience in teaching an undergraduate class for which no single adequate text was available. Basically, this book is meant to be an undergraduate-level text, providing the student with a broad, general introduction to the entire area of human sensory phenomena, without the need to resort to a multitude of original reports and highly technical writings aimed primarily at the professional in the field.

I have tried to make the book readable and interesting, avoiding wherever possible highly technical references and reports of original research, except where clearly necessary. The book includes "earthy," everyday examples, and presents sensory phenomena in a manner understandable to the student who has a minimum of mathematical and biological background. I hope it will be relevant to the needs of the average student. Many highly technical references are to be found in the bibliography. For the student or instructor who wishes to go into a topic in greater depth, references and additional bibliographic listings are provided. In addition, each chapter has a short list of suggested readings, mostly from secondary rather than primary sources. These readings are from books of readings, other textbooks, semiprofessional journals, and frequently used reference books. A conscious attempt has been made to list only readily available sources for the suggested readings.

I hope that through the use of this book at least some students of general psychology may acquire an interest in specific areas of sensory/perceptual psychology that may lead them to ultimate careers in the area.

My experience indicates that a course based on this book can be of considerable value for a broad spectrum of nonpsychology students, as well as psychology undergraduates. Students in premedicine and the biological sciences often remain quite naive, often oblivious, to the importance of sense-organ functioning unless they take individual, advanced courses in several separate disciplines. The book is aimed at providing a broad, general introduction to the sense organs which should prove of value to such students.

Graduate students have a strong inclination, even necessity, to concentrate their efforts in one narrow area, often at the expense of other related areas. I hope that the material presented here might be of value to students concentrating solely on visual research, who might otherwise have little opportunity to gain even a passing familiarity with such sensory areas as audition or the chemical senses. For such students, concentrating in one narrow discipline, the book should provide at least the language of the related disciplines. This was a foremost thought behind its preparation—to provide the student with the "language" of sensory psychology, its terms and constructs and some of its methodology. The student doing doctoral research in vision will probably find little of value in the chapters on vision; they are not aimed at his level. But the nonvisual chapters may be of great value to such a student.

Most graduate students must take examinations in several areas as a requirement for advanced degrees. In the case of such nonexperimental, nonsensation/perception students as those in clinical or social psychology, examinations in such areas present a formidable barrier. With its emphasis on the "language" of sensory experience, the text should provide, in one place, at least some of the background information required by such students.

I should like to extend my appreciation to the administrative staff of Utica College of Syracuse University who, by providing time and facilities, made the completion of the book possible. I should like to extend particular appreciation to Mrs. Marion Inglis of the Behavioral Studies Division who saw to the final typing of the manuscript and without whose editorial assistance it would still be little more than a pile of unorganized notes. Appreciation is also due to the numerous professional colleagues who were so generous in providing access to copyrighted material, original photographs, and other vital materials.

Finally I should like to express my most sincere appreciation to Professor Samuel Renshaw (emeritus) of Ohio State University, my former advisor and favorite professor, from whom I received much encouragement as a graduate student, and who stimulated me to pursue such an interesting and rewarding field of study. To him I dedicate this book.

R. J. CHRISTMAN

Uitca, New York
March, 1971

CONTENTS

1

INTRODUCTION

The study of the human senses, the determination of their essential character, their capabilities and limitations, represents the oldest area of interest in modern psychology. Long before interest arose in the application of psychology to such practical problems as learning and the measurement of intelligence, the study of the sense organs* had reached an extreme pinnacle of academic popularity and methodological sophistication. Why should this have been true?

Although philosophical approaches to the mind-matter problem had existed at least since the time of the ancient Greeks, the establishment of a distinct psychological discipline, with its own unique methods and interests had to await the development of related areas whose methods, technology, and apparatus could be adapted to fit the new science. The general scientific awakening commonly associated with the seventeenth and eighteenth centuries provided this opportunity. Heralded by developments in classical physics, chemistry, and the newly discovered "electricity," and spurred on by the uprising of an insatiable curiosity, it was only natural that those interested in the human organism should turn to the sense organs as a most obvious and easily accessible contact with the physical world. Weren't the eyes the "windows of the soul"?

The psychology of sensory-perceptual phenomena was not originated by psychologists. Indeed the very label *psychologist* was not given to students of the sense organs until many years after the interest in the subject was spawned. Rather, physiologists and medical doctors on one hand and physicists on the other were the bellwethers in the development of the new discipline. Men like Frances Glisson, who in 1677 contributed

---

* While the terms *sense organ* and *receptor* may be used somewhat interchangeably throughout the book, it should be recognized that there is an accepted distinction between them. Sense organ refers to the overall physical entity, such as the eye, ear, or semicircular canals; a receptor is some *part* of the sense organ which transduces the external energy. A receptor, for example, changes mechanical energy such as sound waves into neural energy—or in the case of taste, chemical energy into neural energy.

1

the concept of irritability as an attribute of animate tissue, and Giovanni Borelli, who in 1680 suggested that something is transmitted through the spongy ducts (nerve fibers) to "inflate" the muscles, were necessary before others could work out the intricate details of neurosensory functioning (Boring, 1942).

The invention of the Leyden jar in 1745, Benjamin Franklin's experiments in electricity published in 1774, and Galvani's experiments in stimulating a frog's leg and later constructing a battery of the muscle all were important contributions to the rapprochement of the physiological and physical disciplines so necessary for the development of a science of sensory phenomena (Boring, 1942). By the beginning of the nineteenth century the groundwork was well laid for the concerted attack on the mind-body problem—or as it was popularly known, *psychophysics*.

RELATED DISCIPLINES

While the genesis of sensory-perceptual knowledge can be traced to the alignment of the broad physical and physiological disciplines, other and more narrowly defined areas of study suggest themselves as vehicles for obtaining an understanding of the relation between "what goes on out there" and "what goes on in here." Most of the data used to describe the relation between the outside world and the world of experience can be categorized within one or more of these areas. Some knowledge of all these areas is necessary for a proper grasp of the place of the sense organs in the behavior of man. Let us look at a few of these specialized approaches, bearing in mind that they are neither highly definitive nor mutually exclusive. They are merely examples of interrelated disciplines which play a part in the understanding of sensory-perceptual experience.

Physics of the External World

The word psycho*physics*, which will be encountered so often in this book, is indicative of the importance of physics as an associative discipline. It is probably a truism that one cannot hope to understand the relation between experience and the outside world unless one first *understands* the outside world.* While this statement may at first appear to be too obvious for comment, it does describe a situation not always met, and not always completely possible in the light of our limited knowledge of things physical. In the case of one of our sensory experiences, the actual physical stimulus for the experience is not known with absolute certainty. I am of course referring to the olfactory sense, the sense of smell. While it is

---

* "Understanding the outside world" is a relative expression, and one can only hope to approach such an Olympian ideal.

generally but not universally agreed that small particles of the odorant material must make physical contact with the epithelial lining of the nasal passages in order for a chemical reaction to take place, the specific nature of the sensory excitatory action is not known. Indeed, it is thought that there may be some sort of radiation involved, as well as a primary chemical reaction. Neither the chemists with their endless formulas nor the physicists with their vast knowledge of radiation information can provide us with the answers as yet.

In case you glanced through this book before starting to read (a wise procedure before reading any book) you may have noticed that before any detailed examination of the various sense modalities is made, a fairly extensive section is devoted to the nature of the physical stimulus for each.

In vision, for example, it is important to know of the "wave theory" of light, as contrasted with the "corpuscular theory." One should be aware of the nature of intensity, the location of visible light in the broad electromagnetic spectrum, and various other properties such as refractivity and speed of transmission. Simple physical optics involving spherical, cylindrical, and prismatic refraction are encountered in any but the most superficial treatment of vision. Such things need not be understood at the level of sophistication required of the physicist, but at least a working knowledge of the gross properties of visible radiation is important.

In a similar vein, much of the understanding of the auditory sense cannot be achieved without a working knowledge of the physics of sound. Loudness, pitch, and timbre all have their physical counterparts, and a knowledge of one without the other is simply incompatible with a firm grasp of sensory-perceptual relations. With respect to the experiences of warmth, cold, equilibrium and so on ad infinitum, a truly complete understanding of any experience cannot be obtained without some detailed insight with respect to the physical world which elicits it. We *must* understand the external world if the inner world of experience is to make any sense to us.

A primary requisite of any discipline is to develop its own methodology and techniques. The psychology of sensory-perceptual processes has borrowed heavily from physics in the development of its "tools of the trade." Unlike the psychology of testing, which had to begin from scratch, the study of sensory processes was helped as a result of the ready availability of equipment and research methodology. Many psychologists today are experts in the use of complex equipments which to the uninitiated might appear the exclusive interest of the physicist. An experimental psychologist working in sensory-perceptual research would be hard pressed to get along without a knowledge of such equipment as photometers, spectroscopes, audio oscillators, and cathode-ray oscilloscopes. Furthermore, no person today can entirely escape the influence of our computerized society, and an experimental psychologist with no knowledge of computer technology is almost as hard to find as a hospital intern without a stethoscope.

Chemistry

Man has long recognized that he is made up of a lot of chemicals, combined in ways that defy the imagination. The full impact of knowledge concerning the influence of chemical reactions on sensory behavior has however been of a somewhat more recent vintage. One landmark occurred in 1876 when Franz Boll of the University of Rome isolated a brilliant red pigment from the eye of the frog. This substance, which Boll called *visual red* (now known as visual purple or rhodopsin), has since been the source of an almost unbelievable amount of attention. In addition to this light-sensitive substance, other pigments with selective color-sensitivities have since been isolated and studied. Much of what we now know about color vision can be attributed to the work of men who must list their occupations as "chemist."

It would appear that all of the senses, with the possible exception of those which clearly respond to mechanical changes in the environment, are highly dependent upon chemical reactions for their very existence. Even experiences like hearing and touch presumably require chemical mediation at the juncture between individual nerve fibers.

No one can doubt the significance of chemical mediation in the case of taste and probably smell. And at higher neural levels the importance of such substances as RNA and DNA is gaining widespread recognition. Certainly chemistry pervades the entire field of sensory-perceptual experience.

Anatomy of the Sense Organs

The gross anatomy of the sense organs should in many cases be a valid indicator of how they function. When people abandoned the idea that the eye works by squirting out "corpuscles" and decided that it was really a sensing device, utilizing external energy in its modus operandi, they were taking advantage of their knowledge of its gross structure (Wald, 1950). The similarity between the camera obscura and the mammalian eye must have been impelling to some early investigators. It must have been apparent that the eye had the parts necessary to gather light and focus an image on its rear surface. While it may have been unclear just how this was done, the fact that it *was* done must have been almost indisputable. Today many aspects of visual functioning can be inferred on the basis of gross anatomical observation. The function of such structures as the lens, the cornea, and the iris can be assigned rather confidently from their gross structure.

In like manner the design of the external ear and the bones of the middle ear clearly reveal their function. The external ear must serve as a sound-collecting device, while the articulation of the ossicles points to the actual conduction of vibratory or sound motions.

Microanatomical approaches have made it possible to examine individual neural elements, individual cells, and the structural relations between them. Without such techniques the vast knowledge of the retina would be largely lacking. Neural structures in the central nervous system, the skin, and the inner ear are particularly amenable to study by microscopic techniques.

Unfortunately, attributing a function to an organ on the basis of its gross or microanatomy alone can be extremely hazardous. Additional information of a functional nature is necessary. As an example, textbooks for many years described the nature of the end organs in the skin, their distribution, and their presumed purpose. To the chagrin of the early microanatomists, modern experimental techniques have not been able to verify the functions as assigned to many of these so-called sensory nerve endings. Even today, with the vast amount of microanatomical study that has been directed at the skin, our knowledge of just how such experiences as warmth, cold, tickle, and pain are mediated is woefully inadequate.

Another example might be mentioned of anatomical description leading us down the wrong path. The changing of pupil size as a result of activity of the iris is a familiar experience. A logical explanation of this effect might result in the conclusion that the purpose of the pupil constriction is to limit the amount of light entering the eye and thereby protect the sensitive surface inside. This is just about what I learned in high school, many years ago. Actually this is not the situation at all. The maximum range of pupillary area is only about 20 to 1, while light intensity varies in a ratio of thousands. The constriction serves quite another purpose: to permit, under conditions of adequate illumination, utilization of the central path of the optical system, thereby minimizing various optical aberrations and providing maximum acuity and resolution.

While some knowledge of structure is surely essential to an understanding of function, it is clear that structure, by itself, is not enough. The other disciplines we have discussed must play their roles.

Physiology of the Sense Organs

Physiological information is at the basis of our entire discipline. Most of the early investigators in the field were physiologists, and the distinction today between a physiologist on the one hand and a physiological psychologist on the other may often be difficult to make.

With respect to major contributions of physiology, I suspect the key word is "electricity." Physiologists have provided us with an immense collection of data describing the electrical activity of the neural elements, activity at the juncture of two neurones, and activity within a mass of cell bodies, such as in the various ganglia and in the largest ganglion of all, the brain. In addition, electrical activity at the receptors has been studied and we now have a knowledge of how sensory cells are activated which was not possible before the widespread application of electric and electronic equipment and methods.

A great deal of what we know about the role of the brain in sensory-perceptual processing can be attributed to developments in physiological instrumentation and physiology in general. As suggested earlier, instrumentation and techniques developed by physiologists have contributed immensely to the advancement in sensory-perceptual psychology.

Comparative and Mammalian Embryology

The serious student of sensory-perceptual psychology would do well to spend a little time studying the organism from a developmental point of view. Probably no occurrence in the author's past so impressed him with its relevance to the topic at hand, as a course he once took in comparative embryology. Tracing the development of the sense organs ontogenetically from the gamete to the adult, and phylogenetically from the amoeba to *Homo sapiens* can be an extremely interesting and rewarding experience. Much of our understanding of the sense organs is based upon such analyses. Did you know, for example, that the previously mentioned bones of the middle ear are derived from the gill arches of the primitive shark? That an evolutionary process of many eons has resulted in the migration of these structures from the gill area to their present location in the middle ear? Are you aware that the human eye, or at least that part known as the retina, is actually, in the true sense of the word, an extension of the brain? That in ontogenetic development a bulge in the embryological "brain" results in a bulb on the end of a stalk, the former turning inside-out to form the inside rear surface of the eye, the latter forming the optic nerve?

Such facts as these are more than of passing interest. They are fascinating, true. But more than that, they reveal to us how the structures in question probably work. When we know that the retina is actually an extension of the brain we are not at all surprised to discover what a large amount of information processing goes on there.

Direct Analysis of Consciousness

An approach, not often encountered today, involved the direct observation of one's "sensations," and was quite popular during the latter part of the nineteenth century. Because it *did* make major contributions and *does* have some applicability today it should be mentioned.

Introspective analysis of one's innermost psychological behavior was a favorite tool of such men as O. Külpe, Wilhelm Wundt (who founded the first psychological laboratory in Leipzig), and E. B. Titchener, who brought the new discipline to this country via Cornell (Boring, 1942). These men believed that the proper way to study sensory processes was to study sensations. Such a statement should not, on the surface, evoke much criticism, but the manner in which they proceeded to study them *did* leave much to be desired. They felt that sensations were merely one of the components, or elements, of consciousness, the other two being simple images (like memory pictures), and feeling or affective tone. All consciousness, then, was made up of sensations from the sense organs, images from the memory, and affective tone or feeling (the latter generally being assumed to be either pleasant or unpleasant, or some such dichotomy). In the language of Wundt, sensations were the basic elements of consciousness; perception was the combination of sensation and affection.

Research consisted primarily in studying the content of one's consciousness, and in a more analytical manner, the nature of one's sensations. By the time of Titchener, all sensations were allegedly describable in terms of four characteristics, called *attributes*. These essential attributes were *quality* (for example hue or pitch), *quantity* (brightness or loudness), *temporal* (duration), and *spatial*—or as it was sometimes called, *extensity*. An additional attribute of *clarity* was added later.

The idea that one can learn all about his sensory processes by simply "introspecting" and examining his innermost thoughts, has not been considered very seriously for many years. One can't understand the basis for afterimages by the simple expedient of spending many hours looking at them and trying to figure out their genesis. In like manner, the breaking down of theoretical constructs like *consciousness* into hard-and-fast "structures" is repugnant to our modern approach to science, which tends to emphasize operationalism. However, in spite of their defects, these approaches were not as sterile as a modern scientist might have been led to predict. The *attributes* of sensation are still to be found in every book on sensation and perception. Only now we call them by a different name, such as *characteristics* or *modes of discrimination*. While the structuralist theory of these early pioneers has died with them, they did leave a great legacy of knowledge and methodolgy which is still of extreme importance.

Relation of Outside World, Sensations, and Experience

One of the most fruitful approaches, and really the thesis of this entire book, is the examination of the relationship between what our sense organs do and what we think happened to make them do what they did. In simple language, we "see" a light; what did our eyes *do* as a result of some outside event (presumably electromagnetic radiation) that we interpret as "light"? And of course, what sorts of outside events will produce the effect in the sense organ that we have come to call "light"? We have all experienced so-called illusions, wherein the event we think we experience doesn't occur at all. Some misinterpretations occur because of

TABLE 1-1

RELATION OF OUTSIDE WORLD, SENSORY FUNCTION, AND EXPERIENCE

Outside World	Sensory Function	Experience
Electromagnetic radiation from about 400 to 750 mμ	Chemical-electrical response of rods and cones in retina	Light
Electromagnetic radiation of 700 mμ	Chemical-electrical response of *some* cones in retina	Red light
Acoustic vibration from 20 to 15,000 Hz (cycles/sec)	Mechanical-electrical response in cochlea	Sound
Acoustic vibration at 10,000 Hz	Mechanical-electrical response of one part of cochlea	High-pitched sound
Presence of certain dissociated ions in solution	Chemical-electrical response of receptor cells on tongue	Taste of salt
Tilting of the body	Mechanical-electrical response of cells in semicircular canals	Position of head
Flexing the arm	Mechanical-electrical response of sensory cells in the joint	Bent elbow
Moderate temperature rise	Thermal(?)*-electrical response of cells in the skin	Feeling of warmth
Lack of water in the body	Mechanical(?)†-electrical response of cells lining the mouth	Thirst

* A so-called vascular theory suggests that warmth may be mediated by pressure-sensitive nerve endings in the walls of the small blood vessels.

† This is only one basis of thirst. Receptors in the brain are stimulated by lowered water content in the body fluids and this probably serves as the primary indicator of water need.

errors in the transition from the outside world to the world of the sensory organs, others must occur in the transition from sensory action to conscious awareness. In some cases the sense organ may not even be necessary for the experience of a sensation. If you bump the back of your head hard enough you may "see stars." And what about dreaming, hallucinations, and delirium tremens?

Psychophysics, in its broadest sense, attempts to disclose these relations. It is such a basic part of sensory-perceptual experience that we are going to devote an entire chapter to its methods.

Table 1-1 presents, in summary form, these three aspects of sensory experience for just a few of the better understood sensory modalities. Note that in all cases, while the sense organ input may be in the form of mechanical, chemical, or thermal energy, the output is always in the form of "electricity." As we shall see later, this electrical output of the receptor is not an electrical current as we know it, rather, it is a train of more or less coded pulses, apparently produced by chemical means.

CLASSIFYING THE SENSES

How many senses are there? Your answer is as good as mine, since it really depends on how you classify and name them. What about the classical five senses: vision, audition, touch, olfaction, and taste? Aren't all the senses included under these five categories? Hardly. These are merely convenient categories based on gross observation. Equilibrium and position of the head as sensed by the organs of the inner ear appear to be unique senses. The skin is sensitive to warmth, cold, pain, and touch; are these not separate senses? And what about color perception? Inasmuch as there are probably separate receptor cells (cones) in the retina for each primary color, are these not separate senses? Experience and gross observation are not satisfactory bases for classifying the senses.

The structuralists referred to earlier discovered that sensations are indeed quite personal, and what one man might call "red," another would see as "yellow," or perhaps simply as a shade of gray. If we cannot classify our sensory experiences in terms of their inner nature, is there not some other, more acceptable way of distinguishing them?

One answer lies in the nature of the outside stimuli which produce them. Thanks to the efforts of physicists, chemists, and other natural scientists, a large body of knowledge bearing on the nature of natural phenomena is available. We simply refer to a sense modality in terms of the stimulus which produces the experience, and everyone knows what we are talking about. We do not have the problem of the gross nature of the morphological entities nor the sensory interpretation problems of the structuralists.

Let us look at some of the different forms of energy which are capable of producing effects in the organism which might be referred to as sensations.

Chemical Energy

A generalized chemically induced response in irritable tissue is probably the oldest and most primitive forerunner of our now complex sensory functioning. In lower animals at the level of the amoeba, for instance, it is possible that the only environmental change which has the potential for stimulating the animal is chemical in nature. You may find many lower organisms which do not respond to sound or electromagnetic energy, but I know of no organisms entirely insensitive to chemical changes.

Higher animals' dependence upon chemical energy is likewise well known. Both the sense of smell and the sense of taste* are clearly mediated by chemical energy; smell by stimulation of nerve endings in the epithelial lining of the nasal passages and taste by the chemical nature of particles which evoke responses in the sensory cells of the taste buds. As we will see in Chapters 16 and 17, we do not understand these functions adequately, but is a safe bet to attribute their responses to a chemical reaction of some sort.

While energy other than chemical may produce activity in the sense organs, it does appear to be a fact that for every response to the environment by an organism, a chemical reaction takes place somewhere. Living organisms are chemical machines. Electromagnetic energy may stimulate the elements of the retina to action, but the intermediary condition which produces the neural response is chemical in nature. Even when neural energy is released by direct mechanical energy, such as sound waves or tactual vibration, the neural impulse itself, is, basically, a chemical reaction.

Adaptation is an important aspect of the chemical senses, and appears to be a factor in all of them. Most chemical reactions are reversible, but a finite amount of time is required to produce the reverse reaction. In the meantime, the depletion of one or more of the contributors to the reaction results in a general slowdown of the reaction, and hence, an apparent adaptation. Sensory adaptation may be more than this, but at the superficial level, a slowing-down of the reaction due to the depletion of that constituent of the reaction supplied by the organism appears to be a satisfactory if not completely adequate explanation.

---

* As indicated earlier, the "sense of taste" is undoubtedly several senses if we are to be precise in our language. However, for the purpose of simplicity, the word "sense" may at times be used with its popular, loosely defined meaning: sense of smell, sense of taste, sense of vision, etc.

In addition to the obvious senses of taste and smell, numerous other "senses" are of a chemical nature. The use of quotation marks for the word *senses* was not without reason. The reference is to those receptors that may not result in sensations in the popular sense. We have receptors lying deep in the brain which detect conditions in the blood stream that warrant attention. The recognition of water need, oxygen shortage, or blood temperature must be classed as a form of sensory activity. These sensory functions frequently do not reach a level of consciousness aware-ness, and we do not ordinarily think of them in terms of sensations or perceptions. When things are going along correctly we are not even aware of the existence of most of these functions. Yet hunger, thirst, and body temperature changes are conditions meriting attention at a level of insistence equal to or greater than those arising wholly from the outside environment. While we can be certain that these internal sensory organs work in many cases as chemical receptors, their nature for the most part is still somewhat of a mystery—a mystery, incidentally, that is being at-tacked with considerable vigor by our friends in physiology.

In summary, chemical reactions lie at the basis of most receptor activity, and even in the case of those receptors which clearly respond to nonchemical events, some chemical mediation must play a role some-where, certainly in the neuron itself if not before.

Electromagnetic Energy

Most living organisms also appear to be sensitive, in one way or an-other, to one or more forms of electromagnetic energy. In general, the portion of the spectrum to which most animals are sensitive represents only an infinitesimal part of the whole. As shown in Fig. 1-1, the visible spectrum for man ranges from approximately 400 to 750 millimicrons (abbreviated $m\mu$), while the total known spectrum has a range of some twenty-two log units—that is, a range of 1,000,000,000,000,000,000,000,000 to 1. In comparable units the total spectrum has a range of 10^{-5} to 10^{16} millimicrons. Expressing it in another way, if the total spectrum were divided into octaves, that is "doublings" of frequency or wavelength, 70 octaves would be required to encompass the entire spectrum. In contrast, the visible portion of the spectrum would be included in less than one of these octaves.

Figure 1-1 also shows the position of various other functions in the electromagnetic spectrum. In addition to showing wavelengths in meters and millimicrons, this figure also includes corresponding frequencies in cycles (Hz) and kilocycles (KHz). The position of various forms of radiation such as X-rays, ultraviolet, infrared, and radio, radar, and TV waves are also indicated. The schematic expansion of the visible portion

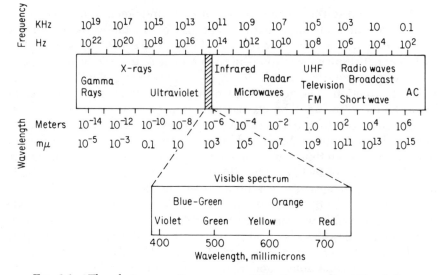

FIG. 1-1. The electromagnetic spectrum. Note the overall width of the total spectrum, more than twenty log units. Note too, the relatively narrow portion which is visible to the human eye.

of the spectrum will of course be considered in more detail in the section of the book devoted to vision and the discrimination of hue or color.

The visual sense, especially in higher-order animals, has achieved a remarkable level of development. The sensitive elements of the human eye have reached such a peak of perfection that they can respond, it is said, to one quantum of radiant energy—the absolute minimum that can be shown to exist (Wald, 1950). The visual sense of lower animals is no less impressive. A broad variety of receptor types and configurations adapt the various species to their environments, in many cases often exceeding the capabilities of *Homo sapiens.*

In general, most animals with sensitivity to electromagnetic energy confine their sensitivities to the restricted portion of the spectrum which produces the sensation "light." There is variability among species, and of course some animals may be sensitive to portions of the spectrum well outside the limits of the normally visible portion. We really do not know with certainty just what portions of the spectrum may affect some living organisms.

At one extreme, however, marked sensitivity to radiant heat, or infrared radiation, appears to be a capability of some forms of animal life. Numerous cold-blooded animals which feed on small warm-blooded creatures can presumably detect their prey by means of specialized infrared detectors. Several types of snakes have receptors for radiant energy which are of sufficient sensitivity so as to enable them to capture their prey with a minimum of assistance from the other senses.

While it is still within the normally visible spectrum, polarized light can be discriminated by some insects. Honeybees, for example, owe much of their navigational ability to a differential sensitivity to direction of light polarization. For centuries, superstitious people have attributed supernatural powers to the moon, specifically to "moonlight." The word *lunacy*, came from the old idea that people behave differently under the light of the moon, or as a function of the phase of the moon. Inasmuch as moonlight tends to be polarized differently than sunlight, perhaps the old superstition is not quite as fantastic as one might think. Perhaps moonlight *does* affect some animals differently than daylight. Certainly, within his state of awareness, however, discrimination of direction of light polarization is a capability denied man; he must equip himself with special polarizing filters in order even to determine the direction of the polarization.

Some animals can sense ultraviolet—that is, wavelengths lying further along the short-wavelength end of the spectrum. The capability of insects to ultilize light in the ultraviolet region has been well documented (Mazokhin-Porshuyakov, 1969). We even have a pretty good idea just how the visual stimulus might appear to the creature (Eisner et al., 1969). Various flowers which to the human eye may appear identical may perhaps be discriminable to the eye of the honeybee, which can allegedly distinguish the ultraviolet content of electromagnetic radiation.

There are also slight differences within the human species. Some people can also see colors well out on either the violet or red ends of the normally visible spectrum. The retina of the eye itself is sensitive to wavelengths in the near ultraviolet which cannot be detected by the eye as a whole. This is due to the yellow coloring in the crystalline lens which, by absorption, prevents some of the shorter wavelengths from reaching the retina. (Insects presumably do not have this filtering capability.) Persons who have had their lenses removed in the course of cataract operations can often see colors in the violet or near ultraviolet which are invisible to the normal eye. Many former patients of cataract operations wear tinted lenses in their spectacles to replace the ultraviolet absorption function.

As was true for the chemical senses, adaptation plays an important role in the electromagnetic-sensitive senses, at least in those which have a chemical reaction as an intermediate stage. Adaptation in the case of color vision has long been recognized, is familiar to everyone, and is usually explained as the result of the chemical breakdown of the color sensitive pigments in the cones. Negative afterimages, on the other hand, are generally attributed to the reverse anabolic process in the receptor organs, although the possibility of some central nervous system contribution cannot be denied.

Thermal Energy

Most organisms, certainly all those relatively high on the phylogenetic scale, react to thermal energy or temperature. As indicated in the previous section, some of this sensitivity is probably due to an extension of the electromagnetic sensitivity into the infrared end of the spectrum. Most sensitivity to electromagnetic energy involves the chemical change of some pigment, not entirely unlike the events occurring in a sensitive photographic emulsion. Indeed, at least one investigator has succeeded in taking the pigments from an animal's eye, crushing them into an emulsion, and making a "photographic plate" which actually works (Wald, 1950). I suspect that the temperature sensitivity of some reptiles to heat from an anticipated dinner may be of the radiant energy/pigment breakdown variety.

On the other hand, there does appear to be some sensitivity to temperature change, both increasing and decreasing temperature, which seems to be mediated by other, perhaps more direct, means. The skin is sensitive to both warmth and cold, and that these sensations are mediated in the same manner as vision, or the snake's infrared sensitivity, appears highly unlikely. Early investigators suggested that there were indeed separate end organs for the receiving of warmth and cold (heat has usually been attributed to a combination of warmth and pain) and they proceeded to "map" them on the skin with an abandon later to be regretted. Now we are not so sure. *Some* end organs do appear to mediate one or the other, but the entire microanatomical description of the skin with respect to temperature sensitivity is up in the air.

The temperature of the blood, as another example, is regulated largely as a feedback mechanism from sensors located within the blood vessels. Just how this is accomplished we really do not know. Perhaps it is simply a sensitivity to expansion and constriction; but then what about changes in blood pressure? How can the sense organs "know" which it is? It would appear that there must be some direct mediation, but its nature escapes us.

One particular problem is the amount of accommodation or adaptation in the temperature senses. If you immerse your hand in ice-cold water and then place it in water of a neutral temperature, the feeling may be one of quite warm water, perhaps even hot. Conversely, adapting to warm water will result in subsequent cool water feeling quite cold. The lukewarm water following a hot shower often feels just like ice water.

It would appear too that the temperature sense is not really a temperature sense at all. It is in fact a *change in temperature* sense. As implied in the previous paragraph, prolonged subjection to any temperature extreme (within rather obvious limits) results in adaptation, such that the original sensation of warmth or cold gradually diminishes and a more nearly neutral feeling takes its place. It has been said that if a live frog is placed in a pan of cold water and the pan placed on a stove, the temperature can be slowly raised to the boiling point, cooking the frog without his ever being disturbed. Certainly you can recall instances where you adapted to bath water, gradually getting it hotter and hotter until you emerged from the tub looking like a boiled lobster. And the last sunburn you got— you probably were not even aware you were being burned.

Much is yet to be learned about the temperature sense (or senses?); it is one of the most fascinating and challenging areas in sensory-perceptual psychology.

Mechanical Energy

Most organisms respond to jabs, jolts, and almost any type of physical contact. The skin rather obviously is a favorite location for these receptors, whatever they might be. While considerable attention has been paid to the sense of touch by classical psychophysicists, their interest was primarily in the nature of the sensation, especially with respect to such things as accuracy of localization and the determination of minimal distances between two points on the skin which could be just barely discerned as being two points, rather than one. The identification of the physiological event which indicates to the organism: "I have been touched" has proved to be quite elusive. Free nerve endings and various encapsulated end organs have at various times been credited with mediating tactual sensitivity. Nerve endings in the hair follicles are probably activated whenever a hair is disturbed. Much remains to be learned with respect to cutaneous tactual sensitivity.

Mechanical energy is important in other than the skin senses. The position of our limbs is known to us, at least partially, through the stimulation of proprioceptors in the joints and movement sensors within the muscles. The proprioceptive and kinesthetic senses tell us when we have moved a limb, and in general just where it is at a given point in time and space. In locomotor ataxia, a disorder commonly the result of an untreated syphilitic infection, the ascending (leg-to-brain) paths of the sensory nerves have been destroyed. The patient walks as if he had some serious impairment to his motory function, hence the name. Actually the problem is not motory at all, but is due to the lack of feedback from the lower limbs. The patient appears to have difficulty in walking because he has to use other cues, such as vision, to indicate where his feet are.

As was true for the temperature senses, there are undoubtedly many internal functions which are mediated by mechanical receptors at a level below conscious awareness. It is likely that the automatic control of pressure functions such as blood pressure, and air pressure within the lungs, are at least partially regulated by stretch receptors in the walls of the involved organs. We alluded in the last section to the possibility that some temperature sensitivity might very well be a sensitivity to mechanical stimulation. Small blood vessels could constrict or dilate as a function of the temperature, and this change could be sensed by means of free nerve endings associated with the vessel walls.

Adaptation plays a role of great importance in the tactual senses. A tight collar, or clothing which may at first appear quite unpleasant, can often be adapted to so that its presence may not only be ignored but even completely forgotten. As was true for thermal receptors, "change" appears to be the key word for the mechanical receptors.

Acoustic Energy

In essence, acoustic energy is simply mechanical energy of a high frequency. While even at its highest frequencies it might still be considered as mechanical energy, there is such an amazing degree of specialization and evolutionary development in acoustic sensitivity that it clearly merits inclusion as a specialized sense. While there is little evidence to indicate that unicellular animals show any appreciable sensitivity to acoustic energy, it is true that almost all organisms higher in the phylogenetic scale do have some sensitivity to acoustic or vibratory stimulation within broadly specified limits.

Phylogenetic evidence tends to indicate, as might be expected, that the acoustic senses have developed primarily from the primitive mechanical energy sensors. The lateral line organs of the shark, for example, are basically cutaneous endings which have acquired a sensitivity to vibratory frequencies impinging on the fishes' outer surface. As another example, the long, facile tongue of most snakes is an organ sensitive to acoustic energy. And too, many arthropods have acoustic sensors in their body and leg regions which are only slightly different from conventional mechanical receptors.

Higher organisms have achieved a level of sophistication in the development of their acoustic sensitivity which is nothing less than miraculous. As an example, the sensitivity of the human ear is so great that were it increased by an infinitesimal amount the results would be disastrous. Brownian movement of the air molecules would be heard as a constant "whishing" sound. Just this sort of thing does arise occasionally under some auditory disorders, and the effects on the afflicted person are indeed serious.

Both the range of acoustic sensitivity and the uses to which it is put vary from species to species. While the frequency range of auditory sensitivity for humans is generally found within the extreme limits of 20 to 20,000 Hz,* there is a marked variability between individuals. Very few persons reach the upper limit of 20,000 Hz, and once beyond the middle teens, sensitivity to the higher frequencies decreases quite rapidly. The range of sensitivity for an adult would probably be closer to 40–12,000 Hz, or even lower at the upper end of the frequency spectrum. Increasing age results in continued lowering of the upper frequency limit.

Many infrahuman animals demonstrate a capability of hearing frequencies much higher than those sensed by man. The familiar Galton whistle, used to call dogs, produces a frequency too high to be heard by humans but is well within the sensitivity range of the dog. Bats are not only sensitive to frequencies in the ultrasonic (above normal human limits) range but are also able to produce "sounds" at these frequencies. (They are sounds to bats but silence to man.) Their remarkable hearing ability enables them to utilize the returning echoes much like a primitive form of radar, providing information about obstacles in their path. Anticollision radar has only recently been developed for airplanes and boats; bats had it millenia ago.

The auditory sense is extremely complex. In contrast to the other senses (except for vision) the amount of information which can be obtained and processed by the auditory sense is almost limitless. Lower animals may simply respond in a general way to acoustic energy or sound. An earthworm, for example may pull himself back into his hole as a result of a vibration or an intense sound. Man and the higher animals, however, have reached such a state of development, with such a sophisticated analyzing capability, that an almost infinite amount of information can be accepted and processed.

Gravity

Probably there is no such thing as a "sense of gravity." However, whether it is mediated by a mechanical sense or whatever, the force of gravity does influence behavior. Due to gravity, fluid and small granules (*otoliths*) in the vestibular apparatus of the inner ear tend to assume a

---

* In accordance with the desires of several professional societies, the expression cycles per second, has largely been replaced by the word *Hertz* (after Heinrich Hertz), abbreviated Hz. When you see the abbreviation Hz, it simply means cycles per second.

normal resting position when the organism is stationary. As the head moves, centrifugal forces move the fluid and granules about in their cavities, stimulating hair cells which eventuates in neural signals indicating movement, and ultimately, the position of the head. To be sure, since this experience is similar to the use of accelerometers in aerial navigation, only *changes* in position are indicated, and other sensory experiences are needed to verify position at any given time.

Fortunately there are other ways in which gravity tells us "which end is up." Our bodies and our internal organs have considerable mass, and pressure on various internal sensors in the customary direction (downward) probably indicates to us that we are right-side-up. Blood is influenced by gravity, and everyone is aware of the experience of blood leaving the feet and flowing to the head when hanging upside down for any length of time. Actually, of course, the blood doesn't really leave the feet and flow to the head, but there are changes in relative pressure that can be sensed, probably by some of the same pressure-sensitive receptors we referred to before.

As was true in the case of many other "internal" senses, response to gravity more often than not occurs below the level of conscious experience. Reflexive behavior is basic to much of our equilibratory sense and automatic adjustments are made without our being aware of them. Persons who have lost the use of their semicircular canals do not have this efficient, automatic feedback system. They must rely more on the proprioceptive pressure senses and the sense of vision to maintain their sense of balance.

Astronauts, of course, survive with no ill effects in an environment completely lacking in gravity. They can determine their body position only through their internal proprioceptive and kinesthetic sense, and of course, vision. Yet they are able to perform physical and mental feats which might tax the capabilities of many of us earthbound folk.

Electrical and Magnetic Energy

In light of our present-day knowledge it is probably safe to say that man has no capability of sensing external electrical or magnetic energy directly. (An electric shock is most likely the result of stimulating receptors such as those for touch, pain, etc., and not the setting off of any special receptors "tuned" for electricity.) Some people believe that ESP (extrasensory perception) is made possible by the reception of some sort of magnetic or electromagnetic energy produced by the sender's brain. Until the existence of ESP can be demonstrated, claims for such sensory processes can scarcely be taken seriously.

Sensitivity to electrical and magnetic energy does, however, appear to be a basic characteristic of some forms of life, and perhaps a fundamental nature of undifferentiated protoplasm. Responses to magnetic or electric currents, often called *tropisms,* are displayed by many lower animals. If paramecia are placed in a watch glass with positive and negative electrodes placed a short distance apart, the little creatures can be seen to move, almost as one, toward the negative electrode. Or if an earthworm is placed on a sheet of paper within an electromagnetic field (plane electrodes above and below it), reversing the polarity of the field will cause the earthworm to roll over. It makes a startling experiment to alternate the fields rapidly and see the worm roll right off his paper platform. Neither of these examples can be likened to a permanent magnet and its attracting iron filings, since the movement of the animals seems to result from their own propulsive behavior.

While such responses may be called tropisms (which of course doesn't explain anything, anyway), and not true sensory experience, they are nevertheless evidence that the animal does have some sort of a sense which can discriminate between the positive and negative extremes of a magnetic or electromagnetic field.

It has been suggested that some birds may utilize the influence of the earth's magnetic poles as navigational aids. While man must carry compasses and delicate sensing instruments to even be aware that such phenomena exist, it is possible that some forms of life may rely on their ability to sense variations in electrical potentials and magnetic fields to insure their very existence.

The ancient art of astrology is based on the belief that the sun and the plants influence our behavior in a relatively direct and predictable manner. While no serious scientist regards astrology as more than entertaining nonsense, there are those who do believe that electromagnetic fields can influence earthly creatures, and that these fields may be produced by the sun, earth and other planets. Frank A. Brown of Northwestern University has conducted experiments which indicate that living organisms may be sensitive to exceedingly weak variations of such phenomena. However, until more is known concerning the nature of their influence we need not pay any concerted attention to them.

What about the gravitational pull of the moon and major planets? Is it reasonable to believe that a force capable of piling ocean water 30 feet high along some coastal areas should have no effect on insignificant living creatures? I know of no animals which can sense the pull of the moon, but that is not to say that some do not exist. We may indeed find that some forms of migratory behavior, for example, are dependent upon the moon and its attractive force.

Deviating somewhat from our original classification of forces, is it possible that some organism can detect other natural phenomena, such as meteorological changes, long before they are detected by humans? Lowering of barometric pressure as a forerunner of serious storms may very well be detected by some animals, thereby enabling them to seek shelter before the full fury of the storm strikes.

SUMMARY

In the first chapter we tried to become familiar with the broad area of sensory/perceptual psychology. We attempted to do this in two ways: First we tried to gain insight in the relationship among the various disciplines which contribute to an understanding of sensory/perceptual psychology. As an admittedly incomplete list, we considered physics, chemistry, anatomy, physiology, embryology, direct analysis of consciousness, and the relation of the outside world to experience. This latter we learned is "psychophysics." Second, we examined a method for classifying the sense organs, based on the nature of the stimuli which produce the experiences. While we must admit that the list is somewhat arbitrary, we recognized chemical, electromagnetic, thermal, mechanical, acoustic, electrical and mechanical energies, and gravity as possible physical sources of sensory experience.

SUGGESTED READINGS

1. From J. J. Gibson, *The Senses Considered as Perceptual Systems* (Boston: Houghton, 1966). Chapter I, "The Environment as a Source of Stimulation," Chapter II, "The Obtaining of Stimulation," and Chapter III "The Perceptual Systems" are suggested as possible readings for the student with particular interest in these areas. These 59 pages suggest an approach more oriented toward an understanding of perceptual problems than toward an understanding of the physics and physiology of the senses. While they are not especially difficult pages, the serious student will be rewarded by being introduced to an interesting approach to the classification of receptors and perceptual systems.
2. Crombie, A. C., "Early Concepts of the Senses and the Mind," *Scientific American*, May 1964. This article of about 9 pages deals with a subject not covered in the text and is written in a manner that should prove to be of interest to the intermediate and advanced student. It is not a complete history of knowledge related to the senses and the mind; primarily it is an attempt to explain the nature of the development of scientific inquisitiveness of the seventeenth century with respect to mental functioning.
3. From E. G. Boring, *Sensation and Perception in the History of Experimental Psychology* (New York: Appleton, 1942). This entire book is

related to the material in this chapter. However, Boring's Chapter 1, "Sensation and Perception," and Chapter 2, "Physiology of Sensation," are of more specific interest. These 94 pages contain the most complete history of the development of sensory/perceptual psychology that I know of. The casual student will find this source somewhat detailed, but the serious, more advanced student can greatly improve his understanding of the field by reading these two chapters rather carefully. The importance of comprehensive and detailed background knowledge cannot be over-emphasized.

4. From E. G. Boring, *A History of Experimental Psychology*, 2d ed. New York: Appleton, 1942). This suggested reading is in many respects similar to the preceding one. While the entire book is one with which the advanced student should be familiar, pages 35–92 are especially pertinent to the material covered in this chapter.

5. Maier, N. R. F., and T. C. Schneirla, *Principles of Animal Psychology* (New York: McGraw-Hill, 1935). I have not included suggested pages or chapters for this reference. As indicated by its title, it is directly applicable to only a small part of this book, but it does have such a wealth of information and at least a general applicability that I must recommend it for the interested student. Of equal importance, it is a very interesting and highly readable book.

6. Wilson, M., and the editors of *Life, Energy* (New York: Time, Inc., 1963). This is a fine book, written in an easy style, profusely illustrated and worthwhile reading for anyone, not just persons interested in sensory/perceptual psychology.

2

DEVELOPMENT OF SENSORY ORGANS

We will be better able to understand the complex functioning of our sensory organs if we examine them against a background of evolutionary as well as individual development. Were we to plunge into the mysteries of vision and audition, for example, without adequate background preparation we might find ourselves lost in a sea of apparently unrelated information, complex relations, and unresolved differences of opinion. To fully comprehend the functioning of our sensory organs we need information on both the development of the species and the development of the individual within the species. Indeed, a preliminary consideration of both phylogenetic and ontogenetic development appears essential to our understanding of the area.

While the old cliché, "ontogeny racapitulates phylogeny" is not perfectly valid, it is true that an understanding of differences among species, both laterally (for similar levels of development) and longitudinally (for levels of increasing complexity of development) can be of extreme usefulness in gaining an understanding of how an organism is influenced by his external world. A subsequent comparison of individual development with phylogenetic development can be extremely rewarding. The remarkable similarity between the embryos of higher animals and the adult stages of many lower members of the animal kingdom appears more than coincidental, and is certainly helpful in improving our understanding of both development of structure and function. It is fascinating to me that both a man and a frog start life in an extremely similar manner. At a sufficiently early stage of development you would be hard pressed to distinguish which is which. Man, however, continues to develop long after the frog has realized his predestined potential and taken his place with his brethren in the neighborhood swamp.

The sense organs develop in a manner which reflects the overall development cycle. The newborn infant can, like the adult frog, perceive movement. The ability to track a moving object skillfully and to perceive form is presumably a later development. But the frog? He never progresses much beyond the movement-perception stage. But in the grand scheme of things this ability is adequate for his catching of his normal quota of insects, and he is indeed ideally suited for his lily-pond existence.

A major portion of this chapter will be devoted to species-related differences and evolutionary development. Ontogentic development will be considered to a greater extent in the chapters devoted to specific sensory/perceptual functioning.

THE PLACE OF SENSORY FUNCTIONING IN LIFE

As we learned in elementary biology, living matter differs from non-living matter in several respects.

1. Assimilation. All living matter has the ability to take in and use other, often nonorganic, material. A fundamental property of protoplasm, and hence all living organisms, is the capability to ingest food and perform some sort of chemical reaction on it such as digestion and respiration or photosynthesis, eventually resulting in the release of one or more forms of energy. Assimilation is probably the most fundamental distinction between animate and inanimate matter, the specific form of which serves as the primary distinction between the plant and animal kingdoms.

2. Growth. Only living matter grows, in the true sense of the word. River deltas seem to "grow," but actually they merely accumulate more individual grains of sand, and no individual grains increase in bulk as is necessary to qualify as true growth. Living organisms change other, foreign material, into protoplasm, and it is this phenomenon we refer to as growth, the creation of additional protoplasm.

3. Reproduction. A third characteristic that distinguishes animate matter is reproduction. A form of growth, perhaps, but more than simple growth. In reproduction a new organism is formed, similar in many respects to the parent, but different in some slight detail, thus allowing for the progress of evolution and the continuous perpetuation, and at the same time, renewal of the species.

4. Irritability. Whether it is ". . . as the sunflower turns on her god, when he sets,/the same look which she turn'd when he rose" (Moore) or a youthful demonstrator tossing a brick through a window, protoplasm has the capability to react to changes in its surround. It is this capability which we refer to as *irritability*. And it is the primitive irritability which has developed (through the fortunate genesis of the nervous system) into the magnificently varied capabilities of sensory processes and ultimately to the pinnacle of higher-level neural functioning that higher animals now enjoy. The subtitle of this chapter, perhaps the entire book,

might very well have included the word irritability, for it is at the basis of all sensory/perceptual functioning.

How did this simple function develop into the complex world of sensation/perception we now know?

The key word is *evolution*. Starting with a generalized "irritability" background, the process of evolution has produced such a variety of sensitivities and discriminabilities in the various species that a mere listing of conditions for which animals are responsive is probably impossible. Each species has developed a sensory capability ideally suited for its own pattern of behavior. (Perhaps the converse is more nearly true; that the animal developed a behavioral pattern consistent with its sensory capability.) Whichever we accept, the fact remains that the differences between species are tremendous, and the fact that so many different kinds of animals *have* survived really points to vast differences in sensory abilities. For example, some birds can locate and recognize small rodents on the ground at distances of hundreds of yards. The normal *Homo sapiens* cannot do this without the aid of powerful binoculars. But then, this keenness of vision represents the key to survival for the hawk; we do not need to see mice at a hundred yards in order to get our dinner and perpetuate our species, but our sensory capabilities *are* adequate for our needs, otherwise *Homo sapiens* would not have outlasted so many of his contemporaries. Similarly, we do not need the dog's keenness of smell, nor the bat's auditory sensitivity to high-frequency squeaks.

Evolution has resulted in a considerable stratification of the various types of animals; some probably survived because of their visual capabilities, some for their sensitivity to chemical stimuli, and some for their auditory abilities. Man probably survived for an entirely different reason: the superb development of his central nervous system, especially that part known as the cerebral cortex. As we progress through this book we will learn of the pronounced limitations of man's sensitivity to changes in his external world and the manner in which his brain compensates for these limitations.

There is another aspect of man's sensory experiences which bears mentioning at this time. Probably because of his higher central nervous system development, man is much more selective in his response to external stimuli. Lower animals are generally invariant (to some degree at least) in their responses to environmental changes. A frog will always flick out his tongue at a moving object if it approximates the size of a fly in his field of vision. My son once had a small monitor lizard with what appeared to be a dreadful temper. Whenever a mouse was placed in the cage with the lizard the behavior of the latter was entirely predictable. He would pounce on the poor mouse, dash it violently against the floor and sides of the cage until it was little more than a bloody pulp. If the lizard were hungry (as evidenced by not having eaten recently) it would proceed to eat the mouse; otherwise it would pay no more attention to the bloody remains. The lizard's reaction to the specific visual and perhaps olfactory stimulus was entirely predictable; whether or not the mouse was then eaten apparently depended entirely on different sensory patterns: those from his organic "hunger" receptors.

In the case of higher animals, and especially man, behavior as a result of external stimuli is much less predictable. We can "tune in" on desired external events, and we can often "tune out" those we wish to avoid. In the case of the so-called "cocktail effect," we can pay attention to one conversation while excluding the effects of dozens of other conversations all around us. A mother who is "tuned in" to her infant's cries can be awakened by a slightest whimper which doesn't even faze the normally sleeping father. Such a capability of selective *attention* greatly increases the flexibility and adaptibility of the sensory/perceptual world of the higher order creatures. While it is beyond the scope of this book, much progress is being made in acquiring an understanding of the neural mechanisms responsible for selective attention, inhibition, and even total repression of the sensory event.

DEVELOPMENT OF SENSORY STRUCTURES

The sensory organs of man have come a long way from the extremely simple, general irritability of protoplasm. This evolution can, to a great extent, be traced from the simplest form of life in organized, logical steps.

Protozoa

The amoeba is probably the simplest form of life in which generalized irritability has begun to be specialized. It has no structures that can be properly classed as neural tissue, yet an amoeba is influenced differentially by different forms of energy and different levels of stimulation to an extent which belies its low level on the phylogenetic scale. It reacts to chemical changes, temperature changes, and mechanical stimuli as well as gravity and some forms of electromagnetic energy. Within wide limits, and subject sometimes to serious errors, it can withdraw from noxious stimuli and wrap its pseudopods around potential food. An amoeba also reacts differentially as a function of the magnitude (intensity) of a stimulus, showing temporal summation (several stimuli, none of which by itself would elicit a response, may, when combined in time produce a response) and adaptation, wherein a stimulus capable of eliciting a response may over time, be simply adapted to, and lose its capacity for producing the response. The simple amoeba is not as simple in its behavior as its morphological structure might lead one to believe. The basic irritability of its protoplasm has developed into a capability for rather remarkable sensitivity and discrimination, and all this without anything which could be called neural tissue.

Simple Multicellular Animals

In the early multicellular animals, a greater degree of coordinated behavior may be found, still without true nervous tissue. In the sponge each cell is an entity in itself (little more than a closely knit bundle of protozoa); but due to their physical juxtaposition, a response in one cell produces by physical contact a response in its immediate neighbor. Thus a very primitive form of "neural" transmission takes place without the need for the presence of true neural tissue.

When we reach the level of the hydras and jellyfish we find for the first time a differentiation in tissue to go along with the differentiation in behavior. Primitive receptor cells are found which are more sensitive to mechanical, thermal, and chemical changes than undifferentiated protoplasm. To go along with the animals' increased response capability (many of these animals have greatly enhanced mobility) fibrous extensions of the receptors may lead to primitive muscle cells. Such neurosensory cells actually combine the sensory and neural functions so clearly differentiated in higher animals. Some of the organisms in this group have their neurosensory cells arranged in a netlike configuration, thus appreciably increasing their potential for coordinated behavior.

Some highly specialized receptor organs can be found in animals at this level. For example, jellyfish are able to maintain their upright positions, in spite of considerable mobility, as a result of the presence of gravity-influenced granules resting on sensitive hair cells in sensory organs called *statocysts.*

Bilateral Organisms

The next stage in development is of extreme importance. As exemplified by the flatworms (Platyhelminthes) and the roundworms (Annelida), for the first time a potential for maximum differentiation and flexibility in behavior is to be found. The replacement of radial symmetry with bilateral symmetry provides a framework for encephalization and concentration of neural functioning at one "end" of the animal. It is difficult to imagine a highly developed organism with no head end!

The presence of a head end permits maximum orientation ability, optimal movement, and the potential for a concentration of specialized receptor organs where they would be expected to be most useful. As a result of this shift from radial to bilateral symmetry worms were able to develop far more variability in their behavior and modes of adaptation than in any lower forms of life. Indeed, some of the more courageous critters even left their protective liquid environment and crawled out onto dry land. Without the shift from radial to bilateral symmetry in such animals as the flatworms we might all be floating around today as jellyfish!

Of great importance to all of us is the fact that at this level the first evidence can be found of simple learning or conditioning based on modifications to the nervous system. Perhaps modifiability is a characteristic of all protoplasm, but not until the development of a nervous system do we find anything much like learning, as we understand it.

Sensory Organ and Neural Dominance

As we move up the phylogenetic scale we cannot but be amazed at the variety and degree of sense organ development we encounter. The development of specialized vibration sensitive hair cells, compound eyes, and remarkable chemical sensitivities are typical of these animals, especially the arthropods. In addition to a fantastic proliferation in kind and complexity of sensory organs for the molluscs and arthropods, a remarkable increase in the amount and complexity of neural tissue is to be found. Animals at these levels for the first time exhibit a wide range of behavior, not nearly as stereotyped and invariant as the lower animals. We find a high level of development of motor behavior. Rapid movements and flying are characteristic of animals at this level. Finally, we find the first evidence of truly social behavior in many of the insects; behavior of colonies, in which the welfare of the group depends on the behavior of the individuals, and the welfare of the individual depends on the behavior of the group.

Central Nervous System Dominance

In some respects the chordata achieve the epitome of sensory development, but not without qualification. As indicated earlier, sensory organs for the lower animals have been developed for specific purposes, and they perform these purposes admirably; in many cases better than those of their higher-level relatives. While many animals from fish through mammals do indeed exhibit remarkable upper limits in their sensory capabilities, we should recognize that much of this advantage must be attributed to central nervous system development rather than sense-organ development. For the first time animals at this level reveal an extreme degree of encephalization and corticalization. Nearly all of the neural capability is concentrated at one end of the animal, and the resultant brain with its higher-level cortex provides for an almost unlimited variability in sensory capacity and overt behavior.

At the same time, divergent developments between species have resulted in the remarkable sensory developments with which we are familiar: the olfactory sense of the dog, the vision of the hawk, and the high-frequency auditory sensitivity of the bat are only a few examples.

SIMPLE NEURAL ACTION

Through the long process of evolution the simple, idealistic neuron as an elementary building block for sensory/perceptual functioning has undergone tremendous change. Indeed, some specialized neurons such as those found in the retina bear almost no outward resemblance to the classical depictions. Nevertheless, although evolution has wrought great changes in the superficial appearance of many neurons their basic structure remains essentially unchanged.

Description of the Neuron

A neuron is a single cell, consisting of three basic parts: a sensitive end called a *dendrite*, a *cell body* or *perikaryon* containing the ubiquitous cell nucleus and other related structures, and an *axon* which serves as the output portion of the cell. Figure 2-1 shows an idealized neuron with its axon, dendrite, and cell body as well as several other structures which may be of interest to us. These include a myelin sheath—a white, segmented, fatty covering found on many axons, and whose presence leads to the identification of the "white matter" of the brain. Other features of importance include the neurilemma, a thin membraneous covering superficial to the myelin sheath, occurring even where no myelin is found; and numerous constrictions in the axon known as the nodes of Ranvier. In the following pages we will only consider those parts of the neuron which appear to be of importance for an understanding of sensory/perceptual phenomena. The interested reader is encouraged to dig deeper into the functioning of the neuron and the nervous system in general if he so desires.

In size, the variability of neurons is tremendous. At one extreme, in the thin membrane of the retina a chain of several microscopic-sized neurons may be found lying end to end, over a distance no greater than the thickness of a sheet of tissue paper. Each neuron may be only a few

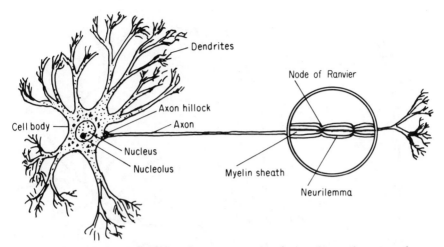

FIG. 2-1. Idealized diagram of a neuron. This figure shows the principle parts of a typical neuron. The drawing is highly stylized and is more typical of a motory than of a sensory neuron.

microns (millionths of a meter) in length. At the other extreme some fibers of neurons may be several feet long, extending the length of the spinal cord, or from the digital extremities to ganglia (clusters of cell bodies) within the torso proper.

As a matter of fact, few neurons look like the idealistic example of Fig. 2-1, which is a *motory* neuron.

Figure 2-2 indicates better than words the extreme difference in external appearance of various neurons as indicated earlier. This figure illustrates diagramatically just a few of the many forms that fully developed neurons may take. Note the extreme diversity in their overall configurations. Even this figure is deceiving when we consider some of the more highly specialized receptor endings such as those found in the retina (rods and cones) and some of the encapsulated end organs found in the skin which are not included in the figure.

How the Neuron Functions

The neuron, like all protoplasm, exhibits irritability. Indeed this is almost its sole function, and evolutionary development has made it ideally suited for its sole raison d'être. While we do not yet fully understand the functioning of the neuron, we *have* come a long way from the ancients who thought of the neural fibers as tubules, carrying "humors" between the various parts of the body.

We now understand, in a gross way at least, the electrical activity of the neuron and its chemical basis. The neuron is *not* an electrical

FIG. 2-2. Some characteristic types of neurons. (a) Multipolar motor neuron of spinal cord. (b) Pyramidal cell of cerebral cortex. (c) Golgi cell of cerebral cortex. (d) Purkinje cell of cerebellum. (e) Bipolar cell of spinal ganglion. (From C. L. Evans, *Principles of Human Physiology,* 14th ed. London: J. & A. Churchill, Ltd., 1968, with permission of publisher.)

conductor like a wire, it does *not* conduct a current of electricity as we understand this useful phenomenon. Rather, it produces, by chemical means, an electrical charge, an increase in negative potential, which traverses the fiber in the form of a "spike" potential until it reaches the end of an axon. The relatively slow transmission speeds of from roughly 2 to 150 meters per second are scarcely consistent with the normally encountered transmission speeds of conventional electric currents.

At the tip end of the axon, a chemical reaction takes place across a short distance (synapse) activating a dendritic structure in another neuron. While it was once supposed that the neural impulse "leaped" across the gap from the tip of one axon to the dendrite of an adjacent cell, we now know better. In fact, a chemical reaction at the synapse, involving the release of *acetylcholine*, results in some manner in a de-polarization of the postsynaptic neuron and a spontaneous firing of it. We shall come back to this action and its accompanying "generator" potential later in the chapter. In the case of motory neurons, activity may be evoked in muscle fibers or glands, rather than other neurons.

In some cases, branching or collateral axon structures are to be found. Frequently these collaterals serve, not to evoke an impulse in an-other neuron, but conversely to *inhibit* the action of an adjacent cell. One level of the retina is particularly well supplied with collateral fibers which inhibit adjacent neurons, thus (as we shall see in a later chapter) enhancing contrast between adjacent visual areas.

All-or-None Principle. What sort of an impulse travels along the fiber? We now know it has a constant level, depending upon the nature and condition of the fiber, rather than the stimulus which set it on its way. In 1871 Henry Pickering Bowditch discovered that a heart muscle fiber responds in just one way: it responds entirely, or not at all. A strong stimulus may increase its rate, but not its strength of firing. In 1905 Keith Lucas extended the principle to skeletal muscle and later gave it its name, the *all-or-none principle*. In 1912 his pupil Edgar Douglas Adrian, in one of the most highly imaginative experiments ever con-ducted, demonstrated the same principle for neural fibers. Adrian showed that when an impulse passes through a portion of a fiber which has been partially narcotized and its apparent strength is decreased, the original strength is recovered in full when it passes beyond the narcotized portion of the fiber. He used a small chamber filled with alcohol vapor to elimi-nate (or reduce) the neural impulse midway in the course of a fiber. At a point where the fiber emerged from the alcohol chamber the im-pulse was the same as it was in the fiber before the chamber. Thus the all-or-none principle was demonstrated for neural fibers (Boring, 1942).

Electrical Activity in the Neuron. At the present time we have a pretty good idea of what goes on in the neuron during transmission of an impulse. As early as 1890 the chemist Wilhelm Ostwald proposed a membrane theory for neural transmission. While he did not actually use living tissue, his hypothesis, involving the transfer of ions through the semipermeable walls of the fiber membranes, was indeed brilliant. Later work by A. Bernstein, who demonstrated temperature effects consistent with the behavior of permeable membranes, was followed by a series of supporting publications by R. S. Lillie early in the twentieth century. Largely due to the work of Lillie the membrane theory of neural transmission is almost universally accepted today (Boring, 1942).

The membrane theory of neural conduction can be understood more easily from a study of Fig. 2-3.

FIG. 2-3.   Membrane theory of nerve conduction. Arrow indicates direction of neural impulse shown at top of drawing. (Adapted from Boring, *Sensation and Perception in the History of Experimental Psychology.* Appleton-Century-Crofts, 1942; based on an original drawing from Forbes, *A Handbook of General Experimental Psychology,* 1934.)

Presumably the resting neuron has a preponderance of sodium (Na^+) and chlorine (Cl^-) ions outside the membrane and a preponderance of positive potassium (K^+) ions inside. The result is a condition (resting potential) in which the interior of the neuron is some 70 millivolts (mv) negative with respect to the exterior surface. Under the proper conditions, the permeability of the membrane increases to such an extent that the outer sodium ions are permitted to flow inward, destroying the resting potential "balance." The immediate result is a decrease in the outside positive charge (or an increase in its negativity, as it is usually described). When a neuron "fires" in this manner the resting potential is replaced by a condition wherein the difference between the outer surface and the inside of the fiber can change about 90 mv—that is, to a point where the outside surface may be 20 mv negative with respect to the interior instead of the original 70 mv positive. This roughly 90-mv "spike" forms the nerve impulse as it moves along the axon.

Upon conclusion of the brief "spike" discharge, a second change in permeability permits positive ions to return from the inside of the fiber to the outer surface, thus restoring the resting potential. This reaction is somewhat slower than that referred to as the discharge or spike potential. The two permeability changes together, in rapid sequence, result in a moving "spike" of negativity which depolarizes the fiber as it moves along and restores the resting potential behind it.

Several characteristics in the behavior of individual neurons are understandable in light of the preceding physiological description. First, a single fiber cannot by any direct means indicate the magnitude of the stimulus which caused it to fire. It has only one level of output—determined by its size, chemical makeup, and perhaps the condition of the organism. It can however fire at different rates, and indeed this appears to be just what happens. Immediately after firing a neuron is in an *absolute refractory stage*; it cannot fire again, since there is no resting potential to be upset by an external stimulation. In a short time the reverse permeability condition allows for a return of the positive ions and the reestablishment of the normal resting potential. The neuron is now ready to fire again. In the meantime, before the normal resting potential has been reached, *some* partial return to normalcy has occurred and the neuron is said to be in a *relative refractory phase*. That is, a stronger-than-normal stimulus may result in a "spike" potential. It is simple to see then how strong stimuli might be discriminated from weak ones. The spike would be the same—complete neutralization of the resting potential, whether it has or has not reached its normal state. The ultimate result of a strong stimulus would be to produce more pulses in a given period of time. In fact, some neurons that can normally fire at a rate of 100 impulses per second may be made to fire at a rate of 1,000 per second with a sufficiently strong stimulus.

In anticipation of later discussions, it should be pointed out that much of our discrimination ability of intensity may also be due to *number* of fibers being fired, as well as rate of firing. A hard pinprick, for example, will set off more fibers than a gentle prick. An intense sound will activate more hair cells in the inner ear than a weak sound.

Generator Potential. In most laboratory experiments neurons are fired by direct electrical stimulation. But this surely is not what happens in the living organism. Where does the electricity from light on the retina come from? Or sound waves in the ear? Or impulses across synapses? It is clear that a receptor must in some way diminish the resting membrane potential of its associated neuron in order to induce it to fire.

The presence of local potentials in sense organs has been recognized for some time, leading Ragnar Granit of the Royal Caroline Institute in Stockholm to suggest, with remarkable foresight, that they be called generator potentials (Granit, 1935). Later, H. K. Hartline at the University of Pennsylvania found what appeared to be a generator potential from a single fiber of the *Limulus* (horseshoe crab) eye, and in 1950 Bernhard Katz of University College, London demonstrated the presence of a generator potential in vertebrate muscle spindles. When the spindle was stretched a slight depolarization occurred which could be viewed on an oscilloscope. Superposed on the shifted local potential were the actual "spikes" or nerve impulses. The stronger the mechanical strain on the fibers, the greater the shift in the local potential, and the greater the frequency of the spikes. It was also found that if a local anesthetic (remember Adrian and his alcohol chamber?) was applied to a fiber, thereby eliminating the spikes, the potential shift remained. Katz concluded that this potential shift was a generator potential, that it was an essential link between the stretching of the fibers and the evoking of the nerve impulse (Miller et al., 1961).

But how does the external stimulus produce a generator potential which can in turn evoke the firing of a neuron? For visual receptors some light can be shed on this difficult question. Based on the work of Hubbard and Wald at Harvard, and others, it seems apparent that the absorption of light in the eye results in a photochemical reaction which does indeed produce a change in the resting potential of the sensitive elements. When this generator potential achieves a sufficient level, the receptor elements fire (Miller et al., 1961). With similar logic, we may guess that the action of acetylcholine at the synapse, in some way alters the resting potential of the second-order neuron, thus causing it to discharge.

With respect to the nonvisual senses, we do not know how the neuron is set into action. All evidence points to the necessity for some shift in the resting potential as induced by a generator potential. Perhaps some generation of a weak electrical current is produced by mechanical means as well as chemical, as appeared to be the case in Katz's muscle-spindle preparations.

UTILIZATION OF SENSORY INFORMATION

Sensory information can be used by the organism in a number of different ways and for somewhat different purposes. Let us examine some of these uses for sensory organ-produced data, bearing in mind that the classification is highly arbitrary and perhaps artificial, being proposed primarily for purposes of convenience and pedagogy.

Maintenance of Arousal Level

Considerable attention has been given recently to the need for stimuli impinging on the organism in order to maintain a currently ill-defined condition known as the "arousal level" (French, 1960). Experiments with human subjects in specially constructed chambers under conditions where they were isolated from all external stimulation have been quite revealing. In order to function properly, the human, at least, must be constantly bombarded with stimuli from the outside world. In an environment of total darkness, devoid of all sound stimulation, and with essentially no tactual stimulation the normal human is in sad shape. He becomes disoriented, restless, and may even experience hallucinations and more serious symptoms of maladjustment.

We now have some fairly good ideas concerning the physiology involved in the arousal-level problem. A portion of the subcortical brain, as a result of varied stimulation from the sense organs, maintains a general level of functioning which keeps the organism in a waking state; a state where it is ready to act. We have long known that external stimuli do not suddenly *start* activity in an inactive sense organ; rather, they tend to *increase* a process already in operation to a point where conscious awareness results. Without this ongoing background stimulation the organism is simply not ready to respond to changes in its environment. More recent work has demonstrated the possibility of manipulating the arousal level by carefully located electroshocks and/or surgery. A cat can be put to sleep in the presence of a mouse by adequately reducing the neural activity from its brain-stem "arousal center." In the normal animal some minimal activity in the afferent (sensory) neural channel is necessary to maintain an adequate arousal level.

While the arousal-level concept is of relatively recent interest to psychologists, and is generally attributed to a fairly high neural structure. It is probably of a much more basic and widespread nature than is generally recognized. An all-pervasive arousal level is probably a condition for survival in all organism possessing true neural tissue, even where a true brain or complex neural ganglion does not exist. In the case of the lowest animals where no true nervous tissue can be found, there is still some sort of arousal level or condition of irritability, dependent upon external stimulation. It is for this reason that maintenance of arousal level has been given first priority as a function of the senses.

Direct Survival

Many senses operate at a subconscious, reflexive-behavior level. Our internal senses are, by and large, of this nature. We may be aware of

hunger, thirst, and internal pain, but the great bulk of our internal receptors which aid in the regulation of blood pressure, body temperature, and
water transfer perform their functions quietly, efficiently, and without
fanfare. Probably they reach a state of awareness only by indirect means;
in some cases it is the adjustment to the imbalance that we perceive.

A goodly proportion of sensory functioning in lower animals is of
this unlearned, reflexive nature, involving in many cases structures analogous to our smooth muscles and associated autonomic nervous system.
In addition to simple reflexes like the human knee-jerk, which certainly
reaches a conscious level, and the pupillary response, which does not evoke
a conscious experience, countless other sensory phenomena with a direct
survival value can be enumerated.

The simple tropisms of lower animals are an excellent example of
such functioning. As we have noted earlier, if you place a number of
paramecia in a watch glass and locate two oppositely charged electrodes
near the edge of the glass, and across from each other, the little animals
will swarm toward the negatively charged pole. This is not the same as a
magnet attracting iron filings; the organisms appear to be traversing
the distance under their own power. Why they go in this direction we
don't know. What is even more strange, you will always find several of
the little rascals going in the opposite direction! Theories of electrically
differing potentials in growing protoplasm might account for the behavior of *most* of the paramecia, but not those contrary individuals. We
have a lot to learn about "simple" behavior.

Animals at a phylogenetic level much higher than the single-celled
paramecia also exhibit tropistic behavior. Moths fly toward a light,
salmon (when their reproductive condition is propitious) swim upstream,
and some fishes navigate by means of magnetic fields. Newly hatched
turtles of at least one species find their way to the ocean for the first time
as a result of a positive phototropism. The sky over the water is brighter
than that over the land, and the newly hatched reptiles are attracted by
the light, thereby finding their way, for the first time, to the ocean.

Many animals, such as the earthworm, are negatively phototropic.
Light, and especially moving shadows produced by the light, cause them
to withdraw into their holes.

As an additional example of the unlearned, complex forms of behavior we call tropisms, or if complicated enough, instincts, we should
include the echolocation behavior of bats and the polarized light sensitivity of honey bees. All of these, and surely countless others, are examples of the way nature has provided her creatures with simple yet
highly specialized sensory capabilities to enable them to compete successfully with their enviroments and other, often more highly specialized,
predators.

Indirect Survival

For want of a better term a number of other sensory uses have been lumped into this category. Our senses enable us to avoid many potentially destructive difficulties. We can see (and hear) the approaching truck in time to step aside. We can spit out the foul tasting substance which might very well be poisonous. The deer can smell the dog or wolf in time to take evasive action, and the dog can often locate his next meal by smelling the trail left by the fleeing rabbit.

At a much higher level of sophistication and development we can hear our neighbor when he tells us that our local emporium has a special today on Scotch. Without communication based on such sensory capabilities, we would have to drink water from the nearest rippling brook, like our subhuman animal friends or our primate ancestors.

When, by evolution, an organism has developed to the point where his tropistic behaviors are inadequate—that is, where much of his invariant behavior has been replaced by a capability for more highly varied behavior—the need for such sensory-perceptual flexibility is apparent. The dog must learn (or know by some means) that one animal (a rabbit) is a delicacy and another similar one (a skunk or a porcupine) is inedible and can be quite troublesome.

It should be obvious to the reader that sensory functions which serve such purposes will be of predominate or almost exclusive interest in this book.

Creation of Pleasure

Some sensory stimulation appears to evoke a reaction we might, for want of a better term, call pleasure (Pfaffman, 1960). Music, rhythm, some odors and tastes, and in some cases gentle physical contact produce feelings of pleasure or joy. While a large portion of human pleasure is undoubtedly the result of learning, there is recent evidence that the concept of "pleasure" goes much deeper.

It may be anthropomorphic to say that a lower animal experiences pleasure; certainly no animal has so reported. We can, however, define the word operationally: an animal is said to experience pleasure if he does nothing to terminate some activity or if he performs in such a way as to continue the activity. One of the oldest parts of the brain, the limbic system, has been found to be of importance in the experiencing of pleasure (MacLean, 1954). If a positive brain area (there are also negative areas) is stimulated electrically as a result of bar pressing, even a hungry rat will often continue pressing the bar that stimulates his limbic system in preference to another bar that would result in his obtaining food (Olds, 1966).

Certainly human infants seem to experience pleasure as a natural result of some forms of simple stimulation. Gentle rocking, stroking, and caressing, and soft rhythmic sounds result in behavior on the part of the infant that gives every indication of being the result of pleasure. Babies may coo, gurgle, and at a later age smile in such a way that we are forced to say they are enjoying themselves. Some of this apparent pleasure *may* arise from simple conditioning, but some is surely of a more direct nature.

SUMMARY

In this chapter we have considered a little more of the background leading to the study of the individual senses. We examined the role played by the sense organs and their general location in the grand scheme of things. We also examined, in some detail, the phylogenetic development of sense organs from amoeba to man, from single cell to multicellular organisms and from radial to bilateral symmetry. We tried to learn, in simple-minded fashion, the nature of the underlying neural activity and how it relates to sensory organ functioning. We considered how the nervous system is set into action by an external source of energy and considered the efficacy of a generator potential in setting off the neural impulse. Finally we examined the uses the organism may make of sensory/perceptual information in maintaining an activity level, meeting the exigencies of life, and sometimes obtaining pleasure.

SUGGESTED READINGS

1. Miller, W. H., F. Ratliff, and H. K. Hartline, "How Cells Receive Stimuli," *Scientific American,* September 1961. This twelve-page article traces in excellent fashion the development of knowledge concerning the underlying behavior of sensory cells. It is excellent reading for those interested in the concept of the generator potential and how it has been studied. References to the work of Granit, Katz, Hartline, MacNichol and others give the article historical significance.
2. Bell, C., "Idea of a New Anatomy of the Brain," from W. Dennis, *Readings in the History of Psychology* (New York: Appleton, 1948). I am recommending this article for its historical interest. Written in 1811 by one of the truly great anticipators of modern sensory physiology, this article summarizes much of what was known about the nervous system at that time which is of interest to our subject. The 12 pages are at times a little tedious in style, but for the reader interested in historical perspective they are certainly worth reading.
3. Mueller, J., "The Specific Energies of Nerves," from W. Dennis, *Readings in the History of Psychology* (New York: Appleton, 1948). This reference

is included because it is a classic in the field. It is the first explicit formulation of the doctrine which describes the relation of sense-organ response to experience, based on the nature of the eliciting stimulus; that experience depends upon *which* neural elements are activated and not *how* they respond. In these 12 pages Mueller describes in logical fashion the development of the theory, its defense, and its significance for future studies. For the serious student interested in historical perspective, this too is a worthwhile, albeit somewhat difficult reading.

4. From E. G. Boring, *Sensation and Perception in the History of Experimental Psychology* (New York: Appleton, 1942). I suggested Chapters 1 and 2 of Boring's classic for the preceding chapter. Chapter 2 of this reference (pp. 52–90) is of particular interest now, and should be read by the serious student. After twenty-seven years the presentation of Boring still has excellent historical perspective and is a must for the serious student. Topics of nerve conduction, sensory conduction, specific nerve energies, projection, and isomorphism are all of importance as a groundwork for later, more narrowly directed emphases.

5. Pfeiffer, J., *The Cell*. Life Science Library (New York: Time, Inc., 1964). The two hundred pages of this reference are well worth the reading, although direct application to the subject matter of sensation and perception is not great. I am recommending this book because I believe it provides one of the finest, most painless approaches to an overall understanding of life and the living cell. It is profusely illustrated, written in a relatively simple style, and above all interesting. It can be read profitably by anyone in the biological sciences.

6. From N. L. Munn, *Psychological Development* (Boston: Houghton, 1938). This older book is worthwhile reading from cover to cover. However, Chapter VI, Development of Behavior from Conception to Birth, pages 165–211, is particularly relevant to our consideration of embryological development. It elaborates on several of the topics discussed in this chapter in a highly interesting and readable manner. This *is* an interesting as well as informative reference.

7. S. S. Stevens (ed.), *Handbook of Experimental Psychology* (New York: Wiley, 1951). See Chapters 2 and 3, Excitation and Conduction in the Neuron and Synaptic Mechanisms by F. Brink, Jr. These 70 pages are probably the most technical of the references suggested to this point. They provide a wealth of information for the serious student and must be highly recommended. This entire volume should be familiar to the serious student who plans to emphasize sensation/perception in his professional future.

8. Mellon, DeForest, Jr., *The Physiology of Sense Organs*, University Reviews in Biology (San Francisco: Freeman, 1968). This is the most technical and topical of the readings suggested for this section. With chapters such as Principles of Stimulus Coding, the Depolarizing Nature of the Trigger, and Origins of the Receptor Potential, this book of 100 pages is particularly intended for the serious student with a sincere interest in the nature of the sensory event.

3

METHODS FOR STUDYING THE SENSES—I

BACKGROUND

The classical definition of psychophysics, "the science of the functional relations, or relations of dependency, between the body and the mind," stems from the great landmark of experimental psychology, G. T. Fechner's *Element der Psychophysik* (Boring, 1942). Published in 1860, this important book brought together, summarized, and elaborated on the new science of mind-body relations. Fechner did not invent psychophysics, but he did describe the existing methods, modify some, and mold the varying viewpoints of the times into a coherent discipline. For this reason Fechner is often referred to as the father of psychophysics.

Like most scientific progress, psychophysics developed as a child of the times, a product of a broader, general evolution in knowledge, as one aspect of the developing Gesellschaft. The early part of the nineteenth century saw a tremendous upswing in science. Astronomers were discovering sophisticated observation and mensuration techniques, physics was growing by leaps and bounds, and physiologists were starting to measure everything in sight. An attempt to quantify the heretofore philosophical discipline of psychology was inevitable.

The study of sensation as a separate discipline owed much of its early impetus to the Bell-Magendie law. While it was not a completely new idea that sensations and responses should have separate neural bases, it remained for Charles Bell to show, in 1811, that sensory and motory nerves at the spinal cord are indeed separate. With Magendie's more convincing experiment in 1822, the groundwork for studying sensory processes was well laid. Johannes Mueller's expansion (1826) of the Bell-Magendie principle into the doctrine of specific energies of nerves was another important step leading to the developemnt of a science of sensations, and its principle tool, psychophysics. (See readings from Chapter 1 for both Bell and Mueller.)

In 1834 E. H. Weber established what Fechner was later to call Weber's law: that two sensations are just noticeably different as long as the intensities of their stimuli bear a constant ratio to each other. While we now know better, Weber believed that the same ratio between two stimuli would always result in a just noticeable difference. The skin, for example, according to Weber, could always appreciate the difference in two weights if said difference had a ratio of one-thirtieth, regardless of the absolute values of the weights. We normally encounter Weber's law written in the form $\triangle I/I=k$; where I is a stimulus value, $\triangle I$ is a barely noticeable increment of I, and k is a constant for a given observer and a specified condition.

Another milestone occurred when Fechner proceeded to modify and extend Weber's law into what has come to be known as Fechner's law. Fechner's law can be stated: $S=k \log I$, where S stands for a sensation, k is a constant, and I is a measure of stimulus intensity in threshold units. Like Weber's law, Fechner's law works to some extent, but it would be grossly gratuitous to say that Fechner succeeded in actually measuring a pure sensation as he originally believed.

In spite of the relative inadequacies of Weber's and Fechner's Laws, and the criticism of those who objected to the measurement of the "incorporeal mind" the new science did grow rapidly (Boring, 1942).

Three basic psychophysical methods were described in great detail by Fechner in his now famous book. In addition to the original three, today there are numerous other measures that may be obtained by conventional and near-conventional psychophysical techniques, along with as many modifications as there are experimenters using them. Moreover, modern scaling techniques and the application of methodologies borrowed from mathematics and engineering have greatly enhanced the potential for sensory measurement.

FECHNER'S METHODS

Let us take a brief look at Fechner's three methods. Later in this chapter we will describe them in more detail and include some additional approaches.

Method of Limits

In the method of limits or *minimal change*, a stimulus is changed in successive, discrete steps until a point is reached where the subject changes his response. One can start with a stimulus which cannot be detected, and in discrete, usually equal steps, increase the intensity until the subject changes his response to "I see it," "I hear it," or what have you. Or, the stimulus can be above threshold to start with and decreased in successive steps until the response indicates it can no longer be detected. Such a procedure results in an absolute threshold, usually abbreviated AL for absolute limen, or more traditionally, RL for reiz limen.

The method of limits can also be used to evaluate stimulus differences in the manner of Weber's procedure. In this case "differences" between two suprathreshold stimuli are manipulated in serial steps until the subject reports "same" or "different" depending, of course, on the direction of the change. Also called the method of just noticeable differences, this method results in a DL or difference limen.

Method of Right and Wrong Cases

The method of right and wrong cases was the second method promulgated by Fechner. More commonly called the *constant* or *constant-stimuli method,* this technique involves the presentation of the stimuli in random or quasi-random order. The subject merely expresses his response in terms of "experience it" or "do not experience it," usually simplified to "yes" or "no." This method results in a psychometric function, a curve of percentage "yes" (or "no") plotted against stimulus magnitude. In a modification of the method, known as the *constant stimulus-difference method,* differences of varying size are presented in random or quasi-random fashion, the subject reporting on the existence or nonexistence of a difference. The stimuli for which differences are judged may be presented simultaneously, as in the case of visual stimuli, or sequentially as in the case of auditory signals. This method is one of the most flexible and useful of all the psychophysical methods. It can be used for the obtaining of numerous additional measures as well as absolute and difference thresholds. Because of its broad application it has been the subject of considerable controversy with respect to details of its use and interpretation of its results.

Method of Average Error

In this method the subject is provided with a standard stimulus and some means of manipulating a comparison stimulus. It is also called the *production method,* and rather appropriately the *method of adjustment.* The subject, himself, in adjusting the comparison stimulus, produces any error that may occur. Most of the psychophysical measurements obtainable by the previously described methods can be obtained by the method of average error. One advantage of the method is that reliance on verbal behavior such as "yes," "no," "larger," "smaller," or "equal," is eliminated. On the other hand, sensory experiences are probably confounded with motory activities, and just what is being measured may be subject to some dispute.

While these methods may result in measures with similar names, it should be emphasized that they are not completely interchangeable. A threshold determined by an adjustment method may not be the same as one derived from a constant method. Similarly, such indexes as intervals of uncertainty and difference thresholds are influenced by the method used to obtain them. The final determination of which method is to be used must depend on the nature of the situation and the use to which the results are to be applied. To fully understand the various techniques as presented in detail in the following pages, this fact must be borne in mind.

USES FOR PSYCHOPHYSICS

A great number of different measures can be obtained by conventional psychophysics, and more recently developed techniques have greatly expanded this potential. Let us examine briefly some of the measures which psychophysical techniques make available to us.

Absolute Threshold (AL)

This was one of the three measures of primary interest to Fechner and the other early workers in the field, and can be obtained either directly or indirectly by most of the major psychophysical methods. The absolute threshold is that point where a stimulus reaches the level of consciousness as evidenced by positive response on the part of the subject. An example might be the minimum intensity of a spot of light (wavelength and spot size would have to be held constant) that can just be detected. A mariner searching for a very dim star is utilizing his absolute threshold for light intensity.

There are numerous ways in which the absolute threshold can be determined. It can be calculated mathematically as in the constant methods (a level observed 50 percent of the time), directly as in the method of limits, or manually as in a production or adjustment method. When we discuss the principal methods in detail we will see just how the AL is determined by them.

In all fairness it should be pointed out that the concept of an absolute threshold is not without its critics. The classical idea that there is a physiological point where a stimulus suddenly has an effect on the organism is not accepted by many modern workers. Rather than a threshold stimulus being that point where something is "pushed over the brink" and immediate awareness results, modern thinking takes into consideration ongoing processes of the organism and the idea that a threshold is little more than a point in a mathematical-temporal curve. Continuity is especially stressed by contemporary researchers who use such tools as probability theory and detection theory, emphasizing the signal-in-noise nature of threshold measurement. In spite of such criticism, I feel that a description of the classical AL and its interpretation is warranted. Just bear in mind that perhaps it should be interpreted as a useful predictive construct and not as some immutable natural limit.

Difference Threshold (DL)

This is the second measure emphasized by the early workers and described in detail by Fechner. The object of this measure is to determine the smallest change in a stimulus which can be detected by an observer. For convenience, a frequency of 50 percent detection is normally accepted as defining the point of the difference threshold. Perhaps it might be better to call it the *absolute threshold for a difference,* rather than the difference threshold, since most of what was said concerning the absolute threshold also applies to the determination of the difference threshold. Most of the simpler psychophysical methods can be used for its determination, and the same sort of healthy skepticism of the measure is pointed to by modern theorists.

But, as in the case of the absolute threshold the concept of a difference threshold has utility as a predictive device, even if not based on an absolutely sound theoretical structure. For example, there has been research accomplished by three organizations as diverse as a large liquor distiller, a large soap manufacturer, and the United States Air Force, all of which involved the determination of difference thresholds by rather conventional techniques. In one the problem was to determine the amount of chance variability in caramel coloring that could be tolerated (not easily detected) in separate batches of whiskey, one was concerned with the amount of perfume to be added to soap, and the other involved the size of disks of light on a vertical display panel.

Sensory Equivalence

This measure determines how one stimulus must change in order to be equivalent (or equal) to another in some specified attribute. For example, how intense must a pure tone of 100 Hz (cycles per second) be in order for it to sound as loud as a tone of 1,000 Hz? Actually, we can give no simple answer to this question, but must resort to rather complex and detailed curves which include the actual level of the sounds as well as their differences. For example, if the 1,000-Hz tone has an intensity of a normal voice level, or 70 db (decibels), the 100-Hz tone must be about ten times as intense in order to result in an equivalent apparent loudness. On the other hand, if the amplitude of the 1,000-Hz tone is quite low, then the 100-Hz tone may have to be 40 db more intense (10,000 times as powerful) in order to result in equivalent loudness.*

We can, by means of psychophysics, ask many other questions involving sensory equivalence, such as: how intense must a red light be in order to appear as bright as a green light, or how much pressure is required on the tips of the fingers to be equivalent to a given pressure on the forearm. Questions such as these are certainly intriguing and often of considerable value in our modern world. As in the case of equivalent sound intensities, however, the result of most sensory equivalence studies are complex, many-faceted relationships, never as simple as Fechner's law would lead us to believe.

Rank Order

Several of the psychophysical methods are ideally suited for developing psychological scales of sensory experience. That is, scales of such things as loudness, sweetness, and pain, and with some reservations scales of even less concrete experiences such as pleasure or love.

The simplest scale for describing experience-bound data would seem to be a nominal scale wherein experiences are simply given names, and no attempt is made to order or in any way set values to them. Indeed, this was all the ancients thought possible. Today we can go much farther, deriving ordinal, interval, and even ratio scales. In this and the following two sections we will examine briefly the uses of psychophysics which may result in ordinal, interval, and ratio scales.

Often encountered in the case of subject matter which does not easily lend itself to quantification, ordering is a rather straightforward uncomplicated procedure. Very simply, given a series of stimuli, what is their correct order according to some specified attribute? For example, rank the American League shortstops with respect to their worth to their respective teams. An ordinal scale such as this is probably superior to a nominal scale which would simply have such statements as "good fielder," "fair hitter," "hits in the clutch," etc. Another example might be to rank ten paintings for their artistic merit. Rank order is probably the simplest of several methods for obtaining numerical data from situations wherein subjective judgments might appear to be the sole alternative.

* The interested reader should not worry too much at this point about the meaning of db or decibel. For the time being it is sufficient to understand that Hz is a measure of frequency and db is a measure of intensity or power. Its meaning and full significance will be considered in detail at a later time.

Sensory Distance

A cup of coffee with a teaspoon of sugar is sweeter than one with a half-teaspoon of sugar. A cup with one and one-half teaspoons of sugar is sweeter than one with a single teaspoon. But are the differences in sweetness the same? Several methods lend themselves to the establishment of scales for sense differences, such that defined stimulus values along a continuum result in equal sensory or experiential intervals.

As another example, is the difference in pitch between C and G for different octaves on the piano the same? Certainly the differences in frequency are not the same, but for pitch (the psychological experience of frequency) the two sensory intervals certainly approach in distance the equality they were intended to achieve. On the basis of such data it is possible to construct a scale of pitch which meets the mathematical requirements for an interval scale.

As we will discover later, specialized techniques have been developed to study sensory distance. One noteworthy procedure requires the subject to bisect a sensory distance. For example, what pitch is halfway between C and G? Or how much sugar makes a cup of coffee midway in sweetness between a cup with one-half teaspoon and one with one and a half teaspoons? While results of such experiments are not always clear-cut and precise, agreement among experimenters and subjects does tend to be rather remarkable, and the existence of interval scales for sensory experience is not beyond reason. Unfortunately, they too are not as simple as Weber and Fechner might have anticipated.

Sensory Ratios

The most sophisticated outcome of psychophysics should be, I suspect, the development of sensory scales with equal sense ratios. Such an accomplishment would make possible such statements as "twice as loud," "three times as sweet," and "half as painful." With the development of such scales we would also have the capability of adding and subtracting stimuli with predictable results. We might know, for example, when two stimuli could be expected to produce twice the sensory experience of one. This is indeed a difficult area, and only for a few restricted experience modalities do we have anything today approaching satisfactory ratio scales. I feel, however, that this is one application of psychophysics with a tremendous future. It is necessary before we can hope to achieve anything approaching a complete understanding of sensory organ/central nervous system functioning.

Let us look at some of the psychophysical methods in somewhat more detail. The interested reader is encouraged to obtain additional details from the readings at the end of the chapter. The reference by J. P. Guilford is particularly recommended.

METHOD OF LIMITS

Also called the method of minimal change or serial exploration, as indicated earlier, this basic method can be used for the determination of thresholds, both absolute and difference. Indeed, this is the primary purpose of the method of limits—to determine thresholds. Let us examine the method in somewhat more detail as it has been utilized for the determination of the two types of thresholds.

Absolute Threshold (AL or RL)

The relation between a physical continuum and its corresponding psychological continuum is not as straightforward as, for example, the relation between the position of a needle on a voltmeter and the voltage being fed into the meter. Perhaps there is no such thing as a point where a stimulus "suddenly" has an effect on the organism, like the straw that breaks the camel's back. Rather, there is likely a range wherein experiencing or failing to experience a sensation is largely a function of chance—that is, the result of countless, often indeterminate factors of attention, background noise, physiological processes, and heaven knows what else. Moreover, the criterion of what constitutes a suprathreshold stimulus must also be taken into consideration. As a consequence, the point where a stimulus may be said to evoke a response in an organism must be defined statistically. By convention, the absolute threshold is usually defined as that condition in which the signal is detected 50 percent of the time.

It should also be pointed out at this time that the definition of an AL does not always imply a *detection* threshold. While often we are interested in determining a threshold for detection there are other AL's of interest to us. For example, we may have an AL for light detection, but we might also have an absolute threshold for color discrimination, for form recognition (the optometrist's familiar chart), and for even more complex perceptual processes. It should be rather obvious to the reader that the amount of light necessary to read the optometrist's chart would be appreciably greater than that required to simply know that it is there. The AL is a threshold for a psychological experience and is not restricted to a threshold for detection.

Procedure. For the following discussion we will refer to the AL for detection, but the same logic and general procedure could be applied to the other, more sophisticated threshold functions referred to earlier. An AL is determined by presenting to the subject series of stimuli, chang-

Direction of Presentation

Stimulus Value, db re .0002 dyne/cm^2	A	D	A	D	A	D	A	D	A	D
40						X				
38						X				
36		X				X		X		
34		X		X		X		X		X
32		X		X		X		X		X
30		X		X	X	X		X		X
28	X	X		X	−	X		X		X
26	−	X	X	X	−	−		−	X	−
24	−	−	−	X	−				−	
22	−		−	−	−		X		−	
20	−		−		−		−		−	
18	−		−						−	
16	−								−	
14	−								−	
12	−								−	
	27	25	25	23	29	27	21	27	25	27

Ascending threshold − 25.4 db.
Descending threshold − 25.8 db.
Absolute threshold   − 25.6 db.
Range of uncertainty − 25.4 − 25.8 db = 0.4 db.

FIG. 3-1.   Sample record sheet for method of limits. Calculation of absolute threshold for 600-Hz tone.

ing in magnitude by small, discrete steps. For one series of presentations the stimulus is started at a level below the threshold and increased by increments until the subject provides a positive response. There may or may not be a secondary cue to indicate when the stimulus is presented. In determining the AL for tone perception, there might be a light to indicate when the stimulus is being presented. The subject then indicates by pressing a button, for example, when he hears the tone. To prevent erroneous responses due to suggestion the light cue may be omitted.

Along with the ascending series of presentations, descending series are normally employed. In this case the starting stimulus is suprathreshold and is reduced by small increments until the subject can no longer detect it.

A sample work sheet for a method of limits determination of an absolute threshold is shown as Fig. 3-1. In this example an AL for tonal
detection was determined with 2 db intensity increments for ten series of
presentations. The first presentation (A for ascending) was clearly subthreshold, with a level of 12 db; the second presentation was 14 db, the
third 16 db, etc., until the subject gave a positive response at 28 db. In
the second presentation series (D for descending), a clearly audible signal
(36 db) was used as the starting point. (In actual practice, a short preliminary investigation may be required in order to locate the approximate
AL before setting up the detailed experiment). Note that in successive
runs the subthreshold and suprathreshold starting points are widely varied
in order to discourage guessing and similar unwanted contamination
effects.

Difficulties and Limitations. There are several problems and possible
sources of error inherent in the method of limits which must be avoided
or in some way controlled. One of these is *errors of habituation.* A subject
may get into a habit of saying "no . . . no . . . no . . ." for so long that he
completely misses the point where the stimulus is indeed above threshold.
In the descending direction, if the subject expects five or six successive
suprathresholds signals he may continue reporting them as "yes" when he
can in fact detect nothing. A personality factor of extreme carefulness may
enter into a person's judgment, a refusal to change his response until he is
sure beyond the shadow of a doubt that a change at threshold level has
occurred.

Other subjects commit errors of anticipation. They *expect* the signal
to change; perhaps they count the number of subthreshold signals and
decide that the next one simply *must* be above threshold; perhaps they
are just trying too hard to please the experimenter. In any event, errors
of anticipation are of serious consequence in the determination of the AL.
On the other hand, errors of habituation and anticipation are only exag-
gerations of normal behavior. All subjects lie somewhere along a continuum of habituation and anticipation.

Both of these errors, habituation and anticipation, can be controlled to
a large extent. Probably the most important consideration is adequate
motivation and training, along with good instructions. Ideally, all subjects
should operate with the same self-instructions and the same criterion for
certainty/uncertainty. Considering individual personality differences, such
an ideal situation is not likely, but with adequate instructions and training a subject *can* at least establish his own standards and adhere to them.

Several methods are also available to detect subjects highly prone to
such errors, and thereby allow for additional instructions and training, or
as a last resort, elimination of the culpable subjects. If we start with a
subthreshold stimulus and keep repeating it without changing its value

a good subject will not make the error of anticipating, that is a "yes" response. Similarly, repeating a suprathreshold stimulus several times without decreasing its value will serve as a check for anticipation in the opposite direction. Habituation can be detected by occasionally slipping in an increment much greater than normal, or by starting a series with a suprathreshold stimulus when the subject expects a stimulus at a level below his threshold. Such "tricks" are never a part of the actual data collection. They are simply thrown in now and then to keep the subject on the ball and to insure his proper level of performance.

Results. A number of measures are obtainable with the method of limits. We can, for example, locate a threshold for the ascending series of presentations. Note that in Fig. 3-1 the value required for detection in the first ascending series was 27 db (halfway between the highest undetected and lowest detected values); the value for the second ascending series was 25 db; and so on for the five ascending series. The average of these five was 25.4 db, the AL for the ascending series. For the descending series the mean AL is 25.8 db. Note that we seem to have an indication of a slight habituation effect. If there were a true "physiological threshold" and if we had a perfect subject, the AL should be the same for both the ascending and descending series. Since, however, the ascending and descending series rarely result in the same value for the threshold, the true absolute threshold is usually taken as their arithmetic mean. In Fig. 3-1 the AL would be 25.6 db.

The difference between those judgments based on the ascending series and those based on the descending series may be of significance in some cases. Called the range of uncertainty (RU), it is a measure of the difficulty of the task and the performance of the subject. If there were no range of uncertainty (RU=0) one would suspect that the increments used were too large or that one had a subject with amazing discriminative capability.

Several other measures can, if desired, be obtained from this method. Given enough repetitions (normally more than ten series would be used), one can calculate the variability (standard deviation, standard error of mean, etc.) for the various threshold measures, thus having an index of the subject's consistency or a comparison between subjects.

If the alternated ascending and descending series are presented in sufficient quantity and over a long enough time period, it is possible to show the curve of learning, as indicated by decreasing range of uncertainty and/or increased consistency.

Difference Threshold (DL)

The method of limits can also be used to obtain difference thresholds. By definition, the DL is defined as that difference between two stimuli which is detected 50 percent of the time. When used in this way, it is a stimulus difference rather than a stimulus value which is detected, and the method is sometimes called the *method of just noticeable differences.*

Procedure. In this method a standard and a comparison stimulus are presented together and compared for equality. As a function of serial increments (or decrements) to the comparison stimulus the subject indicates whether they are alike or different. In some cases he may be required to indicate which one is larger, brighter, sweeter, etc. The two stimuli may be spatially separated, as in the case of visual stimuli, or temporally as in the case of acoustic signals. One advantage of this method for determing DL's is that it does it directly; the subject reports on just noticeable differences (jnd's) or just *not* noticeable differences (jnnd's) depending upon the direction of change. If the two stimuli are the same to start with, then the subject discovers a just noticeable difference; if the starting point has two stimuli which are different, then the point to be located represents, a just *not* noticeable difference.

An example of a work sheet for this method is shown as Fig. 3-2. In this hypothetical experiment, a standard weight of 10 grams was com-

Direction of Presentation

Weight of Comparison Stimulus, grams	A	D	A	D	A	D	A	D	A	D	
20		H				H				H	
18		H		H	H	H		H		H	
16		H		H	H	H		H		H	
14		H		H	=	H	H	H		H	
12	H	=	H	=	=	=	=	=	H	H	
10	=	=	=	=	L	=	=	=	=	=	
8	=	L	L	L	L	L	L	=	L	=	
6	L		L		L		L	L	L	L	
4	L		L		L		L		L		
2	L				L				L		
Lu	11	13	11	13	15	13	13	13	11	11	(12.6)
Ll	7	9	9	9	11	9	9	7	9	7	(8.6)

Point of subjective equality = 10.6 g.
Range of uncertainty = 8.6 – 12.6 g. = 4.0 g.
Constant error = 10.6 – 10.0 = 0.6 g.
Difference threshold = 2.0 g.

FIG. 3-2. Sample record sheet for method of limits. Calculation of difference threshold for lifted weights with 10 gram standard.

pared with a variable or comparison weight to determine the DL, or that increment in weight which could be detected 50 percent of the time. We will, of course, get two DL's one for a comparison stimulus greater than the standard and one for the situation when the comparison stimulus is the lighter.

In the first ascending series the comparison stimulus first had a weight of 2 grams and was called "lighter," a 4-gram weight and a 6-gram weight were also called "lighter," but both the 8- and 10-gram weights were called "equal" to the 10. The 12-gram weight was called "heavier" and brought the first series to a conclusion. In the first descending series the comparison stimuli of 20-, 18-, 16-, and 14-gram weights were all called "heavier" than the standard 10-gram weight. The 12- and 10-gram weights were judged to be equal to the standard and the 8-gram weight was called "lighter."

As can be seen from Fig. 3-2 two separate limen must be determined for each series, Lu and Ll (u and l for upper and lower) and then averages of each must be calculated. Does this mean that our DL is both 2.6 (12.6 −10 and 1.4 (10−8.6)? That would not make much sense, two DL's for a single standard stimulus. Look again; the average value for the comparison called "equal" is really 10.6 grams [(12.6+8.6)/2] and not 10. In other words, the comparison stimulus, in order to be judged equal to the 10-gram weight had to weigh, on the average, 10.6 grams, an error of 0.6 gram. In the language of the psychophysicist the PSE (point of subjective equality) is 10.6 grams and the Constant Error is 0.6 gram. Such constant errors in the method of just noticeable differences are not at all rare and are due to such procedural influences as time differences, space differences, fatigue, or set. Even when highly balanced designs are employed some constant error is often found; the PSE is not identical to the value of the standard stimulus.

The DL then must be the average distance between the PSE and the mean Lu or Ll. In our example the difference threshold, that difference which can be detected 50 percent of the time, is exactly 2 grams (12.6− 10.6 or 10.6− 8.6). Or, looking at it another way, the DL is one-half the Range of Uncertainty (Lu−Ll).

Difficulties and Limitations. The method of just noticeable differences is applicable to most situations where a DL is needed. It should be emphasized, however, that a DL determined by a method of limits is frequently not the same as one derived by the constant methods (see next section). Both methods provide for a measure called a *difference threshold*) but apparently they are not measuring the same thing—perhaps equality is not the opposite of difference!

We also know that if a subject were to continue after his first report beyond "equal" he might again return to "equal," especially if the increments are exceedingly small and the task difficult. How we can handle such a situation is not clear, so we generally avoid it by stopping as soon as one transition beyond the last equal judgment has been made.

Many of the same difficulties mentioned with respect to AL determination also apply to DL determination. I recall one subject, for instance, who would go through an entire series of responses: "low . . . low . . . low . . . low . . . equal . . . high" without the experimenter ever having changed the comparison stimulus! Such subjects, of course, are simply not suited for their tasks, and unless they can be adequately trained they are useless. Indeed, in this case one is making a personality evaluation and not running a psychophysical experiment.

Measures. While the primary measures obtainable are the DL and the Range of Uncertainty, the method of just noticeable differences also allows for additional measures. Rather obviously, a Weber fraction ($\Delta I/I$) can be obtained quite directly. Also separate DL's for ascending and descending series are obtainable, and indications of habituation and anticipation effects are subject to measurement. The interested reader is encouraged to refer to the readings at the end of the chapter for additional details of the methods and its applications.

There are several variations to the method of limits which should be mentioned. One possibility involves a continuous change in the stimulus, rather than changes by discrete steps. At least one type of audiometer (an instrument for measuring hearing sensitivity) presents a pure tone below threshold and gradually increases its level until the patient reports he hears it. This incidentally, is an automatic equipment which records the instantaneous sound level at the point indicated by the patient, and then proceeds to repeat the procedure for additional frequencies until an entire audiogram has been plotted.

When the writer was a graduate student he had access to a visual-acuity device, a car mounted on a track which moved either directly toward or away from the viewer. By means of an acuity chart (like the one your optometrist uses) mounted on the little car, one could determine his threshold (in distance) for reading the letters on the chart. Distance could then be transposed into the familiar 20/20, 20/40 index of visual acuity. Furthermore, the threshold being measured was a resolution threshold, and not a detection threshold such as we have been considering through most of this chapter.

In addition to continuous and systematic presentations such as these, some experimenters have used an haphazard method and one known as the up-and-down method. Methods derived for computer programing "search" in a predetermined but yet flexible manner and are highly effective for automatic determination of both absolute and difference thresholds. Some programs "zero in" to determine thresholds quickly and accurately, leaving the experimenter with little to do except read a tape. Variations to the method seem to be limited only by the experimenter's imagination.

THE CONSTANT METHODS

The constant methods are probably the most frequently used, most flexible, and universally applicable of all the psychophysical methods. Indeed, one often uses one of the other methods to locate parameters

Fig. 3-3. Sample graphic determination of an AL by the constant-stimulus method.

approximately, and then adapt one of the constant methods for the experiment proper. Mathematics and procedures for the constant methods have been worked out in almost unlimited detail, and a thorough review would go far beyond the scope of this book. Consequently, we will limit ourselves to highlights only, and the interested reader may go to the original sources if he so desires.

There are two basic forms of the constant method: the constant stimulus method and the method of constant stimulus differences. The unique characteristic of both methods is the calculation of parameters based on percentage of occurrence.

Absolute Threshold (Constant-Stimulus Method)

In the determination of the absolute threshold, a large number of stimuli are presented to the observer in a randomized order, and he merely indicates whether each stimulus is detected or not. The result is a table of percent detections for the full range of stimuli. These may then be plotted on a curve and the 50 percent point taken as the threshold.

Figure 3-3 is an example of a simple determination of an absolute threshold by the constant-stimulus method. The data in the table at the bottom of this figure have been plotted in the curve. A line of best fit has been drawn through the nine points, each point having been determined by the percentage of times the stimulus at the indicated level was detected. A line drawn from the 50 percent point cuts the curve at an intensity level of 21.6 db, and this is taken as the AL. The distance between the 25 and 75 percent points (the middle 50 percent) defines the range of uncertainty, in this case 19.1 to 23.7 db.

It must be emphasized that there are numerous more sophisticated and probably more precise methods of calculation. There are interpolation methods, median methods, extremely complicated curve-fitting methods, and methods which involve the use of tables of mathematical weights aimed at maximizing the influence of those judgments near the limen. Literally hundreds of articles and dozens of often vituperative arguments arose in the past concerning the use of the constant methods. One should not spend undue time on these academic, generally sterile, arguments of philosophical interpretation. For most purposes a simple graphic method such as shown in Fig. 3-3 should be entirely adequate.

Difference Threshold (Constant-Stimulus Difference Method)

This is the most often used of the psychophysical methods. In this method stimuli are presented in pairs, either simultaneously or sequentially, depending upon the sense modality involved and the purposes of the experiment. Unlike the calculation of a DL by the method of limits, in the constant-stimulus difference method, pairs of stimuli are randomized. The subject judges whether the variable stimulus on the right (or on the left, or the second stimulus) is less, equal, or greater than the standard. Ideally, such factors as sequence and position are counterbalanced, with the standard stimulus being presented on the left (or first) half of the time, and on the right (or second) half of the time, in some sort of random arrangement. Or the effects of spatial and temporal arrangement can be retained and teased out in the data analysis if desired. The flexibility of the technique is tremendous, and almost anything of a psychophysical nature can be examined by some modification of the constant-stimulus difference method.

Many of the older, academic discussions referred to earlier also apply to this method. At least one of these arguments should be mentioned. The thinking goes something like this: Any stimulus difference can fit one of three categories: A difference so small that it can never be detected, a difference so large that it can always be detected, and a great gray area where the difference can be detected some of the time. It is this range of uncertainty that presents the problem. What is equal? Is equality a positive attribute or is it negative, the lack of something—this something being, perhaps, the ability to detect a difference. I am not certain that true equality ever does exist. With fine enough measuring instruments we might never find two eggs, for example, that weigh precisely the same. Two things are only equal to the extent that we cannot detect a difference.

Some experimenters have argued that three category judgments including "equal" should not be permitted, that a subject must respond with "greater than" or "less than" to all stimulus pairs, even when they are physically alike. Difference thresholds may be smaller when the subject cannot take the easy way out and say "equal" whenever in doubt. Other researchers insist that the perception of equality is a legitimate psychological experience, and that omitting it from the acceptable responses of the subject adds intolerably to the artificiality of the situation.

Some additional arguments concern the methodology used to calculate the numerous possible psychophysical measures. What is the significance of a range of uncertainty for two-category judgments as contrasted with a three-category procedure? Considerable argument and a lot of complex mathematics has resulted from the dilemma of two-category versus three-category judgments. The best solution is that first each situation must be examined for its own unique requirements, and second "you pays your money and you takes your choice."

A third category of "equal" or perhaps better defined as "not different" judgments can be included, with the stipulation that subjects should

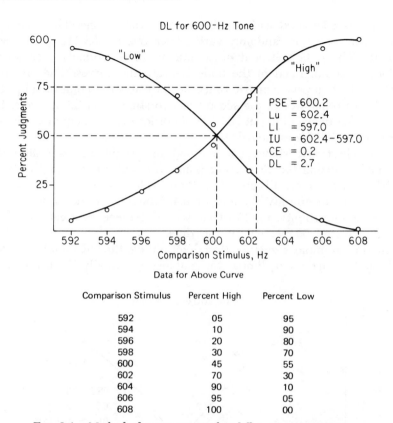

DL for 600-Hz Tone

PSE = 600.2
Lu = 602.4
Ll = 597.0
IU = 602.4 − 597.0
CE = 0.2
DL = 2.7

Data for Above Curve

Comparison Stimulus	Percent High	Percent Low
592	05	95
594	10	90
596	20	80
598	30	70
600	45	55
602	70	30
604	90	10
606	95	05
608	100	00

Fig. 3-4. Method of constant-stimulus differences; two-category judgments. Subjects judged whether a comparison stimulus was "higher" or "lower" in pitch than a 600-Hz standard tone.

be encouraged to make positive judgments and avoid judgments "equal" whenever possible. As in all the psychophysical methods, standardized, clear, and forceful instructions to the subjects are very important.

For calculation purposes the "equal" judgments may or may not be included. In the case of DL's they would appear to be useful, if not essential; if a PSE is the objective of the study, then inclusion of equal judgments in the calculations probably adds very little, since they affect only the precision of the measure and not its absolute value.

Sample Problems. Figure 3-4 shows a graphic analysis of data obtained from a constant stimulus difference experiment based on two-category judgments.* In this experiment a standard auditory tone of

* Actually, in this experiment I permitted "equal" judgments, but for the purposes of drawing the psychometric functions I divided the equal judgments proportionately. For example, if a particular condition had 80 judgments "high," 20 judgments "low," and 10 judgments "equal," the latter would have been divided eight "low" and two "high."

600 Hz was compared with a subsequent variable tone. The second or comparison tone was randomly varied from 592 to 608 Hz in two-cycle intervals. The data collected on a number of individuals over several sessions, is summarized in the table beneath the curves. The crossover point for the two psychometric functions indicates the point of subjective equality. In other words, the second of two stimuli, on the average, had to have a frequency of about 600.2 Hz in order to sound equal in pitch to a preceding 600-Hz standard.

This chart also shows one method for calculating the difference threshold, utilizing the 75 percent points for both judgments "low" and "high." Again called Ll and Lu, these values are about 597.0 and 602.4 for an uncertainty interval of 5.4. The DL is then one-half the interval of uncertainty, or 2.7. That is, a difference as great as 2.7 Hz can be detected 50 percent of the time.

In this example a method for determining the DL similar to that used for the method of limits was employed. Actually there are many

Fig. 3-5. Method of constant-stimulus differences; three category judgments. Subjects judged whether a comparison weight was heavier (high), lighter (low), or equal to a 100 gram standard weight.

Data for Above Curve

Comparison Stimulas	Percent High	Percent Equal	Percent Low
84	00	08	92
88	02	15	83
92	10	30	60
96	30	38	32
100	60	30	10
104	85	15	00
108	95	05	00

methods for calculating a difference threshold, as experimenters in the field are far from being in agreement as to which method is best. However, as long as we define it adequately, we may use any legitimate method we choose, bearing in mind that had we used some other, perhaps more sophisticated method, the results would not have been precisely the same.

In Fig. 3-5 an example of three-category data has been plotted. In this case a standard weight of 100 grams was compared with a variable ranging from 84 to 108 grams in 4-gram steps. Note the rather large constant error (3.8 g), probably a time error, since one weight was hefted subsequent to the other, and no counterbalancing was used.

An even greater variety of techniques for determining a wide range of measures is available when "equal" judgments are included in the calculations. And even more differences of opinion are found than was true for the method of limits. Consequently a DL is not present for this example. If we use half the distance between the 50 or 75 percent points as we did before we would be omitting, perhaps wasting, the "equal" category entirely. Some of the techniques do indeed include the "equal" judgments, but their complexity and their disputed status militates against their inclusion in a book of this depth.

Regardless of what technique is used, the three-category presentation does have an advantage in facilitating comparisons of one condition with another. Comparing different curves with their distributions of "equals," for example, can be enlightening to the extent that "uncertainty" can be observed directly rather than by inference. Once more the reader is encouraged to consult the references if he is interested in the nitty-gritty of the numerous methods of calculations and the arguments of the numerous proponents of one method or another.

METHOD OF AVERAGE ERROR

With this method we obtain a true PSE. Also called the *reproduction* or *adjustment method*, this technique circumvents the need to infer a PSE as in the case of the other methods, since the subject himself makes the adjustment on one of the two stimuli until he reaches a point where he can say "Voilà, they are equal!" A practical application of the method can be found in some modern exposure meters, wherein the photographer adjusts a small spot of light until it is the same brightness as its surround.

In may respects the method is similar to the method of limits. The variable stimulus may originate either above or below the standard, and calculations, for the most part, are similar. The principal differences are that the subject makes the adjustment, and a continuous movement rather than discrete steps are generally utilized. In some cases, unlike the method of limits, "bracketing" is permitted. That is, the subject can go slightly beyond the PSE and zero in on it with successive small adjustments until he is satisfied with his match.

The same general advantages and disadvantages mentioned for the method of limits tend to apply to this method. In addition, we must bear in mind that we are not evaluating a sensory/perceptual experience independent of a motory response. In some cases, the error may be confounded by the subject's motory limitations.

There are numerous variations and possible modifications to the method. It can be used for AL determination when employed with a single stimulus. As another variation, discrete step changes rather than continuous changes may be employed. In this case the only difference between an adjustment method and a method of limits would be the identification of *who* makes the change in the variable stimulus.

SUMMARY

In this chapter we looked briefly into the historical background of the psychophysical methods, including the primary contributions of the two pioneers, Weber and Fechner. In addition, we identified six broad uses for psychophysics: the determination of absolute thresholds, difference thresholds, sensory equivalence, rank order, sensory distance, and sensory ratios. Finally, we examined briefly the three primary psychophysical methods: the method of limits, the constant methods, and the method of average error. In the following chapter we will examine additional techniques designed to evaluate more complex sensory/experiential relations.

SUGGESTED READINGS

1. Stevens, S. S. Chapter 1, "Mathematics, Measurement, and Psychophysics," in S. S. Stevens (ed.), *Handbook of Experimental Psychology* (New York: Wiley, 1954). These 49 pages contain a wealth of background information on measurement in general. Number systems, scales of measurement, and a general approach to psychophysics makes this a valuable background source.
2. From J. P. Guilford, *Psychometric Methods*, 2d ed., (New York: McGraw-Hill, 1954). I would suggest Chapter 1 of this reference for a short (19 pages) introduction to psychological measurement in general. While all of this book is of great significance to experimental psychologists, Chapters 4 through 6 (70 pages) might be considered the "bible" for psychophysical methods. Chapters 7 through 12 (190 pages) have similar importance for scaling techniques (to be considered in the next chapter). Although even

the serious student might not sit down and read this book from cover to cover, it should be available for reference when needed.

3. From R. S. Woodworth and H. Schlossberg, *Experimental Psychology,* rev. ed. (New York: Holt, 1954). Chapters 8 and 9 of this excellent text summarize threshold determinations and scaling methods, respectively, in a total of about 75 pages. While not nearly as complete as the previous reference, these two chapters should be familiar to the serious student of psychophysics and experimental method.

4. From J. F. Corso, *The Experimental Psychology of Sensory Behavior* (New York: Holt, 1967). Chapter 7 of this book is a shorter (40 page) up-to-date summary of psychophysical methods with a somewhat different approach, and including descriptions of scaling. It is suggested for its somewhat broader coverage with less depth, as contrasted with the preceding references.

5. Thurstone, L. L., "Psychophysical Methods," in T. G. Andrews (ed.), *Methods of Psychology* (New York: Wiley, 1948). These 34 pages, comprising Chapter 5, provide an excellent coverage of the area of psychophysics. It is written in an easy, readable manner and is highly recommended.

4

METHODS FOR STUDYING THE SENSES—II

The early psychophysical techniques discussed in the preceding chapter, were primarily concerned with determining thresholds and similar physiologically (so the early workers believed) limited constraints on sense-organ performance. Only incidently did they aspire to the development of interval or ratio scales of sensory functioning. While such operationally observed constructs as difference thresholds and just noticeable differences did indeed foretell the development of true phenomenal experience scales, the final development of such scales remained for the future, with more "tools of the trade" being designed specifically for their determination.

In this chapter we examine some of those methods in a somewhat logical sequence, reflecting both historical and procedural perspective. These approaches are both simpler in concept, and in some cases, more sophisticated than the three psychophysical methods considered in the previous chapter.

We conclude this chapter with a brief look at three modern approaches to determining the relation between the external world and the world of experience. While these three approaches are probably too broad to be categorized as psychophysical methods, their inclusion in a book of this type is imperative. They reflect the direction of the future and should be familiar to the contemporary sensory/perceptual psychologist.

METHOD OF RANK ORDER

An order-of-merit technique, because of its simplicity and apparent validity, has much to recommend it. Many evaluations do not lend themselves to quantification, and a rank ordering is the best that can be hoped for. Ordering may be be done directly, with no (or little) reliance on objective measures, such as: "rank seven different odors on a scale of pleasantness-unpleasantness." In this procedure, no attempt is made to equate differences within the scale; that is, no assumption is made that the interval between the fifth and sixth odors is in any way comparable to the difference between the first and second. While this lack of an interval scale may appear to be a drawback, the fact is that in many cases the absence of scores or other quantitative data make any other approach impossible.

Several other examples might be mentioned. Many colleges provide a rank order of their graduates as well as the individual cumulative grade average. In this case rank order, even when a more sophisticated rating is available, is used for purposes of ease of interpretation and comparison.

Determination of automobile-racing champions is based on a form of ranking wherein points are awarded for finishing first, second, and third for each race and then accumulated throughout the season. At the end of the season the driver with the most points is the champion. At our local track the winner of each race receives 50 points, the second place finisher 48 and on down to 2 points for finishing last, Unfortunately. when one driver consistently finishes a half-lap ahead of the bunched second, third, and fourth cars, the point spread for an individual race is incapable of showing this marked supremacy. The winner gets only 2 points more than the second-place finisher whether he wins by a full lap or by six inches. When applied to psychological problems the same lack of direct quantification must be recognized.

There are, however, a number of approaches which, by means of pooling several rankings, attempt to arrive at scales that *do* show relative position with the rankings. Simply averaging the rank of each individual over all the rankings is an obvious step in that direction. In our racing example, over many races the man who always wins would have an average rank of one; the more evenly matched second-, third-, and fourth-place cars would vary in their finishing orders from race to race so that their average rank would be greater than two, thereby resulting in a significant numerical advantage for the consistent winner. The accumulation of points from race to race would accomplish the same thing.

A number of additional, more sophisticated approaches for deriving scales from rank-order data have been advanced at various times. Each of these methods attempts to meet the problem of interpreting pooled results. The characteristic being rated may be distributed normally in the population, distributed rectangularly, or distributed in a markedly skewed fashion. A pooling technique which may be satisfactory for one form of distribution may be quite misleading for another.

Another approach, while not precisely ranking, facilitates the "ranking" of large numbers of data. Ranking one hundred values would be exceedingly difficult, and in the long run probably meaningless. One approach provides for a limited number of slots, ten for example, and the rater places the data in them according to some a priori instructions. He may approximate a rectangular distribution by apportioning the data equally among the various slots, or he may approximate a normal distribution if so instructed. As in all examples of rating-scale formation, instructions to the rater, whether implicit or externally induced, are of extreme importance.

Guilford (1954) suggests five or six methods for deriving scales from rank-order data and the interested reader is referred to this source for detailed procedures. One of the methods entails the comparison of each rank with every other rank on a paired comparison basis. This is an indirect application of the following basic procedure.

METHOD OF PAIRED COMPARISONS

This is a second technique useful when the stimulus cannot be measured in objective terms. It has probably been used most often in the case of evaluating aesthetic judgment. As the name would imply, the procedure for this method is to compare each stimulus with every other

	Standard								
Comparison	10	9	8	7	6	5	4	3	2
10									
9	9								
8	10	8							
7	7	7	7						
6	6	6	6	6					
5	5	5	5	5	5				
4	4	9	4	4	6	5			
3	3	9	8	3	6	3	4		
2	10	9	2	7	6	2	2	2	
1	10	1	8	7	6	5	1	1	2

Summary for Single Rater

Soap	10	9	8	7	6	5	4	3	2	1
Preference	3	4	3	5	8	7	4	3	5	3

FIG. 4-1. Method of paired comparisons (sample work sheet for one rater). Ten bars of soap, varying in perfume content, were presented to a single subject in all possible two-bar combinations. The subject made 45 judgments as to which of the paired bars were the more pleasant to smell.

stimulus on some basis such as beauty, artistic merit, etc. Since a total of $N(N-1)/2$ different pairs can be made from any series of stimuli, the evaluation of ten stimuli would require 45 separate judgments. It is clear that when the number of stimuli becomes large the method becomes quite time-consuming and rather unwieldy. (For 100 stimuli a total of 4,950 individual judgments would have to be made by each rater.)

A sample work sheet and summary table for the method is shown as Figs. 4-1 and 4-2. In Fig. 4-1 the result of ten stimuli being examined with a paired comparison technique by a single rater is shown. The sample numbered 6 appears to be the choice of this rater, who selected it over every other sample except for the 5. Actually, a rating based on one observer and resulting from just 45 comparisons would be highly subject to chance variability and certainly not very meaningful.

The presentation in Fig. 4-2 provides a more meaningful analysis, based on a large number of comparisons by several raters. This was an experiment performed for a large soap manufacturer and the stimuli were ten bars of soap varying in the amount of perfume they contained. The question asked was something like this: "How much perfume should be put in a new brand of soap? If too much sweet perfume is used the soap may be rejected by potential male users; if too little perfume is used

Code Numbers of Soap

	10	9	8	7	6	5	4	3	2	1
10		.52	.55	.60	.85	.83	.80	.75	.70	.60
9	.48		.51	.63	.80	.78	.55	.55	.50	.49
8	.45	.49		.65	.70	.70	.50	.55	.40	.35
7	.40	.37	.35		.65	.60	.48	.35	.30	.20
6	.15	.20	.30	.35		.48	.32	.18	.10	.02
5	.17	.22	.30	.40	.52		.40	.22	.20	.15
4	.20	.45	.50	.52	.68	.60		.54	.40	.30
3	.25	.45	.45	.65	.82	.78	.46		.55	.32
2	.30	.50	.60	.70	.90	.80	.60	.45		.40
1	.40	.51	.65	.80	.98	.85	.70	.68	.60	
Means	.31	.41	.47	.59	.78	.71	.53	.47	.42	.31

FIG. 4-2. Sample summary table for method of paired comparisons (proportion of time soap numbered on top was preferred to number listed on side). This table presents the summary results of a large number of subjects such as the one illustrated in Fig. 4-1.

and the final product smells like soap, women may refuse to buy it. But is there a happy middle ground where both men and women may like the smell of the soap? Or must separate 'his' and 'hers' soaps be manufactured, differing primarily in their perfume content?" This was the problem we attempted to solve by a paired comparison technique, with subjects choosing between all possible pairings of the ten samples. Figure 4-2 presents part of the data, but does not indicate whether the data were for the males, the females, or the combined results. While these data are not extremely revealing, they do indicate that samples 5 and 6 were preferred almost three-fourths of the time and except in comparison to each other, were clearly preferred over all the other samples. It would appear, too, that there is not much to choose between these two.

This last statement hints at another use for the paired-comparison technique. We once did an experiment for a distillery in which the problem concerned the necessary amount of quality control in coloring the final product. When a bartender pours a drink for a customer at the bar from a newly opened bottle, it won't do for the customer to notice a difference in the color of his drink, as compared with his neighbor's which came from the just-emptied bottle. The customer is likely to exclaim "Who watered my drink?" It therefore behooves the distiller to insure that all their batches of the same spirits have the same color, at least within the normal discriminatory limits of the sober customer. This was the problem we attacked. Subjects matched samples for coloring (which of each pair is darker?) and the result was something like a difference threshold for caramel coloring, but determined by a paired comparison technique. The smaller the DL, the greater would be the amount of precision required on the part of the distiller.

The careful reader may have already noted the similarity between the constant-stimulus difference method and the method of paired comparisons. In the former, each stimulus is compared with a standard; in the latter, each stimulus is compared with every other stimulus. In an experiment such as the soap-smelling one, the rater probably would not even know which method was being used. Many of the sophisticated data-analysis techniques mentioned with reference to the constant-stimulus difference method can (with necessary modification) also be applied to the method of paired comparisons. As before, their complexity, controversiality, and specialized nature militate against their inclusion in a book of this broad coverage and limited psychophysical emphasis.

SCALING METHODS

The idea of scaling things is not new. Industrial psychologists, military commanders, and others have for many years used scales to aid in the evaluation of competence and in some cases, personality, of their charges. Generally referred to as *rating scales,* they have been developed of a purely nominal, ordinal, and in some cases numerical nature. Considerable effort and indeed, success have followed. But such scales as those found in the military's Officer's Evaluation Report, as an example, differ in a fundamental nature from the scaling procedures we will discuss in this section. Such scales merely locate an individual along some continuum, perhaps psychological; they do not attempt to relate this position to some other physical, measurable continuum in a quantitative manner. The purpose of scaling as considered in this section is to relate a continuum of behavior (experience) to a continuum of some physical event in a meaningful, quantitative way.

Indirect Method

When Fechner suggested that just noticeable differences were equal unless always or never recognized, he was stating the basic premise of the indirect method for constructing a sensory-physical scale. If we could accept the formula of Fechner for a sensory experience, we should be able to plot a curve such as shown in Fig. 4-3. If Fechner's $S = k \log I$ were perfectly valid this curve would, if the stimulus values were expressed in log units, be a straight line. The curve of Fig. 4-3 is indeed an hypothetical function, for, as we indicated earlier, Fechner's law simply does not hold throughout the range of most sensory experiences.

Actually, in order to derive a scale such as this that would be valid, it would be necessary to calculate a number of jnd's (DL's) and fit a

Fig. 4-3. Hypothetical function relating magnitude of the sensory experience to the magnitude of the stimulus.

curve to these points. We would not need to measure all the possible jnd's, but with a sampling of ten or fifteen the best-fitting curve would be a good indication of the relation of the experience and the physical event.

The result would be an interval scale of sensory experience. It would not be a ratio scale unless we took the liberty of calling absolute threshold "zero," and this would be a presumption open to serious question.

As we indicated earlier, the magnitude of a jnd, like other psychometric values, is not entirely independent of the manner by which it is determined. The DL obtained by a constant-difference method is not necessarily the same as a jnd arrived at by a more direct method. Consequently, the meaning of a scale derived by such indirect means is problematical.

Direct Methods

Modern proponents of scaling techniques lean to the use of more direct methods in lieu of the older, indirect psychophysical method. Such approaches, while admittedly somewhat subjective, do tend to eliminate or greatly reduce the effects due to different methods referred to earlier. In addition, better handling of the sticky "zero" problem is possible when direct methods are employed.

Two forms of the direct method are worthy of some moderate elaboration.

Single-Stimulus or Direct-Magnitude Estimation. We learned that in the constant-stimulus method, a stimulus is presented in a pseudorandom fashion and the observer reports its presence or absence. In the scaling technique of Direct-Magnitude Estimation a single stimulus is again used, but now all stimuli are above threshold and the subject simply assigns some value to each. In normal practice the experimenter gives a standard signal to the subject to serve as an anchoring point and informs him of its assigned value, such as five, ten, etc. The subject then proceeds to assign values to each of the entire series of stimuli, based on his impression of their relationship to the standard and—and this is very important—to the instructions provided by the experimenter. In some cases, the standard signal may be given before each variable, thus approximating somewhat more closely the method of constant-stimulus differences. In other applications the standard may vary, being as an example, the preceding variable stimulus. The important consideration is, however, the subject *assigns* values to each sensory experience.

Relating the assigned numbers to the stimulus values is then a relatively straightforward procedure, generally followed by curve fitting and the derivation of the physical-sensory scale.

For a technique as subjective as this, the importance of instructions given the subject cannot be overemphasized. Procedures too are of extreme importance if results are to be repeatable and generalizable. Stevens outlines in great detail some of his musts such as: use a standard of intermediate value, keep sessions short (10 minutes), use a simple number such as 10 for the standard, use one standard only for a given session, let the subject present the stimuli to himself, do not suggest what values should be assigned (except for the standard) (Stevens, 1956). It should be clear to the reader that any departure from these suggestions, such as utilizing the weakest or lowest stimulus as the anchoring point, would influence the final results.

Fractionation Method. A method to determine sense ratios was used by Merkel around 1890, in which he attempted to derive a sensory magnitude scale by means of doubling a sensory experience (Woodworth, 1954). The method was pretty much forgotten until revived in the 1930's by S. S. Stevens, who pointed out its value as a tool for developing a scale for loudness. Stevens, however, achieved his greatest success by a process of halving the experience, rather than doubling it—hence the term *fractionation.*

It would appear that the most direct way to obtain a ratio scale is more appropriate application of a fractionation method. It is perhaps the only method that can be said to provide a true ratio scale. The underlying assumption, of course, is that people can recognize equal sense ratios— that is, equal relative distances on a psychological continuum—and that they can make appropriate ratio responses, not merely matches as in the case of conventional phychophysics. As a matter of record, the success with which observers *can* produce ratio scales would probably astonish the Webers and Fechners were they to observe research in a modern psychophysical laboratory.

A typical fractionation experiment goes something like this. Utilizing a scalable standard stimulus, the observer either adjusts or selects an appropriate variable stimulus which stands in some specified ratio to the standard. The subject might, for example, adjust a variable stimulus to a point where it is one-half as loud as the standard, or twice as bright, or one-half as sour. To be sure, many judgments must be averaged to reduce chance variability, and if the scale is to be representative of more than one person, many subjects would need to be used.

Combining of a large number of subjects does not always result in a practical scale. There is always the possibility that a scale based on the average of a large number of subjects may be representative of none of them. Most of us are aware how multiple plateaus in each individual learning curve may disappear when curves for several persons are combined. The whole may obscure the nature of the parts. In spite of such negative instances, however, the remarkable success achieved by such workers as Stevens *does* seem to indicate a bright future for the development of true ratio scales of sensory experience.

There are many modifications and variations in the procedure. One approach involves an adjustment in which the subject halves a difference between two stimuli—that is, he locates the midpoint between two sensory experiences. Such a bisecting procedure has been used by Stevens to verify results obtained by the simpler fractionation method. It is also theoretically possible, although difficult in practice, to fractionate in thirds, quarters, or any simple fraction. Such complications make the task of the subject more difficult, but are not impossible.

There are also several different ways in which a scale may be derived from fractionation data. In general, these methods are relatively simple, relying on commonly used measures of central tendency and simple arithmetic. For the person interested in deriving scales by fractionation techniques the suggested readings by S. S. Stevens at the end of the chapter are particularly recommended. Certainly anyone wishing to use any of the methods in research of his own should be familiar with these readings.

SIGNAL-DETECTION THEORY

This most recent approach to the study of sensory experience should be familar, at least in principle, to all the students of sensory-perceptual relations. Since it does entail some rather complex thinking, no attempt is made here to provide enough information to enable the novices to successfully apply the method. If however this section gets across the general idea and significance of the approach, it will have achieved its purpose.

Background

Some fifteen years ago the principles of statistical decision theory were translated into a theory of signal detection, primarily for use in the description and ultimate prediction of radar signal reception (Peterson, 1954). It was recognized that radar signals are specialized conditions in a background of noise, and their reception or nonreception does not follow any simple threshold analogue, but rather some function which should include a statement of probability. The theory of signal detection accepted the principles of decision theory, in that general hypothesis acceptance or rejection was not considered to be adequately descriptive. To the contrary, in a general decision procedure, statistical hypotheses rather than general hypotheses are evaluated. For those not familiar with the terminology, a general hypothesis is a deductive logic statement such as "all birds have wings." If we find one bird without wings, then we can reject the hypothesis. A statistical hypothesis, on the other hand, requires special rules for rejection, and can be rejected only at some probability level.

Several years after the adoption of the theory for radar-signal detection, the theory came to the attention of several workers at the Massachusetts Institute of Technology, who recognized the generality of the theory and its possible applicability to problems of human signal detection (Swets, 1961). Indeed, to these men the theory appeared to provide a framework for describing the behavior of the human observer in a large variety of detection and perceptual tasks. Swets and others then proceeded to adapt the theory to the human, the result being signal detection theory applied to human observers.

Sensory Thresholds

One of the key aspects of signal-detection theory is its rejection of the concept of a sensory threshold. Classical psychophysics tended to believe that a sensory threshold was an immutable attribute of the sense organ and its associated structures. It was presumed that there was a definite point in a physical continuum beyond which a sense organ would invariably respond. Variability as observed in a psychophysical experiment was due to chance factors and should be eliminated to the extent possible. If this chance variability could be eliminated then, Eureka! the threshold would be there, standing out clearly for all to see.

While perhaps not entirely rejecting something as fundamental as the all-or-none law in the case of extremely simple structures such as muscle fibers or individual neurons, the proponents of sensory detection theory took a different tack. Even if it were true that there is a point where a single straw will break the camel's back, we are not going to find this point. An analogue to noise in an electrical system will prevent our identifying this point with anything approachng optimum precision. Furthermore, why should we wish to find this magical point anyway? The aim of science is prediction, and we can only predict accurately if we include *all* the influences involved. To the modern detection theorist, a threshold is a statistical concept, a probability of detection based on factors, probably too numerous to enumerate. The emphasis is not that a true threshold does not exist, rather it is more like "Who needs a threshold concept? We can predict behavior better if we use the constructs of sensory detection theory and include the influences of noise, the operating characteristics of the receiver (organism), and general probability considerations."

Description

In the basic experiment utilizing detection theory an observer must decide whether an experienced event arose from noise (random influences) alone, or is due to the presence of a signal in the noise. A signal is presumed to shift the overall distribution (noise plus signal) and the degree of shift should, it is clear, indicate the strength of the signal. While this is basically what is done in all psychophysical methods (although perhaps not recognized as such), the unique feature of detection theory is its approach to the data analysis and interpretation.

One aspect of experiments using this technique is the concept of a probability density function such as exemplified by Fig. 4-4. This curve is based on the assumption that any observation may rise either from noise alone or from noise plus a signal.

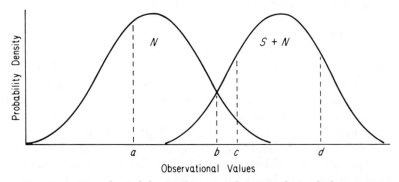

Fig. 4-4.   Hypothetical density function of noise and signal plus noise.

In Fig. 4-4 the probability density functions have been plotted for noise alone and for the condition combining noise and a signal. The distribution labeled N represents the probability density function for a positive response under a condition of noise alone; the distribution labeled S+N is the probability of a positive response when the signal and noise are combined (as in most instances). Since the observations will be of a greater magnitude under the S+N condition, the average for this distribution will be higher than the average for the N distribution. Note, too, that when the observation has a value of a, the probability of detection (experiencing) the combined event is simply the probability of experiencing the noise. As signal strength is increased through b, (equal probability) to d, the likelihood of an error in which noise is identified as signal approaches zero.

This last statement points to another advantage of the detection theory model. Levels of confidence in accepting or rejecting various hypotheses concerning the presence of a signal can be manipulated with extreme facility. Statements concerning the probability of rejecting the hypothesis that a signal does not exist when it does indeed exist, and conversely, that a signal exists when only noise is present can be made with ease and precision.

There are numerous other concepts developed for the application of sensory detection theory, too involved to consider in this section. The concept of an ROC (receiver-operating-characteristic) is useful in describing the nature of the sensory process. It is possible also, to control the nature of the criterion, and to manipulate such aspects as payoff for correct versus incorrect decisions. In summary, the technique, while difficult in its conceptual framework, holds great promise for an ultimate understanding of sensory-perceptual phenomena.

INFORMATION THEORY

Still another approach, borrowed from a discipline other than sensory psychology but useful in many instances, is that involving information theory. While it is generally more applicable to such areas as linguistics or decision making, information theory can in some cases be very helpful as a framework for understanding sensory-perceptual phenomena.

As described by its proponents, one unit of information is that amount of information which reduced uncertainty by one-half. If you have a deck of 64 cards divided, equally according to suits, and I ask you to identify the one card I am thinking of, your uncertainty would encompass the entire pack; the one I am thinking of could be any one of the 64 cards. But, if I give you one piece of information, "I am thinking of a red card," now your uncertainty only involves 32 cards, the red ones. If I then tell you that the card I have in mind is a heart, your uncertainty would be again reduced by one-half, since only 16 of the 32 red cards are hearts. In the language of information theory, I have given you two *bits* (short for *binary digits*) of information, each of which enabled you to reduce your uncertainty by one-half. It should be apparent, if you continue the subdivision to the end, that I would have to give you 6 bits of information to assure your identifying the card I am thinking of with no possibility of error, and no guessing. There are, then, 6 bits of information in a sample of 64 items. If the deck had contained 128 cards, 7 bits of information would be represented, and so on in powers of 2. This is the key—powers of 2—and the amount of information in any symbol, or statement is measured by the amount of uncertainty reduction according to a power-of-2 law. Notice that $2^4 = 16$, $2^5 = 32$, $2^6 = 64$, $2^7 = 128$, etc.

Usually the numbers do not come out as nice and even as in the example. In identifying a letter at random from the alphabet we would need 4 bits of information to identity a letter from a 16-letter alphabet, and 5 bits of information to identify a letter from a 32-letter alphabet. To identify a specific letter in a 26-letter alphabet we would need between 4 and 5 bits of information. We would, of course, settle on 5 bits to be certain of never missing the desired letter. For precise calculation purposes, the number of bits in a 26-letter alphabet would be found as $2^b = 26$, or that power two would have to raised to in order for it to equal 26. Actually, it would be something like 4.6 bits of information.

The information theory approach, it should be noted, is related to the detection-theory model, and the two can be combined profitably for statistical analysis purposes. Many of the conventional psychophysical approaches can be used, with design and interpretation in terms of information theory concepts and the broad conceptual background of communications. Psychophysical experiments in the broad area of learning and learning theory are particularly amenable to the information theory approach.

USE OF COMPUTERS

This section does not discuss actual methods for psychological research. Rather, the purpose is to convince the reader of the importance of understanding a tool for research, the modern digital computer. In some instances and for some purposes, an analogue computer may be ideally suited, but for general purpose use and overall flexibility, the digital computer has no peers.

A psychophysicist (or almost any psychologist, for that matter) who, fifteen years from now, does not have an understanding of the basics of computer technology will be as hard to find as a pop singer without a guitar. The age of the computer is with us and the serious student must keep up with the times.

What can computers do for us? First of all, the erstwhile laborious process of reducing data collected in a psychological experiment can be all but eliminated. Rapid and accurate calculations are a stock in trade of the modern digital computer. I have, for example, a very simple program to process grades for my classes, using a time-sharing system with a Flexowriter such as shown in Fig. 4-5. I merely enter the grades in any order by typing: "DATA 76, 84, 92, 63, . . ." and then "RUN." The computer prints out the size of the sample, the mean, the standard deviation, and the standard error of the mean. Then it proceeds to rank the grades, printing out each grade in order with its rank, its deviation from the mean, its standard score, and its precentile rank. If I desire, I can also get an histogram of the distribution, all in a form ideal for posting on the classroom walls. The total job takes perhaps five minutes, almost all occupied by the slow printout of the automatic typewriter. How long would it take me manually to calculate 25 or 30 standard scores and percentiles?

Experiments can be designed to capitalize on the capabilities of the computer as a calculating tool. Data can be collected automatically on punched cards or magnetic tape. In some cases the processing of the

Fig. 4-5. Sample teletypewriter unit for computer time-sharing. (Courtesy Teletype Corporation, Skokie, Illinois.)

data and the final statistical analysis may be completed before the subject leaves the laboratory.

Computers can in many cases be programmed to run experiments. Not only can they process the final data, but they can also generate and present the stimuli in a preplanned (or truly random) fashion, and make necessary changes as a function of the subjects' responses. Completely automatic experiments can, conceivably, be designed.

Another use for the computer is to store and retrieve information. While it may not be one of the more important uses for the psychophysicist, the capability of storing vast amounts of information in a small space and retrieving all or part of it on demand, is an important capability of the modern computer.

Computers, under the control of qualified experts, can be used to simulate—that is, model—many human functions for concentrated study. Models of neural activity, pattern recognition, and signal detection have all been achieved with some degree of success.

This does not mean that every psychologist interested in sensory-perceptual phenomena should have such a complete knowledge of computer technology that he could program such complex models. To do this well requires a thorough knowledge of computer programming in the language of the computer. When complex programming in computer language is required, the average psychologist might better obtain the expert assistance of an interested and cooperative professional programmer. And too, computers with the size and complexity to handle lengthy modeling programs are expensive and not always available to the average psychologist.

For routine work, however, the qualified sensory psychologist should understand, at a simple-minded level, how a computer works. He should be familiar with its parts, its input and output capabilities, and what it can do for him. He should understand elementary programming. Time-sharing systems with limited capabilities are becoming readily available at nominal cost. Modern time-sharing systems frequently have executive programs that permit the scientist to use simple programming language such as BASIC or FORTRAN. The sensory-perceptual psychologist should be able to write his own programs in such a simple language, and most certainly be able to use simple time-sharing systems such as exemplified by the console of Fig. 4-5.

SUMMARY

In this chapter we have presented additional methods of a more recent, and in several cases more sophisticated nature, for the investigation of psychophysical problems. We examined the older methods of rank order and paired comparisons. More recent, and more sophisticated scaling methods were discussed briefly, and their importance for future, highly definitive research was indicated. A brief look was directed at the application or signal detection theory to psychological problems, and the significance of this trend was noted. The application of information theory to psychological problems was mentioned, and the importance of the computer as a tool in modern research was stressed.

SUGGESTED READINGS

1. Miller, G. A., "The Magical Number Seven, Plus or Minus two: Some Limits on Our Capacity for Processing Information," *Psychol. Rev.* 63

(1956), 81–97. This is a classic article on the human's limitations in making absolute sensory judgments. Limitations in the number of absolute steps in psychological continua are discussed in terms of units of information theory called "bits," and the manner in which people mitigate this problem by utilizing linguistic coding is considered. This is a thought-provoking article, one requiring a little effort to read and understand, but well worth the trouble.

2. From J. P. Guilford, *Psychometric Methods*, 2d ed. (New York: McGraw-Hill, 1954). As suggested earlier, this reading is from the "bible" of psychophysical methods. Chapters 7 and 8 (142 pages), dealing with the Method of Paired Comparisons and the Method of Rank Order, are particularly useful for the serious student and are quite complete. Chapters 9–11 elaborate on scaling and rating techniques; these 102 pages do for scaling what the earlier chapters do for the more basic psychophysical methods. Recommended for the serious student.

3. Stevens, S. S., "The Direct Estimate of Sensory Magnitudes: Loudness," *Amer. J. Psychol.*, 79 (1956), 1–25. This is a highly recommended reading which describes a scaling technique in considerable detail as employed in the scaling of loudness. This article also provides the "suggestions" emphasized by Stevens to insure validity of a scaling procedure.

4. Stevens, S. S., "The Psychophysics of Sensory Function," in W. A. Ronsenblith (ed.), *Sensory Communication* (New York: Wiley, 1961). This reference of 33 pages is somewhat more general than the preceding reference. It describes somewhat more varied techniques and is an important reading for the person interested in the general problem of scaling.

5. Stevens, S. S., "Calculating Loudness," *Noise Control*, 3 (1957), 11–22. This is another description of the methods and results of work aimed at the establishment of a "loudness" scale. It is somewhat less technical than other references and is recommended for the student interested in the area. It is aimed somewhat more at the "semiprofessional" or educated layman.

6. Swets, J. A., "Is There a Sensory Threshold?," *Science*, 134 (1961), 168–77. This article is recommended for the student with an interest in the detection-theory approach to psychological research. While its title sounds as though it were aimed purely at the question of thresholds, the coverage of the article is somewhat broader and presents a brief description of the entire approach. It is one of the shortest descriptions of the method I know of, although it is not especially easy to read and understand.

7. Swets, J. A., W. P. Tanner, Jr., and T. G. Birdsall, "Decision Processes in Perception," *Psychol. Rev.*, 68 (1961) 301–40. This article of some 39 pages of text is as complete as any short article I am aware of. In addition to explaining the approach, the authors include five sample experiments utilizing the signal-detection method. It is recommended for the serious student with the necessary background.

8. Attneave, F., *Application of Information Theory to Psychology* (New York: Holt, 1959). This is an excellent short description (88 pages plus a

short appendix) of the application of information theory to psychological problems. It starts out at an elementary level, using the game of "Twenty Questions" as an example of information-theory application, and proceeds in orderly steps to establish a basic understanding of the technique. It is highly readable and a must for the student interested in learning about information theory as applied to psychological problems.

5

LIGHT AND VISION

INTRODUCTION

You may be surprised to learn that the brilliant Plato thought of vision as being due to particles being squirted out of the eye and falling on an external object. Today Superman has a similar talent that would have thrilled (and vindicated) Plato—a capability of emitting rays from his eyes to destroy the enemies of society who challenge the peaceful existence of Clark Kent and his friends.

But less than fifty years after the death of Plato the Greek mathematician Euclid was to recognize that the eye is indeed sensitive to some substance arising from the outside. To be sure, the theories of Euclid, Galen, and others were not entirely adequate in that they failed to recognize the cameralike nature of the eye, believing that a cone of rays emanates from the external object and is perceived by means of the lens, then thought to be the sensitive element of the eye.

Other, later individuals, such as the Arab Philosopher Alhazen and Leonardo da Vinci, approached an understanding of the basic functioning of the eye, but it remained for Johannes Kepler in 1604 to describe the eye as we know it today. Except for detailed functioning, his description of the eye as similar to the camera obscura, a device for projecting an inverted image on a screen, was complete and accurate. With elaborations by Christopher Scheiner, René Descartes, Christiaan Huygens, and Sir Isaac Newton, our knowledge of the gross anatomy of the eye has needed very little in the way of modern refinement.

NATURE OF LIGHT

But what is the nature of the substance which emanates (or is reflected) from objects in the external world? Since man became aware of the general functioning of the eye, his understanding of the nature of the visual stimulus has taken two distinct approaches. One theory, advanced by Newton, held that light is made up of particles, or corpuscles, while the theory advanced by Christiaan Huygens supported the existence of waves or pulses in a universal medium (ether). The argument is not completely settled today. Indeed, modern thinking tends to support both protagonists.

Light behaves much like Huygens' theory would predict, traveling at different speeds in media of different density in accordance with Descartes' law of refraction, which developed the concept of a refractive index for light-tranmissive materials. The apparent bending or refraction of light as it passes from one medium to another (air to glass, for example) is strong evidence for the wave theory of light, thus supporting Huygens' theory.

Moreover, light of different wavelengths is bent at different angles. When Newton passed white light through a prism, breaking it down into the spectral colors, he was probably not aware of the evidence he was amassing in support of his rival's theory. While Newton did not understand it, we now know that each of the spectral hues he obtained is of a different frequency and wavelength, and that the visible spectrum is just one small part of a very great range of electromagnetic radiation.

These electromagnetic waves (see Fig. 1-1), ranging from 10^{-14} to 10^6 meters in wavelength for the known spectrum, travel, in a vacuum, at a velocity of 3×10^{10} cm/sec, or about 186,000 miles per second. As mentioned in Chapter 2, visible light represents only an exceedingly small portion of this total spectrum—slightly less than the equivalent of one octave from the seventy required to represent the entire spectrum.

As Newton first demonstrated, visible light can be broken down further, as was shown in Fig. 1-1. Violet light has a wavelength of about 400 mμ (about 1/70,000 inch) while red light has a wavelength on the order of 700 mμ (about 1/40,000 inch). Other spectral hues lie in between these two extremes.

While it is difficult to measure it in terms of frequency, light can be described in this way if we so desire. Using the formula: $f = s/\lambda$, where s is the speed of transmission and λ is the wavelength, we can calculate the frequency for any point on the electromagnetic spectrum. Note from Fig. 1-1 that a radio wave with a wavelength of about 300 meters has a frequency of 1,000 kc (10^6 Hz). Radio station KDKA in Pittsburgh puts out a radio signal with a wavelength of 300 meters. Contrast this with a visual wavelength of 500 mμ (green light) which has a frequency of between 10^{14} and 10^{15} Hz, or 10^{11} and 10^{12} kc.

But, light also behaves as if it consists of small packets of energy called *quanta*. The response in the retina of the eye is such that it can be understood only in terms of a quantum theory. It would appear that the chemical reaction in a single element (rod or cone) requires a minimum of one quantum of energy in order to take place. To be sure, we cannot see a single quantum of visible energy, largely due to the fact that absorption and reflection in the less than perfect transmission portions of the eye permit only about 10 percent of the energy to actually reach the sensitive elements in the retina. A total of five to eight quanta *are* sufficient to elicit the experience of a flash of light. This is still a remarkable sensitivity; the eye, under optimal conditions, can detect a candle at a distance of more than 15 miles!

Much of our knowledge of the quantal behavior of the eye is due to the pioneering work of Selig Hecht and his associates at Columbia University (Hecht et al., 1942). Starting out with an assumption of maximum sensitivity of the retinal elements, these researchers demonstrated the sensitivity of individual photoreceptors on a statistical/probability basis.

A quantal theory of light is also useful in understanding the relation of intensity and time factors in vision. It has long been known that there is a reciprocal relation between the intensity and the duration of a visual stimulus. The eye integrates energy over time (on the order of one-tenth second), and a weak stimulus presumably requires more time for the chemical reaction to take place. For a sufficiently intense stimulus, time is of less significance, but for stimuli near threshold a finite amount of time is required for the chemical integrative process to run its course. A pure wave theory of light could not adequately foresee such a relationship.

EVOLUTION OF VISION

As I indicated before, sensitivity or irritability to some portion of the electromagnetic spectrum appears to be a universal characteristic of protoplasm. Note again Thomas Moore's beautiful recognition of a positive phototropism: ". . . as the sunflower turns on her god, when he sets,/ the same look which she turn'd when he rose." Most organisms, both animal and vegetable, demonstrate some sensitivity to radiation in the general range we refer to as light. It would appear that even animals possessing highly specialized light-sensing organs may still retain a "general" sensitivity to light. It has been demonstrated that animals as high in evolution as the sparrow are able, in some unknown manner, to sense the presence of light without the use of the normal visual mechanism. Several workers, including Underwood and Menaker (1970) have showed that blinded sparrows evidence testicular response to variations in light and dark periods (simulating day-night relationships) even when the eyes are totally blinded and the retina is nonfunctional.

There are several cases on record of individuals in Russia, mostly women, who could literally "read" with their skin. They were able to identify printed characters, both in shape and color, simply by running their finger tips over them. Even when a thin sheet of glass was interposed between the finger tips and the printed matter, some of the subjects could still identify the printed characters, apparently as a result of their radiations in the infrared region.

The well-developed visual organs of higher animals have come a long way from the general sensitivity of the sunflower, the phototropism of the single-cell animal, or the testicular response of the sparrow.

Just as specialized cells and groups of cells developed to facilitate reproduction and assimilation, so did specialized cells develop to enhance the irritability function. Probably the earliest "sensory" cells for electromagnetic radiation were little more than ordinary cells with an increased amount of dark pigment, thus producing a reduction in reflection and an increase in absorption of the impinging energy. A further refinement such that these pigmented areas were able to react to the absorbed light energy in a differential manner was a much later development, and was essential for the ultimate genesis of color discrimination.

Pigmented Patches, Eyespots

The very simple protozoan, *Euglena,* provides us with an example of a very early stage in the development of light sensitivity. As seen in Fig. 5-1, *Euglena* is quite a simple, single-celled animal. At the anterior end

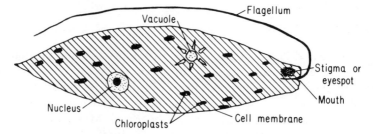

FIG. 5-1.   The Protozoan *Euglena.* This simple creature is one of the earliest organisms to possess a light sensitive organ, the eyespot. Note, however, that the presence of "chloroplasts" gives credence to the argument of some biologists that it is really a plant, rather than an animal. (Modified from *Principles of Animal Psychology* by N.R.F. Maier and T.C. Schneirla, 1935, with permission of McGraw-Hill Book Company.)

of its body, near the base of the flagellum, however, it has an "eyespot," a small patch of reddish pigment sensitive to light. The action of the flagellum which propels the small creature is dependent upon the illumination falling on the "eyespot," thus determining whether *Euglena* will swim into or out of an area of brighter or dimmer illumination. (Maier and Schneirla, 1935).

In more complex, multicellular animals light sensitivity is often mediated by pigmented cells scattered over the skin, as in the case of the earthworm. While basically an inhabitant of darkness, because of factors such as humidity and temperature, the behavior of the earthworm is however not nearly as simple as pure negative phototropism might predict. Under proper conditions the worm may go toward an area of brighter illumination, apparently as a result of the interaction of such factors as the humidity and temperature of its environment.

Most organisms have their patches of pigment concentrated in such manner that they appear to provide the animal with a crude indication of direction. Some planaria, or flatworms, for example, have paired clusters of pigmented cells, known as *ocelli*, at the anterior end; and some marine worms are blessed with several pairs of ocelli sensitive to light. Sea urchins, on the other hand, have numerous pigmented spots scattered about on their bodies.

Even when the species has well-developed, specialized light receptors, some still retain the capability for generalized photopic sensitivity. As an example, the crayfish, in addition to its typical compound eyes, also has photosensitive nerve fibers near the under surface of its segmented abdomen (Kennedy, 1963).

Visual Pits and Simple Eyes

The next evolutionary stage in the phylogeny of the eye appears to be the development of pits or indentations which include the sensitive pigments. These would appear to serve several purposes for survival: for one thing, some mechanical protection of the sensitive pigments from the outside elements would be expected to result from their being located at the bottom of indentations in the animal's surface. Too, if the pits have any appreciable depth, shadowing could serve as indication of the direction of the light source.*

The *limpet*, a marine shellfish, has a relatively simple visual pit. For his quiescent existence, hanging on a rock by his single "foot," the limpet probably needs little more than simple sensitivity to light, and perhaps, moving shadows. In the case of the limpet, the designation of sensitive pigment might be an oversimplification. It would appear that the limpet has something on the order of a primitive retina, a layer of tissue made up of many individual cells with neural fibers proceeding to the central nervous system.

Oliver Wendell Holmes was probably not aware of its unique visual

---

* In many lower animal (fish, snakes) sensory cells for stimuli other than light are frequently found in pits in the skin. These may serve as chemical receptors, or in some cases receptors for acoustic or vibratory stimulation, as well as for temperature. The temperature-sensitive pits in some snakes is a good example, known to everyone.

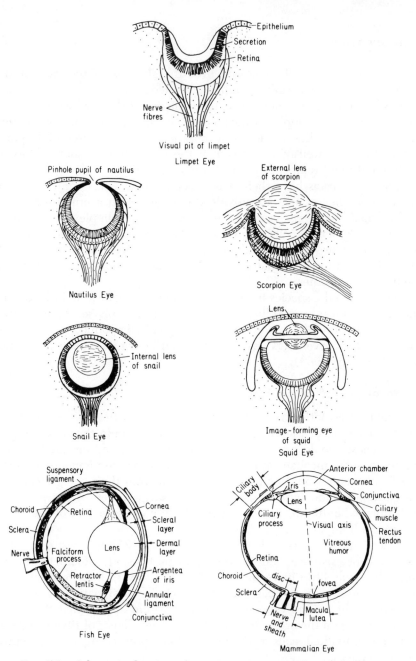

Fig. 5-2. Schematic drawing of representative eyes. Note the progression from the simple pit of the limpet to the last drawing, depicting the mammalian eye. Notice too the nearly spherical shape of the fish's lens, presumably designed to move back and forth, rather than to change shape, in the action of accommodation. (Above figures from G. L. Walls, *The Vertebrate Eye*, 1942, courtesy of the Cranbrook Institute of Science; the first five figures are from a modification by R. L. Gregory, *Eye and Brain*, 1966, courtesy of World University Library.)

capability when he wrote of ". . . the ship of pearl, which, poets feign, sails the unshadowed main . . ." The *nautilus*, a cephalopod mollusk related to the squid and octopus, is indeed a remarkable animal, apparently achieving an astounding level of visual functioning, all without the benefit of any lens or focusing device. The eye of the nautilus is like a pinhole camera, the Camera lucida of the ancients. (See Fig. 5-2.) Thus a primitive focusing effect is obtained and the animal is said to be able to respond to the slightest movement of its anticipated dinner. Its simple structure hardly provides the nautilus with much in the way of detailed pattern vision, and surely the amount of light admitted to the eye must be quite limited. But for its existence, the pinhole camera apparently provides a primitive form of vision that is adequate for the needs of the creature.

In anticipation of later developments, we can see that improvement would result through the formation of a transparent membrane to cover and protect the visual mechanism inside. And a still later stage in evolution would see the formation of a simple lens, either from the primitive corneal layer, or immediately behind it.

Although the visual mechanisms we are describing seem to portray an increasing complexity in the style of phylogenetic development, they do not in fact portray a simple phylogenetic series. Actually, to trace any specific complex eye of higher-order animals back to its primitive ancestors is a difficult if not impossible task. In the process of evolution many directions were taken before the present levels were reached. Some of these directions were unsatisfactory and the species became extinct. Many other developments led to blind ends—that is, species which were served

Fig. 5-3. Scanning eye of *Copilia*. The eye of this minute arthropod appears to have a pair of lenses and a single receptor element. It would appear that the muscle attached to the receptor causes the latter to move back and forth, thus providing a scanning effect. (From *Eye and Camera* by George Wald, 1950, Scientific American, Inc. All rights reserved.)

adequately by their unique organs but from which no important or significant developments evolved. Some primitive eyes evolved into the mammalian eye, while another parallel development resulted in the compound eye of the arthropods, each satisfactory for its bearer, but neither evolving from the other.

One of the most fascinating examples of an animal appearing to take the wrong turn and ending up in a dead end is that of *Copilia,* a tiny arthropod about the size of a pinhead. (See Fig. 5-3.) The eye of this creature has a well-developed primary or objective lens mounted on the end of a stalk, but only a single receptor with its own smaller lens. The receptor is attached to a small muscle and it is believed that this muscle moves the receptor back and forth in the focal plane of the lens, thus scanning the image much like some modern electronic devices built by man.

Compound Eyes

A direction of evolutionary development which apparently proved to be quite successful resulted in the existence of so-called *compound eyes.* There are probably more creatures with compound eyes in existence today than any other type of visual apparatus, and the situation in the past was probably not much different. The earliest known eyes, from the trilobites of the Cambrian period five hundred million years ago, appear to have been compound eyes.

While many still retain some simple ocelli, most arthropods have compound eyes which are ideally suited for detecting movement. (See Fig. 5-4.) Compound eyes consist of numerous (1 to 30,000) units, or *ommatidia,* each of which is a separate receptor, many having relatively simple, direct connections to the central nervous system. Such a proliferation of individual "eyes" makes for rapid visual processes and the ability to detect shadows or contours moving across the surface of the organ with a minimum of delay. You usually have to move a shadow over a housefly only once before it flies away.

While each ommatidium is indeed a single receptor structure it is a disarmingly complex and sophisticated entity. At one end, each ommatidium has a simple lens facet and a secondary lens cylinder. The waveguide nature and high directivity of each ommatidium should be rather obvious; only light traveling in a direction parallel to the optical path of the element is likely to activate it. If light is coming from the proper direction it will pass through the transparent tissues to a light-sensitive element, consisting of several cells in a flowerlike cluster. By the facilitation, not yet well understood; of another cell known as the *eccentric cell,* a nerve impulse is evoked in a fiber leading from the receptor.

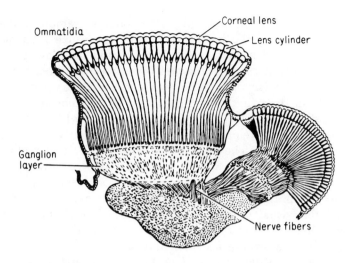

FIG. 5-4. A compound eye. The eye of the mayfly, Chlo-
eon, is unique in that it has a double-segmented compound eye. The larger component presumably provides
detailed vision, while the smaller part to the right permits coarser, wide-angled vision. (From *Eye and Camera*
by George Wald, 1950, Scientific American, Inc. All rights
reserved.)

Form vision with the compound eyes of the arthropods must be quite
rudimentary. But for the high-speed movements and simple behavior
of insects, the compound eye is an ideal arrangement.

While probably not planned that way, the development of the compound eye has had a fortunate spinoff. The relatively large size of the ommatidia (in some species) and their direct linkage with afferent neural
fibers make them an ideal subject for laboratory research. Much of what
we know about the neural and chemical activity in light-sensitive organs
was gleaned from research on compound eyes. For this purpose, the eye
of *Limulus* (horseshoe crab) has been found to be of particular value.

Complex Eyes

With the exception of a few oddballs like *Copelia,* those higher
animals which did not perfect compound eyes, moved in a direction of
increased complexity of the simple eye. The compound eye of the arthropods did not work too well except for such short distances as concern
these small creatures, and it did not provide much in the way of pattern
or form vision. The simple pinhole device, on the other hand, did not
provide adequate sensitivity to dim light nor adequate image formation.
Moreover, such primitive eyes did not permit much in the way of accommodation for varying distances.

Through evolution, the principle of the nautilus' simple pinhole eye was adopted, and with the further development of such refinements as protective coverings, lenses, focusing systems, and multilayered retinae, progress was in a rather straightforward direction. An ultimate in sophisticated visual mechanisms (up to now, at least) was the result, culminating eventually in the paired visual organs of the vertebrates.

Several "stages" in this development can be seen in Fig. 5-2. The scorpion, as an example, developed a fixed "lens," apparently in contact with its sensitive retinal layer. The snail, on the other hand, developed an internal lens (probably also fixed focus) bathed in its own intraocular fluid, probably not greatly unlike the aqueous fluid in our own eyes (and, incidentally, not dissimilar to the saline solution of the seawater which originally bathed the visual organs of all animals). Many other organisms developed similar, perhaps more highly specialized structures, often permitting primitive form of accommodation.

The scallop, a bivalve mollusk (see Fig. 5-5), sports a row of bright blue eyes along the edge of its shell. Did you ever think when you ate a

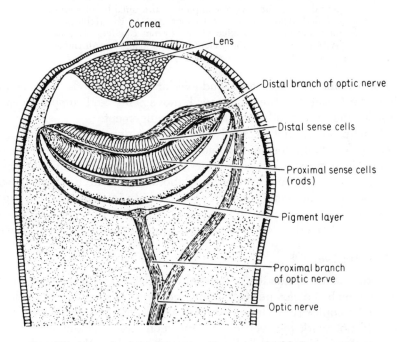

Fig. 5-5. Detail of scallop eye. Note the double-layer retina. The layer farthest from the lens is made up of cells not-unlike conventional rods, while the layer closer to the lens is made up of cells which fire at the cessation of a stimulus. (From *Inhibition in Visual Systems* by Donald Kennedy, 1963, Scientific American, Inc. All rights reserved.)

platter of French-fried scallops that the tasty little creatures had pretty blue eyes? Each of these eyes has a simple cornea and what appears to be a fixed-focus lens. Curiously, the scallop has a double-layer retina, one layer responding to the onset of a visual stimulus, the other discharging when the light is terminated. Many higher order animals appear to have both "on" and "off" receptors, but few are as clearly delineated structurally as in the case of the scallop. We will in a later chapter consider in more detail man's visual receptors which indicate the onset of a signal and the termination of a signal.

While most higher-order animals adjust their eyes (accommodate) for distance by changing the shape of their crystalline lenses, the octopus appears to have a more primitive approach. His hard crystalline lens moves back and forth like the lens of a camera, adjusting according to the distance of his prey. While the octopus does have a rather large eye and a very well-developed retinal structure, the limited range of its ac-commodative capacity is probably an important factor in restricting the size of the creature's dinner table. Normally it seizes its prey at a dis-tance of two to three meters, presumably the accommodative range of its eye. At other, shorter distances the octopus must rely on chemically sensitive disks in its long tentacles.

The Vertebrate Eye

There was once a science teacher in high school who when asked a question she could not answer would reply "That is one of the wonders of science." If there was ever a "wonder of science" the vertebrate eye is surely it. The eye is truly a magnificently designed and almost perfectly conceived instrument. Its range of sensitivity is greater than any camera-film combination I know of, its absolute sensitivity approaches that of the finest man-made instrument, and its ability to resolve fine detail is almost unbelievable. As an example of its excellence of design, most organs of the body have capillaries coursing through them, supplying nutrients and removing waste products. But a cornea with blood vessels in it would not be very transparent. So, the cornea is serviced directly by the aqueous fluid behind it, rather than by intrinsic, semiopaque blood vessels. Fur-thermore, this aqueous fluid is completely renewed every four hours to insure adequate conditions for survival of the tissue it caters to. It is obviously important too that the lens of the eye be transparent. Early in life, even the pigmented cell bodies disappear from this structure, and barring unforeseen metabolic problems later in life, it maintains a remark-able degree of transparency.

The great variety of specialized development for various species is noteworthy. A hawk soaring hundreds of feet in the air can distinguish a small rodent scurrying along the ground. Some animals not only can detect and utilize light, but can also discriminate different wavelengths within the visible spectrum. We take this color vision for granted, but it is indeed a remarkable evolutionary development. Still other animals survive with a minimal dependency on their visual abilities, substituting the sense of smell, or an acute sense of hearing. Most rodents, bats, and similar animals that live in burrows in the ground, dark caves, and the like utilize senses other than vision for most of their survival functions. Owls have apparently developed such a sensitivity to light that their vision in daylight is severely impaired, and dogs' distance vision is notoriously poor. While man is possibly the only mammal with true color vision, some lower animals (e.g., birds) are said to have excellent color vision.

When we do find a remarkable visual capability or limitation for a particular species, we should not necessarily attribute it to the eye itself, at least not to that part of the eye which we can see, and generally refer to as the eyeball. It is the magnificence of the computer behind it which gives the eye much of its advantage over man-made optical instruments. The eye actually has many optical defects if examined by itself. It is often somewhat misshaped, its range of focusing is not always adequate, and the medium through which the light must pass is not always very transparent, frequently containing loose cell bodies, scaled epithelial cells, and various debris floating around in it. But as an extension of that amazing neural computer known as the brain, the eye can perform unbelievable feats.

DEVELOPMENT OF MAMMALIAN EYE

Let us look briefly at the development of an individual eye, which in a limited sense tends to recapitulate some of the general phylogenetic development of all mammalian eyes. The old schoolboy tongue-twister, "ontogeny recapitulates phylogeny" has long been demonstrated to be of limited truth. As a result, those instances where it *does* seem to apply take on an added interest.

The Retina

The *retina*, or light-sensitive surface of the eye, develops from the very early, poorly differentiated and still hollow forebrain of the embryo, and the first evidence of this development heralds the overall development of the eye. Indeed, a thickening of the forebrain wall, called a *placode*, identifies the eventual location of the retina, and can be observed in an embryo of less than four millimeters. Early in development the paired placodes begin to migrate laterally and, at the same time, an outward bulging of that part of the brain wall including the placode results in the formation of the *primary optic vesicle*. (See Fig. 5-6). At such an early stage this simple vesicle is little more than a hollow swelling in the wall of the forebrain. Concurrent with the development of the optic vesicle, the ectoderm layer in front of it thickens, forming a lens placode which will eventually develop into the lens of the eye.

As the optic vesicle develops further, it undergoes a complex invagination process: the base of the vesicle constricts so that the primary optic vesicle takes on the form of a hollow ball on the end of a hollow tube (see bottom drawing of Fig. 5-6). Simultaneously, as can be seen from this figure, the froward wall of the vesicle invaginates so that the result is a double-walled structure, known rather appropriately as the *optic cup*. This double-walled entity is destined to become the retina; the optic nerve will arise from it and proceed by way of the stalk to the brain, and the *hyaloid artery* will enter the eye through the same stalk to nourish the developing retina and its associated structures. While the hyaloid artery will eventually atrophy and fade away, other blood vessels will continue to service the inside layers of the adult eye. These vessels pass through a narrow slit in the cup known as the *choroid fissure* which eventually closes up, enveloping itself around them.

At an early stage the sides and rear of the optic cup are made up of two layers with a space between them. The inner of these two layers develops into several layers of cells and becomes the retina proper (sensory area), the outer layer develops a pigment, *fuscin*, and becomes the black-pigmented layer. These two layers merge together as the space between them disappears, and the combination becomes the retina as we know it.

Before the choroid fissure has closed completely, the nervous layers of the retina undergo considerable development. The outermost layer of cells differentiates (in man, at least) into the sensory neuroepithelial *rods* and *cones*, the second layer of cells proliferates into *bipolar cells*, while a third layer is made up largely of *ganglion cells*. These latter send out fibers which converge from all parts of the retina, leaving the eye by way of the still open choroid fissure, and proceeding to the brain. Note that this development results in a retina which is "backwards," in that light must pass through the nerve fibers and the nonsensitive cell layer in order ultimately to arrive at the sensitive rods and cones.

The Lens

Meanwhile, back in the embryo, the lens plate or lens placode has not been sitting idly by watching the remainder of the eye develop. Arising from the ectoderm layer of the embryo, a thickened placode develops into an indentation (lens pit) and subsequent invagination not entirely unlike that of the optic vesicle. Known as the *lens vesicle*, this hol-

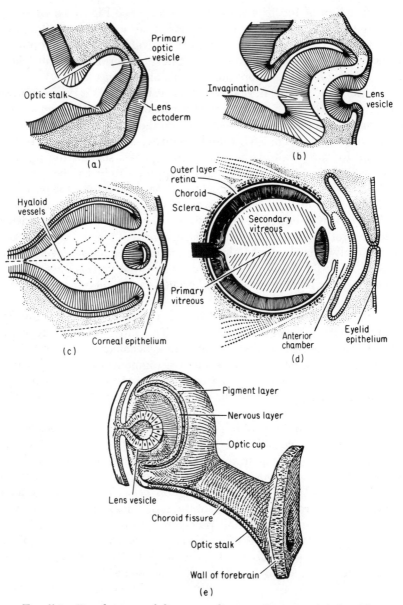

FIG. 5-6. Development of the mammalian eye. Drawings (a) through (d) show the orderly progression from the original "bulge" to the nearly developed eye. Drawing (e) presents an interesting cross-sectional view of a stage somewhat between (b) and (c). [(a) through (d) are from A. W. Ham, *Histology* while (e) is from I. C. Mann, *The Development of the Human Eye*. They are reproduced with permission of J. B. Lippincott Company and Cambridge University Press, respectively.]

low chamber, or bulge into the main cavity of the eye [see (b) and (c) of Fig. 5-6], pinches off from the primary ectoderm layer. Subsequently, the wall of the cup come together, forming a sac with a thick wall on the side facing the retina and a thin wall on the other side. At a sufficiently early stage the large primary optic vesicle is almost filled by the smaller lens vesicle. The thin wall of the lens vesicle develops into the lens epithelium, while long cells in the thick wall continue to grow so that by about the seventh week of development the entire cavity has been obliterated. The elongated cells lose their relatively opaque nuclei and become the lens fibers. With the formation of a lens capsule from the epithelium, the lens is essentially complete.

The tissue of the lens proper is entirely nonvascular. During its early development, however, blood vessels from the hyaloid artery spread over its rear surface. Along with additional vessels on the front surface, the gross structure is known as the *vascular tunic* of the lens. It flourishes during the period of rapid development, and at birth has usually disappeared along with the hyaloid artery, leaving a structure of remarkable transparency and flexibility.

Additional Structures

The remaining structures of the eye, of course, develop along with the retina and lens. The chamber between the lens and the retina becomes filled during the second month with a fibrillar jelly, known as the *vitreous body,* presumably a "secretion" from the inner surface of the eye. Other fiberlike growths attach themselves to the lens and become the *suspensory ligaments* for later growth and attachment to the ciliary muscle.

During the seventh week tissue surrounding the optic cup begins to differentiate and specialize into two accessory coats. The outer coat is more dense and becomes the white fibrous tissue known as the *sclera* or *sclerotic coat.* Actually, this coating corresponds to the *dura mater* of the brain, with which it is continuous by way of the optic nerve. In the front of the eyeball, the sclerotic coat is quite transparent and we recognize it as the *cornea.*

The inner of the two coats covering the optic cup is called the *choroid.* Located between the sclera and the pigmented layer of the optic cup, this later acquires a high vascularity and corresponds to the *pia mater* of the brain. Even in embryos as young as six weeks the choroid plays an important role in the blood supply to the retinal surface.

While we could examine the development of countless other structures of the eye, we will not do so at this time. Suffice it to say that their developments are orderly and can very often be understood in the light of the phylogenetic scale. We will examine additional structures in the following chapter where we consider the anatomy and physiology of the adult eye. For the student interested in the embryological development of such parts of the eye as the iris, the ciliary body, or the eyelids, numerous excellent embryology texts are available.

The thoughtful reader should surely have noticed the close relationship of the eye and the brain: the extension of the forebrain to form the retina, the relation of the choroid and the pia mater of the brain, and the common origin of the sclera and the dura mater. This was the principal reason we spent so much time on the embryological development of the eye and introduced so many new terms. A student of the eye must realize that it is a remarkable instrument, not just because of its optical qualities, but of even greater importance because of its profound data-processing capabilities.

SUMMARY

In this chapter we have tried to present a little on the background of vision and the development of the visual organs. We examined first the nature of light, its location on the broad electromagnetic spectrum, and its characteristics as both a wave and a particle phenomenon. As a second step we traced the phylogenetic development of vision, beginning with highly primitive light sensitivity, progressing through the formation of pigmented patches, simple visual pits, and culminating finally in the evolution of compound and complex eyes. The last part of the chapter traced the ontogenetic development of several structures of the human eye, with an intent to show some comparability of ontogenetic and phylogenetic development, and the remarkable nature of the eye as an extension of the brain.

SUGGESTED READINGS

1. From N. R. F. Maier and T. C. Schneirla, *Principles of Animal Psychology* (New York: McGraw-Hill, 1935). While I recommended this entire reference for Chapter 1 as general reading, some parts are of particular significance to the development of visual systems. The first 266 pages are replete with illustrations and descriptions of visual mechanisms of lower organisms. The interested reader can obtain a great deal of valuable information from scanning all these pages and then reading those of specific interest.
2. Wald, G., "Eye and Camera," *Scientific American*, August 1950. This is an interesting, well-written, and relatively short description of the eye. Background history is provided, and although omitting considerable detail about visual functioning, the analogy between the eye and the camera is carried all the way through the nature of the sensitive emulsion. These 10 pages are interesting and quite easy to read.

3. Newton, I., "A New Theory of Light and Colors," in W. Dennis (ed.), *Readings in the History of Psychology* (New York: Appleton, 1948). This reference is included for its historical significance. These twelve pages represent, in full, Newton's transmission to the Royal Society of London information on his discovery of the physical basis of color. It is worthwhile reading if for no other reason than to gain the flavor of such pioneering work.

4. From R. M. Evans, *An Introduction to Color* (New York: Wiley, 1948). Chapter II of this excellent book, titled "The Physical Nature of Light," does what it is supposed to do in a very acceptable manner. These 14 pages go into the matter in somewhat more detail than required at this point in the consideration of sensory/perceptual processes. However, the material is highly readable, and the inclusion of several pages on such topics as general receptors and photometry will help prepare the reader for more specific visual problems to be considered later.

5. From M. Wilson and the editors of *Life*, *Energy* (New York: Time, Inc., 1963). Although this book was recommended for Chapter 1 and the general approach to energy I feel that Chapter 4, "The Search for the Ends of the Rainbow," is particularly germane to the present chapter on light energy and visual sensitivity. Like the remainder of the book, this chapter is well written, well illustrated, and interesting. The 20 pages of this reference are well worth reading for anyone.

6. DeBeer, Sir G., *Embryos and Ancestors*, 3d ed. (Oxford: Clarendon Press, 1958). A nice little book for the student interested in embryology, especially from a theoretical point of view. In 197 pages the author provides evidence for a refutation of the recapitulation theory, providing his own alternative explanation. While it is not a particularly easy book, the serious student, by reading selectively, can gain much from exposure to it.

7. From Tom N. Cornsweet, *Visual Perception* (New York: Academic Press, 1970). This is an excellent book, more germane to sensory/physiological functioning than to perception, as the title might indicate. It is a relatively advanced book, and its 450 or so pages do not lend themselves to a single evening's casual reading. It is, however, highly applicable to this chapter, as well as to Chapters 7, 8, 9, 10, and 11. It is recommended for the serious reader, especially one interested in the status of contemporary visual research.

6

STRUCTURE OF THE EYE

Before we can examine the functioning of the eye we should gain some understanding of its structure. The reader is referred to Fig. 6-1 for an overall schematic presentation of the adult mammalian eye.

CORNEA

If the eye is the window of the soul, then the cornea must be the pane in this window. Except for an exceedingly small amount of light that finds its way through the nearly opaque walls of the eyeball itself, all of the light reflected from external objects must pass through this window to get to the sensitive retinal layer behind. Developing from the same embryonic layer that produced the dense white protective sclerotic coat, the degree of transparency of this structure is indeed remarkable.

Description

The cornea is a tough, nonvascular sheet of tissue approximately 0.6 mm in thickness. It is formed from bundles of connective tissue fibers, lying one upon the other to form a laminated whole. The external surface of the cornea has a thin epithelial layer which is constantly being renewed by cell division. This epithelial layer provides, among other things, the medium for the elimination of carbon dioxide. This is one of the reasons why you are told not to wear your contact lenses continuously. Carbon dioxide build-up between the cornea and the contact lens might become excessive and the concentration in the trapped fluid would not allow for adequate evacuation of the poisonous substance. Superficial to the epithelial layer is a thin (several microns) double layer of tears (oily on the outside and watery on the inside) which forms the optically smooth surface.

The cornea performs several critical functions. In addition to protecting the delicate internal parts of the eye, it permits light to pass through

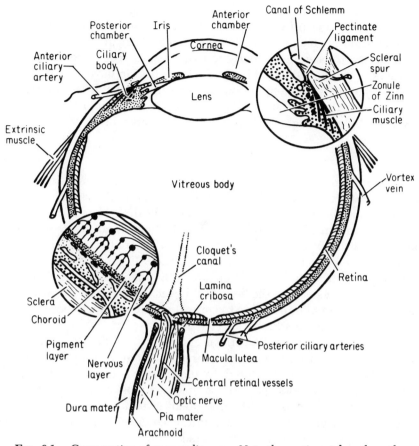

FIG. 6-1. Cross section of mammalian eye. Note the sections taken through the retinal and ciliary portions. (Taken from A. M. Ham, *Histology,* J. B. Lippincott Company, with permission.)

to the retina, focusing the image on the sensitive surface. Popular belief often holds that the lens of the eye focuses the image on the retina. In animals living on dry land, this is generally not true. The cornea actually does most of the focusing (refraction) of the image on the retina, while the lens is responsible for only small adjustments (accommodation) to compensate for changes in distance. As a matter of fact, the cornea acts like a fixed-focus lens, such that about two-thirds of the total refractive power of the eye is supplied by it. In operations for cataract in which the lens of the eye is removed, the cornea (plus some corrective lenses) must supply the entire refractive power for the system.

In the case of fish, living in a watery milieu, the converse is true. Differences in refractive index between the fishes' cornea and the water are not sufficient to permit complete image formation. Consequently, for animals living entirely in the water, the lens is responsible for the greater part of the image-formation function. Indeed, gross visual examination reveals a thicker, more nearly spherical lens in fish, as contrasted with most land-dwelling animals. Many fish also appear to have an accommodative mechanism dependent upon movements of the lens forward and backward, much like a camera, rather than the shape-adjusting technique employed by most higher-order land-dwelling animals.

Potential Disorders

The cornea is susceptible to a great many possible defects and physical injuries. As exposed and unprotected as it is, damage from foreign material must be relatively common. While healing of minor damage is relatively rapid and generally complete, infections, if not treated properly, can result in scar tissue which if sufficiently pronounced can greatly reduce or even eliminate corneal transparency. Damage due to scarring, often associated with malnutrition and other metabolic deficiencies, is particularly prevalent in the less well-developed nations of Africa and the Far East, and blindness due to corneal opacity is much more common in these parts of the world.

While many instances of corneal opacity in well-developed countries may be attributed to infections of a viral, bacterial, or fungal nature, the greater bulk must be attributed to degenerative or metabolic causes. While much of the etiology remains unknown, loss of transparency due to metabolic malfunctions with subsequent swelling and opacification of the cornea is of greater significance in this country. It would appear too, that genetic causes cannot be eliminated entirely.

When the corneal opacity has reached a point where an insufficient amount of light can pass through it, surgery is generally indicated. Using operating microscopes and delicate "micro" instruments, the skilled surgeon can replace the damaged cornea with a section removed from a recently deceased healthy eye, usually obtained from a so-called "eye bank." Although, there often remain problems of tissue rejection and the possibility of transplanting a potentially unhealthy cornea, corneal transplant operations are nevertheless a tremendous step forward in providing "eyes for the blind." Perhaps the comparatively low incidence of rejection in the case of corneal transplants may be due to the lack of blood vessels in the cornea, as contrasted with the high vascularity of other organs which so often resist transplantation.

There has also been some progress in replacing diseased corneas with plastic prosthetic devices. The results from these experiments are often less than satisfactory, however, and much remains to be learned to avoid biological rejection and insure adequate functioning of the prosthetic cornea.

An otherwise healthy cornea can be somewhat misshapen. If the central area of the cornea does not present a perfect section of a sphere to the incoming light, distortion will result and the image will appear blurred. Known as *astigmatism,* this common condition is usually due to an imperfect curvature of the corneal surface. Such a defect, unless very severe, can be corrected by the cylindrical curvature of an eyeglass lens. We will discuss this application in more detail when we examine the use of glasses for correcting visual defects.

AQUEOUS CHAMBER

Directly behind the cornea is the anterior or *aqueous chamber* of the eye, containing, not unreasonably, the aqueous humor, a thin watery fluid that contains most of the diffusible substance of blood plasma, and in about the same concentration as plasma. Continuously replenished and absorbed, this fluid presumably provides the nutrient and waste removal function in support of the nonvascular cornea in front and the lens behind. It is believed that the fluid for the anterior chamber is formed in the posterior (vitreous) chamber and enters the anterior chamber between the lens and the iris (see Figure 6-1). Pressure in the anterior chamber holds the iris against the lens, preventing return of the aqueous fluids to the posterior chamber. Fluids from the aqueous chamber eventually leave the eye by way of the canal of Schlemm, ending up in the venous system of the body.

IRIS AND PUPIL

If you have lovely baby-blue eyes, it is due to the pigments in your *iris,* a relatively flat disk with a variable aperture near the center, known as the *pupil.* In humans the pupil has a relatively round configuration, but this is by no means the universal situation. A variety of shapes are found in different species, with the slit-shaped pupil being typical for nocturnal animals. Note, for example, the shape of the cat's pupil.

Along with the *lens,* the iris separates the anterior chamber of the eye from the posterior chamber. But it does much more than this. A highly complex and vascular tissue, the iris contains two sets of antagonistic muscles. One set, composed of smooth muscle fibers, is arranged in a circular or sphincter configuration near the outer edge of the doughnut-shaped iris. Innervation of these muscles results in a partial closing of the pupil. Another set of muscles, arranged radially near the back of the iris, serves to dilate the pupil. Both of these sets of muscles are activated reflexively as a result of the level of illumination falling on the retina, and through impulses arriving from the sympathetic and parasympathetic divisions of the autonomic nervous system, as well as light-sensitive cells in the retina itself.

While changes in the size of the pupil do indeed tend to control the amount of light entering the eye, this is not the primary function of the iris/pupil structure. Popular descriptions of the eye tell us that the pupil constricts under conditions of high illumination, thus protecting the delicate interior of the eye. The total range of light to which the eye can adapt is much greater than that which can be accounted for by the relatively limited changes in pupil size. An alternate explanation of pupillary changes involves the maximizing of visual acuity rather than the protection of the interior sensitive surfaces.

Under conditions of high illumination the pupil is constricted, thus insuring that most of the light will pass through the center of the optical system, thereby minimizing aberrations due to improper curvature at the extremes of the cornea and lens. Under conditions of low illumination the pupil widens, allowing a maximum of light to enter the eye, even though some of it must of necessity pass by way of the distortion-producing edges of the optical system.

The pupil also tends to constrict for near vision reflexively. This is fortunate, since a smaller aperture produces a greater depth of field, thus no doubt reducing some of the wear and tear on the accommodative mechanism which might otherwise be constantly adjusting and readjusting for small changes in distance.

Can you now see why your eye doctor often dilates your pupils before performing a refraction? With your iris at a maximum opening, vision is most influenced by optical flaws and a minimum depth of field is found. Glasses prescribed under such unfavorable conditions can be more precisely selected and are more likely to be accurate than glasses prescribed under highly favorable circumstances.

The color of the iris is due to a pigment called *melanin,* and has little significance for vision except in its absence. Eyes that are totally lacking in melanin (*albinism*) are, of course, unduly sensitive to light, since the basis for iris opacity is lacking, and light may enter the eye through the peripheral part of the iris as well as the pupil itself. If the melanin is limited to its posterior surface, the iris will appear blue. On the other hand, with additional pigments in other layers of the iris, the apparent color may range from gray to brown. In most Caucasians the development of pigment often occurs subsequent to birth, so that the blue-eyed baby may later develop eyes of a decidedly brown color. In the case of many non-Caucasians, the pigment deposition often occurs before birth.

LENS AND CILIARY BODY

The lens of the eye serves, not to form an image on the retina, but rather to add, in accordance with changes in viewing distance, increments of curvature to that provided by the corneal surface. Changes in the shape of the lens are produced reflexively, and appear as the result of failure of the projected image to focus precisely on the sensitive surface of the retina. In the normally relaxed state, the slight curvature of the lens contributes just enough positive correction to bring objects at a distance into focus. When nearer objects are to be viewed, the lens must assume a more nearly spherical shape to produce a correspondingly sharp image.

Description

The crystalline lens is a remarkable structure, being composed of both living and ostensibly nonliving tissue. In its young, healthy state it can change its shape to accommodate for distances from as short as one foot to as great as infinity, a remarkable range of focus for even our best modern cameras.

As I indicated in Chapter 5, the development of the lens proceeds largely from the inside to the outside. Indeed, after the nuclei-free cells in the core have in effect died from lack of nutrition and isolation from the vascular system, those on the outside continue to grow (at a slower rate of speed). As a result, the mature, overly filled sac with a hard core becomes less pliable and resists assuming a shape either highly spherical, as needed for near vision, or as flat as required for distant vision. The middle-aged owner must then resort to corrective lenses for both reading and far vision, either separate spectacles or, if he is willing to disclose his age, bifocals.

Just how does the lens perform its amazing feat of accommodating for both near and far vision? While we are reasonably certain that the *ciliary body* and *zonule of Zinn* (see Fig. 6-1) are involved in the accommodative process, the complete answer to the question is still somewhat vague. I once heard an ophthalmologist present an excellent description and theory concerning the process. He proposed that the ciliary body did not perform as a muscle, as it is normally described, but rather as a gland. According to his logical hypothesis the lens at rest is in a relatively flat state, adjusted for far vision. When the ciliary muscle (or gland?) contracts fluid is forced through tiny tubules in the zonule (also called the *suspensory ligament*), thus filling the lens sac and causing the entire body to expand into a spherical or near-spherical shape, much like the process of inflating a balloon. Thus the ciliary body is relaxed for far vision and at work for near vision, consistent with physiological events as we know them. It was a brilliant theory, adequate in every detail except one: no one has ever found any tubules in the space between the ciliary body and the lens!

More generally accepted explanations of the accommodative function assume that the normal resting position of the lens is somewhat on the spherical side, and that the attachment of the lens to the ciliary body is such that contraction of the latter relaxes tension in the lens, thereby permitting it to assume its normal near-spherical shape. A relaxed ciliary body, on the other hand, produces tension on the lens, forcing it into its flatter, distant vision configuration. One might ask, "Why not examine a lens after removal from an eye?" To be sure, this has been done, but removal from the eye results in almost immediate changes in the delicate tissue of the interior portion of the lens such that the true shape of the lens in the living organism escapes detection.

One might wonder how such a simple structure as the mammalian lens can produce images so free from serious optical aberration. The old box camera with its simple lens was quite inadequate for eliminating *spherical aberrations* unless only the very center of the optical path was used, thus cutting down appreciably on the light admitting and sensitivity of the system. Even then, chromatic aberration, the differential bending of different wavelengths in the manner of Newton's prism, was inescapable. Optics makers get around the problem by making complex lens systems composed of five or more separate lenses made of materials differing widely in their refractive indices, such as flint and crown glass. The human eye, however, has only a single lens like the old box camera, and it operates with a relatively large aperture, yet neither spherical nor chromatic aberrations are particularly bothersome.

As pointed out in an earlier chapter, there is an excellent computer behind the human lens, filtering and processing the image; but even without this filtering process the lens, cornea, and retinal combination have several features that tend to mitigate the serious effects of aberration. In spherical aberration, at least three mechanisms may be noted. For one thing, the cornea and lens are formed from tissue with slightly different refractive indices, similar, on a smaller scale, to the camera lens' crown and flint glass. Also, the curvatures of the two structures tend to counteract each other, with the cornea tapering off gradually at its edges, while the lens features as increasing rate of curvature near its edges. Finally, spherical aberration is reduced when it might be most harmful (close work, such as reading) by a reflexive constriction of the pupil, limiting the light path to the relatively aberration-free axis of the optical system.

Several mechanisms are also available for the reduction of *chromatic aberration*. Such aberration is most noticeable at the extremes of the spectrum, especially at the blue end, where the light is bent the most. While the retina itself is sensitive to light over a relatively broad spectral band, filtering provided by the yellowish lens prevents much of the unwanted blue light from reaching the sensitive surface, thus eliminating some of the potential chromatic aberration. Many people who have had their lenses removed in the course of cataract operations must wear yellow glasses to replace the blue absorption function of their missing natural lenses. There is also a concentration of yellow pigment in an area of the retina directly behind the lens. Known as the *macula lutea*, this area is most effective in close, critical vision, and the yellow pigment must, by absorption, prevent some of the undesirable blue light from reaching the sensitive retinal elements. And finally, the sensitive elements of the eye directly behind the pupil (cones) have a greater sensitivity to the red and a lower sensitivity to the blue end of the spectrum as compared to the more peripherally located sensory cells.

Potential Disorders of the Lens

Being such a highly specialized structure, and consisting as it does, of part living and part nonliving tissue, and all on the borderline of nutritional deficiency, the crystalline lens is indeed a delicate organ, poised on the brink of catastrophic disorder. Such disorders frequently take the form of *cataracts*, a term used for any opacity or clouding of the lens. A cataract is not a growth and it does not involve the cornea; it is an opacity in the lens itself.

Cataract produced opacity takes on many forms: it may be evident at birth, it may develop from an injury or disease, or it may develop apparently as an inexorable result of the aging process (probably the most common form). It may appear in any part of the lens, it may remain stationary, or continue to develop until the entire lens is opaque.

While the etiology of most cataract formation remains somewhat obscure, there does seem to be an underlying relation with systemic disease processes. Apparently the latent protein molecules making up the lens body are subject to significant structural changes under conditions produced by factors associated with diabetes, German measles, radiation, nutritional and hormonal deficiencies, and the general aging process.

Treatment for cataract formation varies according to the situation. When the cause is known, as in diabetes, early recognition and treatment of the systemic disorder may prevent or at least delay the formation of the cataracts. When the cataracts are well developed, surgical removal of the cloudy lens is the only recourse. Even then, surgical removal of the offending lens does not always produce the desired result. Eyes with congenital cataracts are often predisposed to other serious defects such as *glaucoma* and *retinal detachment*. In children blind from birth the operation may appear to be successful, yet the patient may never learn to fixate properly. In successful cases—and they are many—several devices may be employed to correct the refractive error left from the lens removal. These include spectacles with a relatively large amount of correction (trifocals are sometimes worn to provide correction for distant vision, near vision, and intermediate distances); contact lenses; and plastic lenses inserted directly into the eye. Unfortunately, the latter technique has not been proven to be entirely satisfactory.

VITREOUS BODY

The main body of the eye which gives it its globular shape is known as the *vitreous body,* and is located in the posterior chamber between the lens in front and the retinal surface in the rear. It is a mass of transparent gelled amorphous substance, the origin of which is not known with certainty, but believed to be largely of epithelial origin.

In addition to the gelled substance, liquid similar to that found in the aqueous chamber may also be found in the vitreous chamber. As indicated earlier, the aqueous fluid probably originates in the vitreous body. When parts of the vitreous body has been removed, as in surgery, it may be replaced by the liquid medium.

Along with transmitting light, the vitreous body serves to provide general support for the eye, including holding the lens firmly in place in front and keeping the layers of the retina in the rear in close apposition. Presumably the vitreous body also has a function in the metabolism of the retina.

The vitreous body normally performs its passive light transmission function efficiently and with very little fanfare. As indicated earlier, only a relatively small proportion of the light which impinges on the cornea ever reaches the retina. The remainder is lost through optical scattering and absorption by the various tissues through which it must pass. Furthermore, as an individual gets older the vitreous body tends to lose some of its transparency for reasons not entirely clear. If you look into the eye of an older person with an ophthalmoscope you may have difficulty in seeing all the way to the retina. Your view will be blocked by an unbelievable number of opaque cells and general "junk" appearing to be either suspended or floating about in the semiliquid medium. Some of these particles are probably dead epithelial cells scaled from the lining of the eye, others are perhaps the result of systemic chemical changes in the normally transparent vitreous tissue. Remarkably enough, however, the presence of a great amount of opaque cells in the vitreous does not seem to bother vision appreciably. With a potential range of 100,000 to 1 in light sensitivity, the loss of even 90 percent or more of the transmissibility of the vitreous medium would scarcely be noticed.

RETINA

We can, within the scope of this chapter, scarcely touch upon the complex structure and functioning of this, the most critical part of the

Fig. 6-2. Photomicrograph of monkey retina. Portions of both the outer and inner segments of rods and cones can be seen in this photograph. The part labeled A is the beginning or conical portion of the outer segment of a cone. The inner segment of the cone extends to the line at F, representing the outer limiting membrane. The portion of the inner segment labeled B is the ellipsoid of the cone, while C is a cone nucleus. One can see in this view mostly inner segments of rods, such as illustrated by D, with rod nuclei being somewhat smaller and located deeper in the retina (E). The thin line identified as F is the outer limiting membrane, a thin, perforated tissue, separating the inner segments of the rods and cones, on one side, from their nuclei on the other. (Photograph courtesy of Mitchell Glickstein, Brown University, Walter S. Hunter Laboratory of Psychology.)

eye. Truly a part of the brain, as indicated earlier, the *retina* is a paper-thin (0.2 to 0.4 mm) sheet of tissue containing the light-sensitive elements (*rods* and *cones*) and an amazing network of nerve fibers and higher order neural cells. Slightly over one-half of the vitreous cavity is lined by this remarkable organ. Figure 6-2 shows a photomicrograph of a retina in cross section, while Fig. 6-3 presents a schematic diagram of its structure. Note that the direction of light transmission appears to be in the wrong direction—that is, the light must pass through the entire nervous structure before reaching the sensitive rods and cones which are juxtaposed against the outermost pigmented layer. In some invertebrates the arrangement is reversed, so that the sensitive elements face the direction of the incoming light.

Fig. 6-3. Layers of the retina. Note the arrangement of the interconnections and the numbered layers as referred to in the text. (From S. Polyak, *The Retina,* courtesy Mrs. Stephen Polyak.)

Sensory Layer

While histologists have identified some ten layers of the retina (see Fig. 6-3), we will confine our descriptions to only those layers of significance for our limited purpose. The outermost layer of the retina is the pigment layer, consisting of pigmented epithelial cells which presumably absorb stray light, preventing light from bouncing about in the cavity and activating sensory elements not in the line of vision. The pigment layer does such a good job of absorbing light in the eye that it is virtually dark in there at all times—so dark that it is impossible to look into the eye without a well-directed source of illumination such as that provided by the ophthalmoscope.

The histologists' second, third, and fourth layers are of interest to us in that they contain the sensitive elements, the rods and cones, their nuclei, and their axonal processes. The size and densely packed nature of the rods and cones are something to marvel at. Some elements are as small as one micron in diameter, or about twice the wavelength of red light, some 2,000 being concentrated in an area of about one-third degree of arc. This certainly suggests a tremendous potential for fine resolution and perception of detail. Of the total elements, some 6,000,000 are cones, sensitive to color and able to make color discriminations, while perhaps 120,000,000 can be identified as rods, presumably at an earlier stage of evolutionary development, and sensitive simply to any light within the normally ascribed visible spectrum.

The rods and cones are not distributed randomly throughout the retina. In accordance with evolutionary theory, the color-sensitive (*photopic*) cones tend to be concentrated near the primary optical path, directly behind the lens, while the rods occupy the remainder of the retinal surface. At the extreme periphery there are no cones at all, and in a small spot (*fovea centralis*) directly behind the lens, a depressed area of less than one millimeter in diameter contains nothing but cones. To visualize the size of this area, a dime viewed at arm's length would cover roughly the area of the fovea centralis. This area has a poorer sensitivity to weak light than the rod-filled periphery, but because of the relatively direct one-to-one connections with the higher-order neurons in the retina, the foveal area provides maximum resolution and is the part of the retina one uses for close work. You never read a book out of the corner of your eye; you look directly at it in order to utilize the cones in your fovea to maximize acuity and fineness of resolution detail.

Surrounding and including the fovea centralis, is an area of some 5 by 10 degrees known as the *macula* or *macula lutea*, so-called because of its yellow color which is due to the pigments we considered earlier when we were examining the manner in which the eye mitigates the deleterious effects of chromatic abberation. The macula, while dominated by cones, and providing fairly good acuity throughout, contains both rods and cones, with the latter probably dominating. As one moves peripherally, the proportion of cones diminishes until, in the outer periphery, only rods are found, and vision is said to be simply light-sensitive (*scotopic*). Perhaps "simply light-sensitive" may be the wrong way to express it, since some rods appear to be as much as one thousand times more sensitive to light than their more highly specialized cone neighbors. You are probably aware that when searching for a very dim star you can often detect it out of "the corner of your eye" before you can see it directly.

The chemical-electrical functioning of the rods and cones presents an extremely fascinating challenge to the researchers in the area. While much has been learned of the action of various retinal substances such as rhodopsin, iodopsin, etc. I feel that we might best delay any detailed description of such processes until a later point in the book. When we discuss color vision, including the development of color theories, we will be better able to grasp the significance of such complex and highly promising work.

Nonsensory Layers

Most sensory neurons, such as those found in the skin, extend uninterruptedly to ganglia of the spinal cord or brain before transmitting their impulses to a higher-order neuron. The sensory neurons of the retina, however, are already a part of the brain, so they find several levels available in the paper-thin retina itself.

We described the histologists' second, third, and fourth layers as containing the sensitive elements and their axonal processes. In the fifth, sixth, and seventh layers we find the *bipolar cells* with their dendritic and axonal processes. The bipolar cells serve as links between the sensory rods and cones and the deeper-lying ganglion cells. It is at this level that, to a great extent, the functional resolution of the image is determined. Near the fovea centralis a single bipolar cell may connect a single cone to a single ganglion cell; near the periphery perhaps hundreds of rods may feed into one bipolar cell. Thus maximum resolution and precision of the image is available near the fovea, while much poorer resolution must obtain for the periphery. On the other hand, the large number of rods supplying a single bipolar cell may mean sensitivity to a much lower level of illumination (due to integration of the separate impulses) for the nonfoveal parts of the retina.

The last three layers of the retina include the *ganglion cells* and are furnished with minute blood vessels as well as nonnervous supporting tissue. Ganglion cells are activated by outputs from the bipolar cells and are in effect, the third level of visual processing. The term *ganglion* as used here is actually a misnomer, the cells being so called only because they resemble the large cell bodies frequently found in ganglia. No true ganglia are to be found in the retina.

The unmyelinated axons of the ganglion cells are quite long and exit from the last layer, forming a fine network over the inner surface of the eye, before gathering together to leave the eye by way of the optic nerve. The point at which these fibers leave the eye is known as the *blind spot*, as no rods or cones are to be found there. It is a small area on the nasal side of the retina, and can be observed by anyone with a little practice. It is said that one of the former kings of England would use the blind spot to show his subjects how they would look with their heads cut off.

Several other types of cells are also found in the inner layers of the retina. In addition to the nonnervous supporting cells, both *horizontal cells* and *amacrine cells* are to be found. The purpose of these cells, presumably, is to provide lateral "switching" circuits in the complex computerlike level of the retina. Some of these neurons undoubtedly inhibit the firing of other neurons in some unknown way, thus enhancing contrast effects and light-dark contours, as we will discuss in more detail in a subsequent chapter.

Disorders of the Retina

The usual perfection of embryological development occasionally fall somewhat short of the ideal. Sometimes the inguinal ring does not close properly after the descent of the testicle, and an inguinal hernia is the ultimate result; or, less often, the bones of the skull and the mouth do not close properly during development, again requiring surgical correction. If you look carefully at Fig. 5-6 again you may discover another point where emryological development may fall somewhat short. When the optic cup is formed from the invagination of the primitive brain wall, two layers, originally with a space between them, fuse to form a single, complex layer. These two layers, as we learned in the previous chapter, fuse together, one becoming the retina, the other the pigment layer. But the fusion is not always perfect. Under normal conditions the existing adhesion and the pressure from the vitreous body hold the retina firmly against the pigment layer. With damage to the eye, such as from a severe blow, the loosely attached retina may separate from its pigmented backing tissue, and the disorder known as a *detached retina* is the result. In the violent sport of boxing, detached retinas are not at all uncommon.

Treatment, if the detachment is not too severe, and has not been permitted to go untreated too long, consists of refastening the retina to the tissue behind it. This can be done surgically, or (more recently) by means of a laser beam. In the latter technique, after the retina is properly positioned, a small, intense beam from a ruby laser is used to "spot weld" the retina back in place. The small burn area and its little scab serve to hold the retina in place until normal healing and tissue regeneration can complete the reattachment.

Another very serious disorder, frequently culminating in blindness, is *glaucoma*. Glaucoma actually includes a number of ocular disorders with hereditary, traumatic, or systemic bases whose common symptom involves an increase in intraocular pressure. Some 13.5 percent of the legally blind persons in the United States have glaucoma as the cause of their affliction.

Presumably, an excessive rate of aqueous secretion and/or an insufficient outflow capability is responsible for the heightened pressure. Detection of the excessive pressure can be made by means of a *tonometer,* an instrument which measures the amount of indentation of the cornea for a given area and known force of the instrument's plunger, thus indicating the eye's resistance to the deformation and hence its internal pressure.

Blindness ensues due to atrophy of the optic nerve at the rear of the eye, generally progressing from the blind spot outward toward the periphery, but not necessarily in an orderly fashion. The disorder can often be prevented or delayed by appropriate treatment aimed at reducing the intraocular pressure before irreversible damage has been done. As a first step, drugs which either inhibit aqueous production or increase the drainage rate are often employed. Recently, cryosurgical techniques have been employed in order to destroy portions of the ciliary body, thus lowering its aqueous-producing capability. Advanced forms of glaucoma may require removal of part of the iris to permit escape of the fluids from the vitreous to aqueous chambers, and in some cases the surgical construction of new paths to facilitate drainage of the excess fluid may be indicated.

OPTIC NERVE

The fibers from the retinal ganglion cells leave the eye by way of the *optic nerve* and proceed to the brain. In the case of many lower animals (especially those whose visual fields do not overlap) the optic nerve from the left eye goes to the right side of the brain and the optic nerve from the right eye goes to the left side of the brain. In many, the situation is more complex. It might be best described simply by saying that fibers serving the *left visual field* (in both eyes) proceed to the right half of the brain, while those fibers for the *right visual field* terminate in the left side of the brain. There are crossover fibers along the way, but a general contralateral projection of the visual field does obtain.

Figure 6-4 shows in schematic form how this occurs. The temporal half of the left eye's retina goes by a relatively direct path to the left side of the brain, as does the nasal half of the right eye's retina. The latter must cross the corresponding fibers emanating from the nasal portion of the left eye which terminate in the right side of the brain. In effect, the fibers which proceed to the left side of the brain represents the left retinal areas of the two eyes, or since the lenses reverse the images, the right half of the overall visual field. Note that if the left path beyond the *optic chiasma* (crossover point) were destroyed at a point such as A by a tumor or a wound, one would not lose vision in a specific eye, rather, vision would be lost in the right visual field of both eyes, since the left half of both retinas would be isolated from the brain. If damage occurred at point B, the nasal portion of both retinas would be functionally lost and the

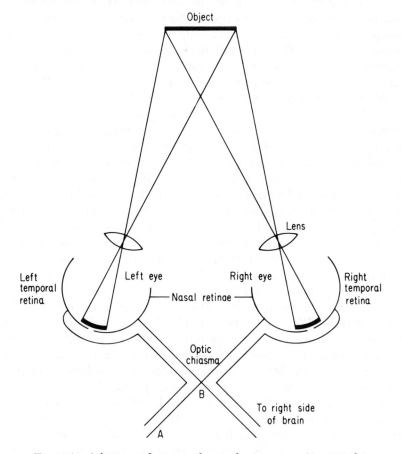

Fig. 6-4.   Schematic diagram of retinal projection. See text for discussion.

result would be a loss of peripheral vision in both eyes. The not-too-rare condition of "tunnel vision" is frequently caused by damage to the optic nerves at the point of crossover.

Beyond the optic chiasma the fibers proceed to lower visual centers such as the *lateral geniculates* and the *superior colliculi* and, after various interconnections, terminate in the projection area of the cerebral cortex in the area known as the *occipital lobes*. The tracing of structure and function beyond the optic nerve is another long tale in itself and would go well beyond the scope of this book.

EXTRINSIC EYE MUSCLES

The last structure of the eye of significance to the study of sensory processes is actually external to the eye itself. It is the assembly of muscles which position the eyes in their sockets. Three directions of movement appear necessary: (1) up-and-down movements such as raising or lowering the eyes; (2) back-and-forth movements as used in following a line of print; and (3) rotational movements about the optical axes, as when we tilt the head to one side, yet maintaining the eyes in roughly the normal orientation to the horizontal.

With three directions of movement it would appear that three pairs of muscles are needed, and this is indeed the situation that prevails. One pair, the *superior* and *inferior rectus* muscles, moves the eyes in an upward and downward direction, a pair of *lateral recti* move the eyes in the horizontal direction, while a pair of *oblique* muscles are wrapped partially around the ball of the eye at one end, thus producing rotational movements when called for. Failure in the proper functioning of these muscles is often noted and may manifest itself in such forms as squinting or cross-eye, properly termed *strabismus*. When such malfunctions interfere with vision or present cosmetic problems, they may often be corrected through surgery, or, if the condition is not too severe, by means of special training and eye exercises.

Numerous additional parts of the eye have been scarcely mentioned in this chapter. We could, for example, have considered the vascular components and the protective sclerotic membrane in considerably more detail. We could have examined the internal appearance of the eye, as viewed through an ophthalmoscope; we might have included a discussion of the conjunctiva, the eyelids, and the tear glands. The structure of the retina could have been delved into to an almost limitless extent. The aim of this chapter, however, was to provide the student with only enough anatomical and physiological background to enable him to profit fully from the material to be presented later in the book. Where additional material of a physiological or anatomical nature is needed it will be presented at the appropriate point in the discussion. The student who has absorbed a reasonable portion of this chapter should now be adequately prepared to grasp the sensory and psychophysically oriented material to be presented later. For those interested in learning more about the anatomy and physiology of the eye, many books are available and college courses with the desired emphasis are not uncommon.

SUMMARY

In this chapter we described the basic structure of the human eye which is of importance to a further understanding of sensory functioning. Examining parts of the eye in a direction of front to back, we considered the cornea, the aqueous chamber behind it, the iris and its pupillary opening, the crystalline lens, vitreous body, retina, and finally the optic nerves with their chiasma and subsequent projection fibers. We also mentioned, without providing great detail, several potential disorders of the eye, such as corneal damage, lenticular cataracts, glaucoma, detached retina, and the visual results of damage to various parts of the optic nerves. Finally, we briefly considered the three pairs of muscles which position the eyeball in its socket.

SUGGESTED READINGS

Selecting several readings on the structure of the eye which would prove to be relatively easy to read, informative, and not too long has proved to be a most difficult task. Consequently, the following readings fail rather noticeably to meet these criteria. Nevertheless, they are all worthwhile reading for the serious student and should not be ignored simply because of their size or depth of coverage. In addition to the references below, any current textbook in the area of neuroanatomy should be able to provide valuable information on the sense organs, especially the one we are interested in here, the eye.

1. Polyak, S. L., *The Retina* (Chicago: U. of Chicago Press, 1941). This is still the classical informative book on the structure of the retina. One would not expect the average student to read its 600 pages as an extra reading assignment. The book does serve as a magnificent source of data and provides interesting descriptions of research technique, as well as one hundred superb drawings and photographs of retinal structures. It is a worthwhile book for thumbing through and reading bits here and there as one's fancy directs. The professional investigator in the area should be familiar with the entire book, but the student interested in vision merely as one aspect of sensory-perceptual experience could not be expected to read and master the entire volume.
2. From A. W. Ham, *Histology* (Philadelphia: Lippincott, 1950). Pages 678–

704 present a highly readable description of the eye, not restricted to histological descriptions, including many of the structures not described in the present text. While it directs its emphasis toward histological examination it does not omit important macrorelations. The curious reader is advised to look into this reference in order to gain a little more detailed knowledge than was presented in the preceding chapter. (Other sections of the book dealing with nonvisual subjects might also be useful to the interested reader.)

3. From R. L. Gregory, *Eye and Brain, The Psychology of Seeing* (New York: World University Library, 1966). Chapter 4 of this reference includes 25 pages and is one of the simplest presentations available. While the last 10 pages of this chapter present material which we will later consider in greater detail, the remaining pages elaborate somewhat on topics we tended to treat lightly, such as the functioning of the iris and the relation of eye movements to the extrinsic eye muscles. It is an easy reference to read and will provide some, perhaps not a great deal, of additional information. The entire book (236 pages) is easy and interesting reading, and the enthusiastic student might very well wish to read it in its entirety.

4. From F. A. Geldard, *The Human Senses* (New York: Wiley, 1953). Chapter 2 of this book, "The Visual Stimulus and the Eye," includes 14 pages of relatively easy reading. It includes a discussion of the nature of light and its measurement, and treats several subjects which we will discuss in a subsequent chapter. It represents fairly easy reading as a background for the material in this and the next chapter.

5. Davson, H. (ed.), *The Eye* (New York: Academic Press, 1962). A large book, an excellent source of information on such topics as physiological optics. It is not a book to read in one sitting, but for general reference application it is perhaps unsurpassed.

7

LIGHT INTENSITY, BRIGHTNESS, AND RELATED CONCEPTS

In most experiences the relation between the external world and the resultant experience can be examined in the light of three distinct parameters of the physical event: its *quantity* or intensity, its *quality,* and its *purity.* The latter two characteristics of the visual stimulus, quality (or hue) and purity (or saturation), will be dealt with in later chapters. The subject of this chapter is the first of the three: the intensity of the visual stimulus and the resultant experience which we generally call brightness (often incorrectly).

THE VISUAL STIMULUS

Before proceeding to the world of experience we should first gain a preliminary understanding of the nature of the physical events which produce the psychophysical or psychological experience of brightness. The amount of light can be expressed in three ways: the amount of light produced by a source, the amount of light falling on a surface, and finally, the amount of light reflected from a surface to a sensor.

Intensity

We might look upon a source of radiant energy in terms of its total radiant flux over the entire visual spectrum. This is satisfactory for many applications but for our purposes it might be more useful to consider the effectiveness of the energy in producing a visual experience. This latter approach results in a photometric measure, and is most commonly employed because of its meaningfulness to an understanding of the visual psychophysical function. (If we were developing an intensity system for a specific camera film, we might very well construct it in accordance with the unique sensitivity of the film's emulsion, rather than the sensitivity of the human eye.)

The luminous intensity of a point of light is commonly referred to in terms of *candles*, an arbitrary photometric unit internationally recognized and used by most laboratories. A standard candle is maintained by the National Bureau of Standards in Washington, D.C. If a source of light is twice as intense as the Bureau's standard candle it has an intensity of two candles, if half as bright, an intensity of one-half candle. In general, the candle is not a measure frequently encountered in the behavioral or biological sciences. To the contrary, visual stimuli are much more likely to be expressed in one of the following measures which are derived from the standard candle.

Illumination

The second approach to light specification involves the amount of light falling on a surface. A standard candle one foot away from a surface provides an *illuminance* (area density of luminous flux) of one *foot-candle*. Illuminance on a surface is, of course, proportional to the luminous intensity of the source, so that a source of two candles provides, for the same distance, twice the illuminance of a one-candle source.

Inasmuch as the light emanating from a point source spreads out in all directions equally, distance influences illuminance in an exponential manner. In technical terms, illuminance varies inversely as the square of the distance from the source to the surface. As an example, doubling the distance from the source to the surface reduces the illuminance to one-fourth its original value. Increasing distance by a factor of 10 reduces the light falling on a surface to one percent of the original. A one-candle source 10 feet from a surface provides an illuminance of $\frac{1}{100}$ foot-candle, not $\frac{1}{10}$ as one might logically believe.

When you use your photoelectric exposure meter as an incident light meter—that is, pointing it at the source of the light rather than at your subject—you are measuring illuminance. You are measuring the intensity of the light falling on your meter's sensitive surface. Indeed, your meter, in order to be used in this fashion, is probably calibrated in foot-candles and has such a scale for your use.

An interesting measure of illuminance, perhaps less often used today than in somewhat earlier times, is the *troland*, named after the American physicist L.T. Troland. The troland is a measure of illuminance on the retina itself, and is perhaps the best defined measure of direct retinal stimulation we have. It is defined as the light falling on the retina, when viewing, through an artificial pupil of one square centimeter, a surface whose luminance is one candle per square meter.

Luminance or Brightness

The third approach to measuring light intensity is a measure of the light coming back from a reflecting surface. Formerly called brightness, *luminance* is perhaps a better term for units of this measurement since it tends to limit subjective influences and can be based on a more rigorous standard. Technically, luminance should perhaps be reserved for the psychophysical correlate of the physical world, with brightness reserved for those situations where subjectivity plays an important role. Brightness should refer to a psychological rather than a psychophysical experience. Occasionally, however, we may in moments of less rigorous presentation relapse into the old habit of saying *brightness* when we really mean luminance.

A one-candle source, one foot from a surface (one foot-candle of illuminance) will reflect light at a level of one *apparent foot-candle* if all of the light falling on the surface is reflected back. This is a definitive ideal, since no known surface can ever reflect back 100 percent of the energy falling upon it. An apparent foot-candle is, then, a unit of luminance. When you use your photoelectric exposure meter in the conventional manner—measuring the light reflected from your subject's face, for example—you are measuring luminance, and in units of apparent foot-candles if your meter is so calibrated. Automatic cameras also measure luminance, but they make the necessary aperture and shutter settings without requiring you to read the meter and make the adjustments manually.

There are several other measures of luminance, some of which may be encountered in this chapter. *Foot lambert* (ft-L) is the more common expression for apparent foot-candle, while probably the most common unit of luminance is the *millilambert* (mL). Actually, the foot lambert and the millilambert are, for all practical purposes, interchangeable, since

$$1.0 \text{ mL} = 1.076 \text{ ft-L}$$

Before proceeding too far with our discussion of light intensity it might be well to consider the use of a numerical scale, perhaps unfamiliar to some readers, but of great importance to the expression of physical or psychophysical values. Because of their great range, many measurements encountered in sensory studies are expressed in logarithmic units, or logs. A logarithm is that power to which 10 must be raised in order for it to equal the value in question. For example, what is the logarithm of 100? This is the same as asking, to what power must 10 be raised in order for it to equal 100? Rather obviously, 10 must be squared or raised to the second power in order to equal 100. Therefore the log of 100 is 2. If you see the value log 2, it simply means 100. Log 8, as an additional example, means 10 raised to the 8th power, or 100,000,000. Similiar relations hold for values of less than one, 10 raised to the -1 power (10^{-1}) is equal to 0.1, so the log of 0.1 is -1. Similarly, the log of .001 is -3. And, since 10 raised to the zero power (10^0) is equal to 1, the log of 1 is zero. For intermediate values one must consult a table of logarithms or use a slide rule.

With this slight departure to explain terminology, let us continue with our discussion of light specification.

The range of light intensity to which the human eye can respond is almost unbelievable. Note in Fig. 7-1 that the total sensitivity range of

FIG. 7-1.   Range of light sensitivity of human eye. Notice that the scale is in logarithmic units and that the range as shown is in excess of 10^{10} or 100 decibels.

the human eye is in excess of -6 log mL to 4 log mL, or from .000001 to over 10,000 mL. This is a range of more than 10 billion to 1! An expensive camera with 10 f-stops might have a range of one thousand to one, but the human eye has the equivalent range of more than 30 f-stops. As we will see in the following pages, the various visual capabilities are by no means equivalent throughout this range. We can resolve form with high precision only when the illumination is relatively high and we are permitted to use our retinal cones. Under scotopic vision, we can detect quite low-level light sources, but the resultant rod vision does not provide for adequate resolution or acuity. With respect to color, we need levels in the photopic end of the scale in order to make confident discriminations. At night, under conditions of scotopic vision, colors are not discriminable and all cats appear to be gray.

SEEING LUMINANCE OR "BRIGHTNESS"

An ability to react differentially to the amount of light falling on a sensitive visual surface appears to be common for all specialized visual organs. Within limits, at least, the manner in which differences in intensity of visual stimulation are registered is frequency of firing of the sensitive elements. The more intense the stimulus, the more rapid the firing. With more complex systems, since various receptors have different absolute thresholds, the overall magnitude of the visual organ response may also increase with increasing stimulation level.

Figure 7-2 illustrates the relatively simple situation for the *Limulus* eye we referred to earlier. Note that the function is linear over much of the range when rate of firing is plotted against the logarithm of the light intensity. This is a commonly found relationship in the study of sensory/neural action, that the sense organ response varies as the logarithm of the stimulus intensity. The common use of logarithmic values for specifying stimulus levels, therefore, serves two purposes: to reduce the tremendous range of sensitivity with its large numbers to workable units, and to depict the relationships in an easily visualized and physically accurate manner.

It should also be pointed out that rate of firing is not something that suddenly commences with the onset of a stimulus. Contrary to the implicit assumptions behind the early threshold concept, a sense organ is not sitting idly by, waiting to be set into action by a suprathreshold stimulus. To the contrary, it is in a steady state of action, sending out trains of pulses, perhaps maintaining a state of "alertness" or readiness to respond in the higher nervous centers. A stimulus *increases* the rate of firing; and it is the interpretation, at a higher level of functioning, of this increase which is recognized as a sensory event. As indicated earlier, the experi-

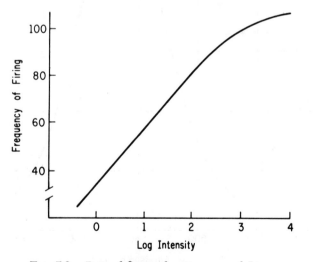

Fɪɢ. 7-2.   Rate of firing of optic nerve of *Limulus*. (Modified from H. K. Hartline and C. H. Graham, "Nerve Impulses from Single Receptors in the Eye," *J. cell. comp. Physiol.*, 1932, 1, 277–95.)

mental methods referred to in Chapter 4 which employ detection theory owe much of their acceptance to knowledge concerning the existence of constant ongoing processes.

Luminosity

While the eye is sensitive to light of wavelengths from perhaps 400 to 750 mμ, it is not equally sensitive throughout this range. When sensitivities are determined for a standard human eye (based perhaps on hundreds or thousands of representative eyes) over the visible spectrum, and plotted on a curve with ordinate values relative to the most sensitive point, the result is a relative *spectral sensitivity curve*, or *luminosity curve*. In obtaining the spectral sensitivity curve of Fig. 7-3, a standard light was employed and the observer adjusted numerous wavelength bands until they matched the standard in brightness (hue and saturation ignored). The point on the spectrum to which the eye is most sensitive (555 mμ) was given the arbitrary of value of 1.00. Based on the amount of energy required for a match at each of the many wavelengths employed, the

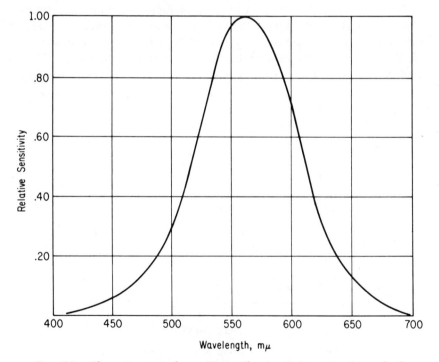

Fig. 7-3. Photopic spectral sensitivity (luminosity) curve of standard eye. The ordinate is in units of sensitivity relative to the peak value, which is given the value of 1.00. The abscissa is in units of wavelength (millimicrons).

relative sensitivity for the remaining wavelengths was calculated and plotted, resulting in a relative sensitivity, or luminosity curve.

The curve shown in Fig. 7-3 was obtained with the light-adapted eye, and is known as the photopic CIE Spectral Sensitive Curve, or the photopic luminosity curve of the CIE standard observer. It was developed as a standard by the Commission Internationale de l'Éclairage, more commonly known as the International Commission of Illumination or ICI, and is a result of pooling measurements obtained by scientists in many parts of the world. It is today the basis for the derivation of all photometric units which presume to assess quantities of light. As suggested earlier, light meters have spectral sensitivities closely adjusted to the CIE standard observer.

Rod versus Cone Luminosity

In the preceding section we explored the relative sensitivity of the light-adapted eye, a function based on the response of the cones. Since the time of von Kries and his advocacy of a duplicity theory, we have been aware of the dual nature of vision, the presence of two types of basic receptors, differing in their sensitivities, both quantitatively and qualitatively. As indicated earlier, the rods are much more sensitive to low levels of illumination than are the cones. In addition to a thousand-fold advantage in sensitivity, the point in the spectrum where the rods achieve their maximum sensitivity is not the same as that for the cones. Whereas the cones achieve maximum sensitivity at about 555 mμ, the rods are most sensitive to light of about 510 or 512 mμ.

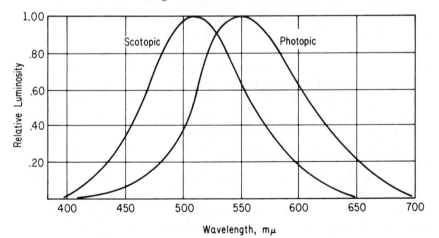

Fig. 7-4. Luminosity curves comparing photopic and scotopic vision. Both curves have been normalized so that their points of maximum sensitivity have been given the value of 1.00. Figure 7-5 shows the *difference* in sensitivity for photopic and scotopic vision.

The difference in sensitivity is known as the *Purkinje shift* and is of significance for vision under scotopic conditions. Johannes (Jan) Purkinje's original observation makes an excellent example. In 1825 he observed that of two flowers which appeared equal in brightness in daylight, a blue flower appeared brighter than a red flower under night or twilight conditions. That is, when the rods of the eye were being utilized under low light-level conditions, the point of maximum sensitivity shifted toward the blue end of the spectrum. Figure 7-4 provides a comparison for the two forms of vision, photopic or cone, and scotopic or rod. It must be emphasized that these are *relative* sensitivity curves. The fact that the rods are a thousand times more sensitive to light than are the cones cannot be determined from this figure. The drawing has been normalized so that the curves for each condition are drawn relative to each point of maximum sensitivity, arbitrarily assigned the value of 1.00. A later curve, showing sensitivity at threshold, will show this difference clearly.

Dark Adaptation and the Absolute Threshold

But what about the eye's absolute sensitivity to electromagnetic energy? Perhaps more basic than relative brightness, studies of absolute threshold can become quite complex and require detailed controls and immense precision in the specification of the stimuli and the condition of the observer. Much of what we know concerning the sensitivity of the eye we owe to the monumental work of Selig Hecht and his students, who over many years at Columbia University have produced much of the definitive literature on the subject. Much of our available data is actually based on the right eye of this exceptional research pioneer.

Sensitivity to light is not an immutable quality of the rods and cones which remains constant regardless of all other circumstances. To the contrary, it is very changeable, and is influenced among other things by prior activity on the part of the visual system. Sensory elements subjected to strong light stimuli temporarily lose their ability to respond to weak stimuli. Known as *light adaptation,* this loss of sensitivity on the part of the eye has been experienced by anyone who has walked from a lighted street into a dark theater. It takes several minutes before the light in the theater is sufficient to provide anything but the most elemental vision.

In order that maximum sensitivity be regained, *dark adaptation* must take place. Both rods and cones have such a capability for adapting to light level. There is also a dilation of the pupil in dim light and constriction in bright light, but the magnitude of this adjustment is quite small and rapid in comparison to the neurochemical adaptation of the sensory elements themselves.

Absolute sensitivity of the eye to light increases by as much as five log units (100,000 times) with a suitable adaptation time. Figure 7-5 is the classical dark-adaptation curve, based on the original work of Selig Hecht. It shows on the abscissa minutes in the dark—that is, adaptation time in total darkness after a two-minute exposure to a light adapting level of 400,000 trolands.* On the ordinate, the absolute threshold in log trolands is shown.

Some interesting facts can be gleaned from this figure. Note for example that the function cannot be adequately described with a single curve. It is necessary to plot one curve for the threshold of the cones and a second curve for the rod threshold. Even if we did not know about rods and cones before, the location of the points in the distribution would

FIG. 7-5. Dark-adaptation curve. The data are from research by Selig Hecht and are based on his right eye. They represent changes in sensitivity after exposure to a light of 400,000 trolands for 2 minutes. The circles are for cone vision, where the color (violet) of the test flash was apparent, the solid circles are for the scotopic condition wherein the stimuli appeared colorless. (Adapted from Hecht, Haig, and Chase, courtesy The Rockefeller University Press.)

* Adaptation of the dark-adapted eye to light is quite rapid. When you go from the dark theater to the bright street you may be "blinded" for a moment, but the adjustment of your eyes is relatively complete in minutes, or even seconds. Hence the two-minute exposure to a bright light of 400,000 trolands was quite adequate to form a common standard level from which to proceed with the slower dark adaptation.

strongly suggest that two "somethings-or-other" must be involved. Whereas the earlier discussion (see Fig. 7-4) on relative luminosities did not show the differences in sensitivity between the rods and the cones, Fig. 7-5 shows this clearly. It can be seen from this figure that the best threshold obtainable for the cones is about 1 troland (log 0), while the rods achieve a maximum sensitivity one thousand times as great, or .001 troland. The range of adaptation is also greater for the rods—something like a thousand to one for increased adaptation for the rods and two or three hundred to one for the cones. Combining both rods and cones the range of sensitivity is over 100,000. That is, the rods, at their maximum dark adaptation level, can respond to 1/100,000 the light required to obtain a response in the light-adapted cones.

There are marked temporal differences in adaptation for the rods and the cones. The cones require about 7 minutes of nonstimulation to increase their sensitivity by a factor of 100 and after roughly 10 minutes in the dark, they have achieved their maximum sensitivity. The sensitivity of the rods, on the other hand, does not exceed that of the cones until the latter have reached their limit. After roughly 12 minutes of adaptation the rods are more sensitive than the cones, and this advantage continues to increase, rapidly at first, and later tapering off, for an hour or more. Some investigators hold that dark adaptation for the rods continues to increase for 24 hours or more. For all practical purposes, however, the rods have reached their adaptation limit within three-quarters of an hour.

Our knowledge of dark adaptation has many practical applications. For such tasks as flying aircraft at night in relatively darkened cockpits, pilots may dark-adapt their eyes before beginning the flight. This is often done by wearing dark red goggles which provide enough light to get around in daylight, but block out the shorter wavelengths, thus permitting the establishment of dark adaptation prior to entering the cockpit. And too, cockpit illumination is often of a low-level, red color in order that the occupants may maintain their dark-adaptation level and be more sensitive to lower level external light.

The results of threshold determinations for the human eye may take on many forms, depending on the methods and stimuli employed. The previous description involved ideal methods and stimuli of maximum efficacy (violet light). Under less favorable conditions the range of adaptation might be closer to 10,000 to 1 or even less, rather than the maximum range of 100,000. We could, for example, determine sensitivity to different hues. Figure 7-6 shows the results of dark adaptation when the stimuli varied in hue. (Thresholds are for detection of light, not recognition of hue; recognition of hue requires considerably more light, and is limited to levels adequate for cone vision.) Note that the curve

FIG. 7-6. Dark-adaptation curves for different hues. Curves show the weakest light that can be seen after entering the dark. Note that we eventually become most sensitive to violet, with our sensitivity to red increasing very little after about 5 minutes. (Adapted from A. Chapanis, *J. Gen. Physiol.*, 1947 with permission.)

for the red stimulus appears to have no rod component. Rods are essentially insensitive to red, hence there is no red component part of the curve. When wearing red goggles as described in the preceding paragraph, light adaptation in the rods does not occur, and they consequently retain their high sensitivity to the remainder of the spectrum. Note also that the greatest range in sensitivity is to be found for the violet light, the hue presumably employed by Hecht. Had we included additional hues, they would have been located between the curves for the white and the red. Orange-red, for example, would show only a slight discontinuity due to rod functioning.

Curves of absolute threshold as a function of light-dark adaptation can take on many other forms as a result of additional variables. If thresholds are determined without the use of an artificial pupil, limiting and keeping constant the effective aperture of the eye, reflexive changes in pupil size will surely confound the results.

The portion of the retina involved is an important consideration. Threshold determinations made with small spots of light limited to the fovea will not show the rod function, since no rods are to be found in that part of the retina. Conversely, a point source in the periphery where there are no cones, will not show the cone portion of the conventional curves of Figs. 7-5 and 7-6.

Ricco's and Piper's Laws

Inasmuch as retinal elements, especially rods, integrate over area (approximately 120,000,000 rods and 6,000,000 cones synapse with as few as 2,000,000 ganglion cells), thresholds are dependent on both the location and area of the target, or more accurately, the location and area on the retina. In the case of foveal stimuli, where interconnections are presumably rather direct and often one-to-one, area and intensity tend to integrate in a simple fashion such that for threshold conditions the product of area and intensity is a constant. This generalization is known as *Ricco's law* and is usually written $AI = C$. It has been found to apply only when the angular size of the test object is no greater than 10 minutes. For the periphery, where retinal interconnections are more complex, *Piper's law* $(I\sqrt{A} = C)$ applies for visual angles within the relatively wide range of 2 to 7 degrees.

The above laws and principles are not always as simple as they have been presented here. There are many additional factors at work, and the interested student is encouraged to learn more about the exceptions and limitations from the suggested readings. In addition to integrative effects within the retina, there are also inhibitory effects; there are effects of contours and the intraocular media. While much has been learned concerning the functioning of the eye at or near threshold, much yet remains to be learned.

Additional Rod-Cone Differences

There are other differences between the functioning of the rods and cones which may result in interesting effects. One of the more curious of these is known as the *Pulfrich phenomenon.* Take a piece of string several feet long and suspend a bob on the end of it. If you swing the bob back and forth in front of you in a right-to-left and left-to-right direction while holding a dark (not opaque) glass in front of one eye, the bob will appear to move in an elliptical or even circular direction. Why? The best explanation is based on rod-cone differences in reaction time. The image in the eye without the filter is mediated predominantly by the cones, while the lower light level in the opposite eye activates the rods. Since rod functioning is somewhat slower than cone functioning, the image from the partially occluded eye is delayed somewhat with respect to the image from the other eye. The brain "sees" the image from the filtered eye slightly in the past, and the result is different images from the two eyes. If the relationship is right, a pseudo-three-dimensional effect results, not physically unlike the usual stereoscopic vision, wherein the images to the eyes do indeed differ.

There are, I suspect, practical applications for this difference in response time of the retinal elements. Driving a car at night probably involves considerable more rod vision than daylight driving. While it is indeed slight, the additional time required for the response from the rods may contribute to the dangers of night driving.

Another difference between the rods and the cones is their directional sensitivity, known as the *Stiles-Crawford* effect. It has been shown that light passing through the center of the pupil stimulates the retina to a greater extent than light entering the eye near the edges of the pupil. While some of the effect may be due to differences in the ocular media, most of it must be attributed to the cone portion of the retina, since the effect occurs only in the light-adapted eye when cone vision is dominant or when red light, to which the rods are insensitive, is used. The best explanation for the effect suggests that the cones behave somewhat more like waveguides than do the rods. Thus, only light from the pigmented layer which enters the cones in a direction parallel to their long axes can have maximum effect. The cones do not achieve the waveguide sophistication purported for the *Copelia* eye, but they do exhibit this characteristic to a greater extent than do the rods.

Areal and Binocular Effects

Some interesting effects, presumably due to the "computer" nature of the retina and lower brain centers, are to be found. If a single point of light illuminates the retina the pupil of the eye will adjust accordingly, presumably as a result of the illumination level. However, if a second point of light, dimmer than the first, is inserted into the visual field, the pupil will not constrict as a result of the increased total light. Actually the pupil will dilate somewhat (location and distance between the two points are important), as if it were trying to adjust to the average level. Known as *Fechner's paradox*, this phenomenon is generally attributed to inhibitory effects produced by means of horizontal connections in the lower retinal levels (bipolar and ganglion cells).

Indeed, it is probably due to such inhibitory effects that our excellent resolution and acuity is achieved. When one element in the retina fires, there seems to result an inhibitory effect in adjacent elements. Thus contours are greatly enhanced and differences between light and dark areas of stimulation tend to increase.

The eye contains both "on" units and "off" units, neurons that fire at the onset of a light and those that fire at its cessation. In all likelihood the interaction of these two types of neurons is also of importance for the inhibitory effects we have mentioned. The importance of borders and contours to perception has long been recognized, and the significance of inhibitory effects within the retina cannot be tossed off lightly. Small, almost imperceptible eye movements result in a complex patterning of "on," "off" responses which apparently serve to maximize the existence of contours and light-dark differences.

An interesting result of inhibitory effects, known as *Mach bands,* can be observed in Fig. 7-7. Near the central division you may notice a thin darker band in the dark area and a thin lighter band in the light area. The generally accepted explanation of these Mach bands involves retinal inhibition. It is said that the dark line is due to increased inhibition in the dark area due to the adjacent light area, while the light band is due to the reduced inhibition produced by the neighboring dark area.

Another interesting paradox, in this case binocularly induced, should be described. If you look at a scene with two eyes and close one, the apparent brightness does not appear to change. The scene appears to be of equal brightness whether you use one eye or two. If, however, you use both eyes, but place a filter over one eye, the scene appears darker than with either both unobstructed eyes or a single unobstructed eye. The effect, not entirely accountable by pupillary change, must be mediated by some sort of interocular inhibition, either retinal by way of the optic chiasma, or at a higher brain level. Probably both direct interocular inhibition and higher level inhibitory effects occur.

CHEMISTRY OF VISUAL FUNCTIONING

What takes place in the rods and cones of the eye that can result in such a range of adaptation level and resultant threshold variability as we

FIG. 7-7. Mach bands. Notice the white and black lines on opposite sides of the separation between the dark and light gray areas. (Photo courtesy of Tom Cornsweet, Stanford Research Institute.)

have reported? Few if any of the other senses exhibit such great adaptation effects. Perhaps some of the adaptation as well as the relatively long time delay in the eye may be due to the additional complexity of the radiant energy/chemical energy/neural energy cycle. For some components of the tactual senses and the auditory sense, mechanical stimulation acts directly to produce a nervous response, hence very little opportunity for adaptation mediated by chemical reaction occurs. With respect to the chemical senses (taste and smell) a chemical reaction with the stimulating material presumably results directly in a neural response.

The Rods and Visual Purple

In the visual sense the situation is more complex. Electromagnetic energy produces a chemical response which is relatively slow, and this chemical response (or an opposing reaction) then results in the firing of the sensory neuron. Such a complicated process takes time, and allows for a considerable amount of adaptation or change in the sensitivity of the overall sense organ. Adaptation is also a quality of the simple chemical senses, and some adaptation is certainly mediated at higher nervous levels, but the exceedingly wide adaptation range of vision indicates to me the efficacy of the "dual" chemical process: a chemical reaction in the rods or cones due to the light, and a second chemical reaction to produce the neural discharge.

While our knowledge of just how external energy can result in the discharge of a sensory neuron is not entirely adequate, we do understand rod functioning in the eye to a better extent than is true for most of the senses. Experimental evidence suggests that first of all a quantum of light must be absorbed by a molecule of photosensitive substance in the outer portion of the rod cell. When the pigmented substance of the eye is removed and subjected to light of various wavelengths, it is found that the absorption spectrum of the substance agrees almost perfectly with the scotopic relative luminosity curve shown in Fig. 7-4. In other words, the wavelength absorbed best is at about 510 mμ, the point of peak luminosity; and relative absorptions for other hues fall almost perfectly on the rod-function curve. Corrections must be made to allow for discrepancies between the two measures, such as the absorption characteristics of the ocular media and the fact that, when determining the relative luminosity curves, light must be measured at the cornea, rather than at the rods themselves. When these corrections are made, the agreement is striking.

What is the nature of the rods that occasions such absorption? In 1876 Franz Boll of the University of Rome discovered in the rod cell of the frog's retina, a red pigment which bleached in light and synthesized in the absence of light, thus meeting theoretical requirements for a visual pigment. The substance, which he called visual red, is now known as *visual purple*. It has since been determined that about 30 percent of the entire rod cell consists of visual purple, or *rhodopsin.*

A contemporary of Boll, Willy Kühne of Heidelberg, proceeded with some fascinating experiments in the study of the remarkable light-sensitive pigment. He was able to obtain an image from the retina, known as an *optogram,* demonstrating conclusively that the eye does indeed behave much like a photographic plate. Kühne, after dark-adapting the eye of an albino rabbit, exposed the eye to a barred window for several minutes. Upon decapitating the animal, removing the eye, and fixing the retina in an alum solution, he was able to see the image of the barred window in the dried tissue.

By isolating rhodopsin it has been further demonstrated that it has an absorption spectrum identical to the actual rods themselves, and of course, the psychophysically derived luminosity curve. Indeed, recent researchers have removed the sensitive rhodopsin, prepared it in emulsion form, and coated photographic plates with it which actually worked in taking simple pictures. It is clear, then, that it is this substance which produces the relative sensitivity function of rod vision.

Since the discovery of rhodopsin nearly a hundred years ago we have learned a great deal about its properties. For one thing, it bleaches under the influence of light: from purple to yellow, and then to transparency. We know too that the unbleached rhodopsin is made up of two molecules, one called the *chromophore,* derived from vitamin A and giving the substance its characteristic color, the other a protein molecule known as *opsin.* Presumably the result of light stimulation is to alter the form of the vitamin A portion and in some manner not yet understood produce an excitation in the neuron. Perhaps the modified vitamin A produces a change in permeability within the cell wall which allows for the passage of ions, much like the neural impulse in a conventional neuron.

After the cessation of the light stimulus it is necessary for the transparent chromophore portion of the substance to revert back to its normal unbleached form. This then, is ostensibly the adaptation we have been discussing. It is probably not the entire story. It has been found, for example, that the entire bleaching-recovery cycle of rhodopsin is not adequate to explain the full range of adaptation. The matter is not settled. Perhaps an interaction of rods such that mutual facilitation and/or inhibition occurs, thereby providing for the unpredicted increase in adaptation range; or perhaps much of the range must be accounted for at higher neural levels. The question remains unanswered.

Did you notice the significance of vitamin A in the chemical reaction? Should you eat carrots to see better? To the extent that carrots are rich in vitamin A, and to the extent that you have a shortage of vitamin A in your system, they might help you see better in cases where dark adaptation is critical. Under conditions of vitamin A shortage, it has indeed been found that dark adaptation is impaired and vision under low-level illumination suffers.

The chemistry of cone vision is presumably more complex, since color discriminability must in some way be accounted for. When we come to discuss color vision in a later chapter we will examine what is presently known concerning the chemistry of the cones.

The Bunsen-Roscoe Law

It was indicated earlier that area and intensity may integrate to provide a threshold stimulation. The manner in which this occurs was described by Ricco's law and Piper's law. If at threshold, the product of area and intensity is a constant (within limits), then an increase in either could be accompanied by a decrease in the other, and the threshold situation would still exist. Inasmuch as the original reaction in the retinal elements is chemical in nature, and since we know that the rate of chemical reaction frequently depends on the concentration of the constituents, we might wonder whether perhaps intensity and time might not also integrate and therefore be somewhat interchangeable. In other words, given enough time, could a weak visual stimulus elicit a response which might not occur for a similar stimulus of shorter duration? This is indeed the case, and the law which describes the relationship is the *Bunsen-Roscoe law*. This states that a constant photolytic effect is determined by a constant amount of *energy*, rather than intensity or intensity level, energy being a combination of intensity and duration. The law can be written $I \times t = C$, where I is the intensity, t is time or duration, and C is a constant. In photographic emulsions, for example, the law works almost perfectly over a very wide range. As you may know, you can change either the aperture or the shutter speed with equally predictable results (so far as exposure is concerned, at least). In the eye, the law does not apply over all time and intensity combinations. For long duration the critical member of the function is intensity, and time has little if any influence, but for durations up to roughly 0.1 second, intensity and duration are, indeed, interchangeable.

SUMMARY

In the first part of the chapter we considered the specification of the visual stimulus which produces the experience of brightness. We described, briefly, three approaches to light measurement: intensity, illumination, and luminance, and a few of their more common units of measurement. A large part of the chapter was devoted to the experience of luminance or "brightness" and the specification of the absolute threshold. In so doing we examined differences between rods and cones, including sensitivity, dark adaptation, response time, and the Purkinje shift. In the course of the chapter we described, with a minimum of detail, the known chemistry of rod functioning. Two well-known laws of vision, Ricco's and Piper's laws, were described as well as the Stiles-Crawford effect, the Bunsen-Roscoe law, and the Pulfrich phenomenon.

SUGGESTED READINGS

1. From M. H. Pirenne, *Vision and the Eye* (London: Chapman and Hall, 1967). This is an excellent little book (205 pages) well worth reading in its entirety. About half of the book is germane to the subject matter of the preceding chapter and the first eight chapters (109 pages) are particularly recommended at this time. Chapters 9 and 10 concern themselves with the limulus and insect eyes and are also worthwhile reading. It is well illustrated, well written, and must be highly recommended.
2. From S. S. Stevens (ed.), *Handbook of Experimental Psychology* (New York: Wiley, 1951). Chapters 22 and 24 are applicable to visual sensory processes. These 120 pages are quite detailed, and must reading for the serious student. For others, a more selective approach may be advisable. Chapter 22, written by Dean Judd, emphasizes the physical correlates of the visual stimulus and is therefore recommended for the student with such an interest. The latter half of the chapter might best be read after we have considered color in more detail. A valuable part of this chapter is the glossary of terms at the end as well as several tables which aid in the understanding of the different approaches to light measurement. Chapter 24, "The Psychophysiology of Vision" (60 pages) by S. Howard Bartley is the best detailed elaboration of the material covered in our Chapter 7 that I know of. This chapter also includes considerable material which will be pertinent to later chapters, such as flicker, movement, etc. For the serious or advanced student, these two chapters are highly recommended.
3. From S. Howard Bartley, *Principles of Perception*, 2d ed. (New York: Harper, 1969). Chapter 4 "Adaptation and Brightness Discrimination" covers most of the material we have presented. It does it in a highly readable manner, and these 30 pages are well worth reading. This chapter is especially useful to the reader who wishes original sources, since Dr. Bartley includes references to original research work in most cases.
4. From F. A. Geldard, *The Human Senses* (New York: Wiley, 1953). Chapter 3 is titled "Basic Visual Phenomena" and includes much of the material included in this chapter. It is easy reading and well illustrated; pages 28–40 in particular should furnish an excellent supplement to the material just completed.

5. Boynton, R. M., "The Psychophysics of Vision," in R. N. Haber (ed.), *Contemporary Theory and Research in Visual Perception* (New York: Holt, 1968). Consisting of 17 well-written pages, this article from the 1964 Proceedings of the International Congress on Technology and Blindness, is excellent. It includes discussions of physical measurement as well as descriptions of psychophysical methods. It discusses thresholds, dark adaptation and in general, most of the topics covered in the preceding chapter. It is highly recommended for additional reading.
6. From C. G. Mueller, *Sensory Psychology* (Englewood Cliffs, N.J.: Prentice-Hall, 1965). Chapter 2 of this reference is short, about 11 pages, but it is well worth reading. The presentation of the rhodopsin cycle and photochemistry is particularly lucid and topical. Professor Mueller's coverage of the electrical activity of the retinal elements and the nerve impulse are also very illuminating. Highly recommended reading.

8

ACUITY, VISUAL CORRECTION

Astronomers in their quest for new, distant stars first recognized the problem of discriminating between small spatial differences in the visual field, and the importance of the resolving power of the eye for this ability. As a result, most early definitions involving visual acuity were originated by astronomers. The early work of the astronomers suggested that the minimum separable difference between two stars that could just be detected was 1 minute of visual angle. This was defined as "normal," with the reciprocal of the visual angle in minutes being the conventional expression for visual acuity. Thus an eye with a minimum separable angle capability of 1 minute was said to have an acuity of 1.0; an eye that required an angle of 2 minutes of arc between two points of light would have an acuity of 0.5 (1 divided by 2).

An acuity of 1.0 was the accepted standard, and even today is the basis for the familiar Snellen chart used by the school nurse and most optometrists and ophthalmologists. (See Fig. 8-1). We now know that this standard is somewhat too lenient, and that a good, healthy eye can resolve a distance of less than 1 minute of arc. Many students may have vision better than 20/20, such as 20/15, which indicates that they can resolve a separable angle of less than 1 minute of arc.* For practical application, however, the use of 1 minute of arc remains the convention.

Let us retrace our steps a bit and examine the significance of visual acuity, beginning with the subject of resolution—the ability of the eye and its retinal mosaic to discriminate between small spatial distances.

LIMITATIONS

Three factors tend to place an upper limit on visual acuity; one of them can, in some cases, be mitigated by means of eyeglasses and one may be improved by means of visual training.

---

* The meaning of such expressions as 20/20, 20/40, etc. will be considered later in the chapter.

FIG. 8-1. Representative acuity charts. A is designed for viewing in a mirror, hence the reversed characters; B and C are the conventional letters; while D is made up of numerals employing the same spacing. E is used for illiterates and also includes an astigmatism detection figure. F is for the use of kindergarten-age children and is printed in color (appearing in black here). (Courtesy American Optical Corporation, Buffalo, N.Y.)

Optical Factors

A most important limitation in visual acuity concerns the optical characteristics of the semitransparent media. In the most simple case of improper optical functioning, the cornea-lens combination simply does not bring the image in focus on the sensitive plane of the retina. As in an out-of-focus camera, the image is in focus either in front of or behind the retina. As we will show later in the chapter, unless the defect is extremely severe, problems of simple *refractive error* can be corrected by means of corrective lenses.

Another possible difficulty may result from departures from the "true" shape of the cornea and/or lens. As indicated earlier, both the cornea and the lens should have surfaces which represent sections from perfect spheres (at least in the functionally central portion). When these surfaces are distorted or misshapen in any way, projection of an image on the retina is disturbed, and the visual experience is known as *astigmatism*. If such distortion involves the portion of the optical path relied on for fine vision, a limitation in acuity must result. As with refractive error, if the disorder is not too severe, corrective lenses can mitigate most of the limitation due to astigmatism.

There are fundamental characteristics in the design of the eye which limit its potential resolving power. As with man-made optical devices, the theoretical limitation based on the wavelength of light can never be attained. Diffraction of light at the pupil margin results in light not perfectly perpendicular to the plane of the retina, and this in turn causes some loss of resolution. Such light may actually bounce around in the eye, resulting in a general "film of light," thus reducing contrast between the image and its background. It is well known that a high degree of contrast between an object and its background is necessary for maximum visibility, and *entoptic stray light* cannot but reduce figure/background contrast. Indeed, some light must enter the eye by way of the sclerotic coat and the eyeball itself. Light may enter by way of the partially opaque iris and contribute to an overall lowering of potential acuity. In the albino eye, with its lack of pigment, this problem is particularly acute.

There are also aberrations due to the nature of the cornea-lens combination. Any lens is in effect made up of an infinite number of prisms. Hence different wavelengths will be refracted differentially, and unless light of a single wavelength is used, chromatic aberration must produce some limitation in resolution. As we indicated earlier, the eye does indeed eliminate some chromatic aberration, but enough surely remains to keep practical resolution well below any theoretically expected level. The nature of the vitreous body probably serves to limit resolution, too. It is not as transparent as air, for example, and with the large amount of solid material suspended in it, more diffraction and general clouding of the visual image must result.

Retinal Factors

The size of the individual elements in the retinal mosaic might be expected to limit visual acuity. Many of you are aware of the limitations of resolution in a photographic film due to grain size and clumping of the individual silver molecules. According to figures provided by Polyak, the average cone in the fovea centralis subtends a visual angle of 24 seconds of arc, or slightly less than $\frac{1}{2}$ minute. It might therefore be expected than a minimal distance to be discriminated could not be less than 24 seconds of visual angle.

While "grain size" of the retinal mosaic may provide a theoretical limit, in practice the cross-sectional size of the retinal elements does not appear to severely limit resolution. Under highly controlled laboratory conditions, one can find measures of resolution where the dimensions on the retina are much less than the width of a cone. In vernier acuity (to be described later), differences of 5 seconds of arc, or one-fifth the diameter of a cone, have been reported. We once showed, in a laboratory psychophysical experiment utilizing a constant method, that at a distance of 20 feet, size differences of less than $\frac{1}{64}$ inch could be detected with statistical significance.

How can the eye discriminate distances on the retina which are smaller than the actual size of the retinal elements? Very small, unconscious movements of the eye may result in a moving image, and the "on-off" functioning of the sensitive cones allows for greater resolution than would be predicted on the basis of rod-and-cone cross-sectional size. There are, for example, very rapid eye movements (30 to 70 per second) of quite short excursion which may provide the "scanning" effect that permits resolution much greater than might be expected on the basis of cone diameter alone.

Interconnections in secondary layers of the retina *do* limit acuity. In the nonfoveal regions where the simple one-to-one connections we described earlier do not exist, acuity is in fact restricted as a function of the retinal mosaic and its bipolar and ganglion cell connections.

Neural Processing

The third factor in determining limits of visual acuity concerns the ability of the nervous system to utilize differences in excitation. As mentioned in the preceding paragraph, the lack of one-to-one correspondence from the retinal elements to the optic nerve fibers places a limit on potential acuity. Similar branching at higher levels may also result in loss of visual acuity.

However, higher-level functioning may be responsible for increased rather than decreased acuity. If higher-level functioning is indeed related to visual acuity, can we not "learn" to see sharply, to have improved acuity? Within limits we can. A professor I once knew emphasized visual training to reduce many visual problems and increase visual skills. He was occasionally accused of teaching people to interpret "blurs." It was said that his training did not improve acuity at all, his patients were merely able to interpret their blurred images better. Is this bad? Indeed, in light of the relatively poor optical quality of the eye, much of our excellent vision is perhaps due to higher mental processes which interpret the relatively inadequate and certainly incomplete, retinal image. You have probably seen many examples of how the eye, using the word in a broad sense, fills in details not even present in the viewed image. Perhaps Dr. Renshaw's subjects who learned to "interpret blurs" were just doing what we all do, only doing it better, and in spite of more serious defects in their image-forming structures.

FACTORS INFLUENCING ACUITY

Before considering in some detail the measurement of acuity or resolving power of the eye, let us examine briefly some of the factors influencing it. Acuity, to be described adequately, must allow for the entire accommodative range of the eye. Inasmuch as the lens achieves maximum accommodation for distance at about twenty feet, this distance is normally used for so-called far point, or distance vision. For near-point vision, acuity must be measured at the normal reading distance. When fitting you with reading glasses, for example, your optometrist may have you hold a printed page in a comfortable position to determine what distance you prefer for reading.

As suggested in the previous chapter when we considered rods and cones, acuity is highly influenced by the portion of the retina involved. Knowing the extent of one-to-one or near one-to-one connections between the foveal cones and the higher neural centers, we might expect acuity to be better when the central portion of the retina (fovea) is involved. This is indeed the case. Figure 8-2 shows the influence on acuity of angular distance from the fovea. Note the extremely rapid loss of acuity as we progress even 1 or 2 degrees away from the direct line of sight. The curve, of course, is for cone vision, involving relatively high levels of illumination.

Since the rods are more sensitive to light than the cones, and since we can best detect a very dim light at a distance of about 20 degrees

FIG. 8-2. Visual acuity on the retina. Note the small
blind spot on the nasal side.

from the fovea, we might expect that under low-light conditions acuity
too would be somewhat better if a retinal area eccentric to the fovea were
involved. It has indeed been found that best nighttime acuity is obtained
when the direction of regard is on the order of 4 degrees eccentric to the
direct line of sight.

As in the case of visual detection, acuity too is influenced by time.
Dimmer objects, as well as smaller objects, require more time to be
resolved satisfactorily. For a given exposure time, more light is required to
see a smaller target than a larger one.

Acuity is influenced by other factors. The brightness of the surround,
even the extreme peripheral area, may influence acuity in the central
area. Some of this effect may be due to entoptic stray light which may
serve to mask somewhat the area of the retina occupied by the image.
There are also, presumably, retinal events which serve to inhibit or
sensitize the more central rods and cones. The interaction is exceedingly
complex and goes far beyond the limitations of this chapter.

MEASUREMENT OF ACUITY

To this point we have been discussing acuity as if it were a single
attribute of the visual sense, simple to define and measure, and subject to
no controversy. This is not the entire story. Resolution ability and resultant visual acuity can be measured in may different ways, with
decidedly disparate results. As in the study of learning, where different

experimental materials and methods result in different "types" of learning, different visual stimuli and methods result in different "types" of visual acuity. Let us examine several of the available approaches to the assessment of visual acuity.

Visibility

Basic to any consideration of acuity as a threshold for discriminating differences in areal location of visual stimuli, is the concept of *visibility,* or less rigorously, visibility acuity.* An object must subtend some finite distance on the retina in order to be visible, and the nature of this distance determines visibility acuity. But the matter is not quite that simple. An important factor is contrast—that is, the relative brightness of the object and the background. Except at very high levels of background where light scattering may actually reduce contrast on the retina, maximum acuity is found with maximum contrast. In general, this rule also applies for the more conventional measurements of visual acuity.

Contrast is a relative attribute, since black is rarely the complete absence of light, and white must have some finite limit. Contrast is usually measured in some sort of ratio between the background and the figure or stimulus. In one approach, the brighter of the two values is always used in the denominator of the contrast ratio fraction as:

$$\% \text{ contrast} = \frac{B_1 - B_2}{B_1} \times 100$$

where B_1 is the brighter of the two and B_2 is the less bright measure.

Another approach results in two different formulas:

$$C = \frac{B_s - B_g}{B_g}$$

and

$$C = \frac{B_g - B_s}{B_g}$$

where C is contrast, B_g is the brightness of the background and B_s is the brightness of the stimulus. The first expression is useful for situations where the stimulus is brighter than the background and provides contrasts from 0 to ∞. The second form of the fraction is used when the background is brighter than the stimulus and results in contrasts from 0 to 1.00.

With ideal conditions of contrast the normal human eye can detect a fine wire on a light background when the thickness of the wire is such

---

* Properly defined, acuity refers to the resolving power of the eye, the ability to see two lines or two points as two, while visibility is simply the ability to detect a visual stimulus as a function of its size.

as to subtend a visual angle of as little as 0.5 second of arc. In terms of the normal visual acuity (as defined by the Snellen chart) such a capability represents a visual "acuity" 120 times greater than the standard one minute of arc.

It is also of interest, and germane to our earlier suggestion of higher-level influences, that the length of the line is of some importance. Longer lines can be detected at lower contrast levels than shorter lines, indicating, rather obviously, some sort of summation effect at a level of functioning at least higher than that of the basic rods and cones.

Gratings

Another approach, particularly useful for basic research, involves the presentation of grating made up of dark lines on a light background. (Light lines on a dark background can also be employed, but with somewhat different results.) As most often used, the threshold for acuity is

Grating   Checkerboard

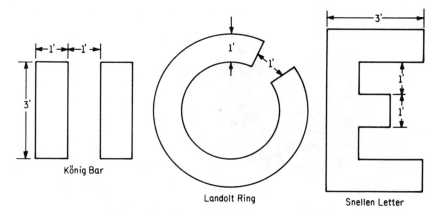

König Bar   Landolt Ring   Snellen Letter

Fig. 8-3. Representative acuity-test material. Note the 1-minute dimensions in both the stroke width and the openings for the bottom figures. Note too that both the König bars and the Snellen letters have overall widths of 3 minutes of visual angle.

that point when the subject can identify the area as being a grating, rather than a uniform gray. A modification of the grating technique features alternate squares filled in the manner of a checkerboard, and is to be found in a few clinical tests of acuity. (See Fig. 8-3.)

The use of gratings combines the more elementary visibility function with the more conventional acuity based on discriminable spatial distances. As a result of this combination, the use of gratings results in acuities poorer than those obtained for simple visibility, but much better than those obtained by the methods normally employed by your optometrist or ophthalmologist for clinical evaluation.

Vernier Acuity

Another type of acuity measurement is that of vernier acuity, which indicates the aligning power of the eye, the ability to align two thin lines. Acuity under this condition is about 12 times as good as the Snellen standard, or on the order of 5 minutes of arc. To express it in another way, a misalignment equivalent to one-fifth the width of a cone can be detected. It is perhaps not fortuitous that precision measuring instruments such as micrometers and machinists' calipers capitalize on the remarkable ability of the eye to align opposing lines etched on their metal scales. (See Fig. 8-4.)

Resolution Acuity

Probably the most commonly used measure of acuity is that of resolution acuity, defined as the reciprocal of the minimum separable threshold, specified in minutes of visual angle. As discussed briefly at the beginning of this chapter, resolution acuity can be measured by determining the

Fig. 8-4. Machinist's micrometer. The remarkable precision obtainable with such an instrument is due, partially, to the use of vernier acuity. Aligning of one line with another provides the highest measure of acuity possible.
(Photograph courtesy of Fisher Scientific Company.)

minimum distance (in minutes of arc) between 2 points of light which can just be resolved. In practice, however, it is more usual to use simple geometric figures, with known separations between their components. Three forms of geometric figures are commonly used and are shown in Fig. 8-3.

König Bars. This is probably the simplest test of resolution acuity, and the one which most closely satisfies the definition. The König bar was originated by Arthur König, a brilliant researcher, whose untimely death in 1901 at the age of 45 deprived the world of one of its truly great potential researchers. A König bar for "normal" vision will subtend an overall visual angle of 3 minutes of arc in each direction, consisting of two bars, each 1 minute by 3 minutes and separated by a 1-minute space. The criterion for resolution is not quite as objective as is true for tests such as the Snellen letters, in that the viewer must decide when he can see the two solid bars as separate and distinct. If we mount the display on a track, and bring it from a distance where it looks like a blob up to a point where it is clearly seen as being made up of two distinct bars, interesting subjective reports may result. There will be a stage where the blob looks somewhat "dumbbell-shaped," and then a stage where the ends of the dumbbell will separate temporarily, frequently rejoining and separating, until the target is finally close enough to be resolved with 100 percent precision. Because of the apparent transitional development of resolution and the potentiality for subjective reports, König bars are quite useful for research in resolution.

When used as just described, König bars also produce the most direct measure of acuity in the familiar 20/20, 20/40 terms. When the target has been brought to a distance of 20 feet with a separable angle of 1 minute, and can be resolved by the subject, we can say that he has normal 20/20 vision; that is, he can see at 20 feet what he should be able to see at 20 feet. However, if the observer requires twice the bar separation of a normal person—that is, he can resolve bars at 20 feet which he should be able to resolve at 40 feet, then he is said to have 20/40 vision.

It is relatively simple to manipulate distance and bar separation to obtain quite precise distance/resolution relations. König bars have been used to study the influence of background area and brightness contrast on resolution. They can also be used to study the influence of figures (noise) in the peripheral visual field at varying distances from the target itself. Subjective reports concerning the development of the clear separation condition are particularly valuable. König bars are also useful for training, their application being limited only by the imagination of the researcher. On the other hand, the subjective nature of the judgments required make them somewhat less useful for clinical applications than the two following techniques.

Landolt Rings. Landolt rings are intermediate between König bars and Snellen letters in their diagnostic/research potential and in their usefulness for clinical application. A Landolt ring is a doughnut-shaped figure with, for normal vision, a thickness of 1 minute of visual angle and an opening of 1 minute. In practice, the opening can be located at various positions on the circle, and the subject (or patient) indicates the position of the opening in such terms as "north," "southwest," etc., or perhaps more simply "top," "left," "bottom," and "right." In some cases the subject may simply indicate the direction of the opening by pointing, thus eliminating the requirement for a verbal response. The underlying assumption is that the subject, in order to locate the opening, must be first able to resolve it.

Landolt rings can be presented individually, as in the case of König bars, or they may be presented on a card in varying sizes, not unlike the familiar Snellen chart. (See Fig. 8-1.) In practice, some clinicians present Landolt rings of varying sizes in a natural fashion as part of a photographed scene, allowing the patient to view the three-dimensional display by means of some sort of stereo viewer. When using a stereoscopic device distance can be simulated optically, eliminating the necessity for long viewing distances in order to evaluate distant (far-point) vision. Such techniques, utilizing acuity test material in realistic surrounds may indeed result in more valid measures than the purely artificial office setting with a chart mounted on the wall.

It is probably safe to say that Landolt rings are gradually replacing the familiar Snellen chart as a simple test of acuity. Their greater flexibility and diagnostic potential are, I suspect, being increasingly recognized by modern clinicians.

Snellen Chart. This is still the most commonly used instrument for determining acuity, especially for screening purposes. Like other measures, charts can be used both for distant vision (20 feet) and nearpoint (reading distance) evaluation. An example of several possible charts is shown as Fig. 8-1. Charts A, B, and C all utilize the familiar Snellen letters, based on a 5×3 minutes of visual angle standard (see Fig. 8-3). All characters for a given distance have stroke widths of 1-minute visual angle and spaces between elements of 1 minute. The line on the chart labeled 20/20 would, of course, have the basic dimensions for the 20 foot viewing distance. The 20/40 line would have elements subtending visual angles of 2 minutes at a distance of 20 feet.

In Fig. 8-1 charts B and C are the conventional wall charts with which you are probably familiar. Chart A appears to be backward. This is so because it is designed to be viewed in a mirror, and is meant for applications where the viewing room is not long enough to accommodate the nominal 20 foot viewing distance. Chart D is similar to the conventional Snellen chart, but utilizes numerals rather than letters. Chart E employs figures all in the form of elongated E's and is for testing illiterates. The patient simply indicates the direction of the "arms" by pointing with his fingers. The last chart is for testing kindergarten children and features familiar objects—in color, incidentally—which can be identified by children of this age.

While the Snellen chart is relatively foolproof, it is not entirely so. When used in the conventional wall card form, dirt, fading, smudges, etc., can greatly reduce the contrast of the printed material, resulting in acuities with appreciable error. When used for simple screening in schools, in industry, or in the military, uneven lighting and glare may make the results suspect. In the simple wall-chart form, the Snellen chart should probably be limited to crude screening and not be relied upon for precision measurement unless extreme care is used.

The Snellen chart, as a tool for acuity measurement, is also available in various other forms, similar to those available for the Landolt rings. Outdoor scenes can be photographed with Snellen charts at various distances and viewed (or projected) in stereoscopic form, simulating true

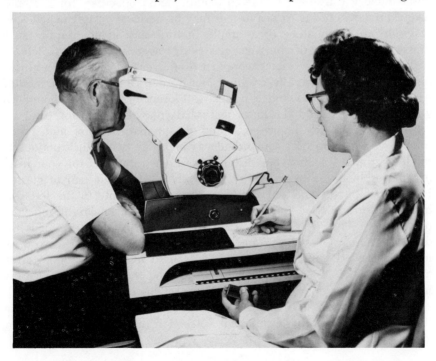

FIG. 8-5. A visual testing device. This and similar equipment by other manufacturers provide built in stimuli and controlled conditions for testing basic visual skills such as acuity, phoria, stereopsis, etc. (Courtesy Titmus Optical Company, Petersburg, Va.)

binocular vision. Still another possibility involves the use of a zoom type projection system, so that the size of the projected image can be varied continuously over a relatively wide range.

Figure 8-5 shows a device used to screen persons for various visual defects, including acuity. It can provide somewhat more analytic results than a simple wall chart, particularly in the hands of moderately trained nurses and assistants. The Vision Tester, manufactured by Titmus Optical Company, has built in slides for testing various eye defects. An adjustment for either near or far vision is available, and testing conditions are fairly well controlled. There are several other commercial devices available which make the testing of visual defects much less subject to error in the hands of nonprofessional than a simple wall chart and test lenses.*

CORRECTING VISUAL DEFECTS

We have already discussed some problems in degraded visual ability and the steps necessary for their correction. If the problem is one of unsatisfactory transmission due to ocular media opacities, for example, surgical removal of the cornea or lens may be necessary. Most deficiencies of vision are fortunately, of a simpler nature and do not require such drastic action. Many of you wear glasses to correct simple visual defects. Did you know that spectacles were first used over 650 years ago, and that their invention is generally credited jointly to a Dominican friar named Alessandro della Spina and a native of Florence, Salvino d'Amato? Of greater importance, do you know just what your glasses do for you?

Exclusive of such features as tinted glass, tempered glass, and special frames, your optometrist can provide as many as twelve instructions to the lens grinder—six for your distant vision glasses and six for your reading glasses, or if you wear bifocals, all twelve for a single pair of glasses. Half of the instructions on your prescription will apply to the left eye, half for the right. But you probably won't see "left" or "right" on your prescription. The "S" you may see at the top of the prescription is the doctor's way of saying "left," and is short for *sinister,* the Latin word for left. For the other lens, the letter "D" is used and is short for *dexter,* meaning "right." "S" and "D" are simply in the tradition of using Latin in all doctors' prescriptions, even medicine for the common cold.

Each lens (or each half of a bifocal lens) can provide as many as three basic corrections: a spherical correction, a cylindrical correction, and a prismatic correction. All lenses will not have all these possible

---

* These include the Sight-Screener by American Optical Company; the Tele-binocular by Keystone View Company: and the Ortho-Rater by Bausch & Lomb Optical Company.

curvatures ground into them. Let us examine the significance of these three types of correction.

Spherical Correction

Look at Fig. 8-6. In (a) of this drawing the point source focuses directly on the sensitive surface of the retina for both far and near vision.

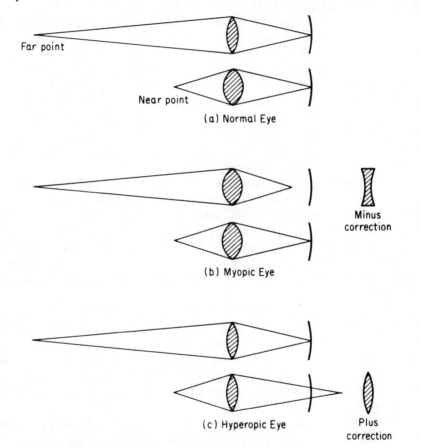

FIG. 8-6. Spherical correction. (a) The normal eye is able to adjust its lens shape for both far and near vision. (b) The myopic eye has a lens which does not get thin enough for far vision and a minus or concave lens must be worn. (c) The hyperopic eye has a lens which will not thicken sufficiently for near vision, hence, plus or convex lenses must be worn.

As a matter of record (and as indicated earlier), while not shown on this diagram, the cornea of the human eye provides about two-thirds of the refraction necessary to focus an image on the retina. The lens, on the other hand, provides the variability in refraction (*accommodation*) to enable proper focusing with changes in distance. Such is possible because the lens is able to assume a thick, relatively spherical shape for near vision, and a thin, less "powerful" shape for distant vision. The two extremes shown in the diagram are indicative of a healthy, flexible lens, the sort of lens you were meant to have and once did have. With a lens like this you do not need glasses, at least not to correct a refractive error such as those illustrated in (b) and (c) of this figure.

The refractive error illustrated in (b) is typical of *myopia* or the myopic eye, also called *near-sightedness.* Note that the lens is relatively thick and focuses the point of light on the retinal surface quite adequately at near-point (e.g., reading distance). But when the visual stimulus is at a distance, the lens does not adequately assume its thin, less-powerful configuration. There is too much refraction for distant vision and the point comes to focus in front of the retina. A positive refractive error such as this was once thought to be due to an eyeball that was too long. Today we are inclined to think that the problem is in the lens/cornea combination, rather than the eyeball shape.

In (b) of Fig. 8-6 the condition known as *hyperopia* or *far-sightedness* is illustrated. In this condition the lens willingly assumes its thin form for distant vision but is unable to take on the thicker, more powerful shape for near vision. Most young people do not suffer from hyperopia, but in the older generation inability to focus properly at normal reading distances is quite common. Did you ever notice an older person whose "arms were getting too short" to permit him to hold his book far enough away to read?

How does your eye doctor diagnose refractive errors and what can he do about them? One approach to examining accommodation of the lens involves a phenomenon known as Purkinje's images. Noting changes in the relative size and location of images reflected from various interocular surfaces, the skilled optometrist or ophthalmologist can determine with remarkable accuracy the extent to which the lens is accommodating for changes in distance.

More likely, however, and certainly as a final step, trial-and-error procedures will be used. These procedures may involve the physical insertion of trial lenses into temporary frames the patient is wearing, or in more elaborate set ups, manipulation of internal lenses in a device known as a *phoropter.*

It is clear from Fig. 8-6, that if you are suffering from myopia—that is, if your lens is too thick—you must make it functionally thinner or less powerful. The answer is obvious: negative or concave lenses to reduce the total amount of refraction in the spectacle/cornea/lens combination. Look through your spectacles at this page. If they make it seem smaller, then you have a concave lens, a negative or *minus* correction for myopia.

If your glasses magnify the image, they are correcting for hyperopia, adding curvature or refraction to the total system. They are then *plus* lenses. Your eye doctor determined the type and amount of correction you needed by inserting lenses of various design in front of you until you said "now it's clear."

When a person gets older, he may suffer from *presbyopia*—that is, he is both near-sighted and far-sighted. His lens works adequately only at some intermediate distance, and he needs negative or minus correction for distant vision and positive or plus correction for reading. Bifocals, invented by that remarkable gentleman, Benjamin Franklin, may be called for with minus correction in the top portion and plus correction in the bottom.

All of the above corrections are called spherical because the lenses are, indeed, much like sections sliced from large spheres. If they are to provide plus correction they are not unlike the conventional magnifying or reading glass, for minus correction they are like the inside surface of a large sphere, if you can visualize such an entity.

The first line of your spectacle prescription will probably specify the amount of spherical correction to be ground into your lens. It will say something like: $+1\Delta$, -0.5Δ, or $+2.0\Delta$. The $+$ and $-$ signs are relatively simple: plus or minus spherical correction. The Δ is the Greek letter delta, and is the symbol for *diopter*, a unit of focal length. The reciprocal of the focal length in meters of a simple lens is expressed as diopter. Thus a lens of one meter focal length is a one-diopter lens ($+1.0\Delta$ or -1.0Δ). A two-diopter lens has a focal length of one-half meter, a four-diopter lens a focal length of one-fourth meter, etc. A lens of 0.1 diopter would have a focal length of 10 meters and would not be much more than plain glass. For any correction less than one-quarter diopter you would probably not need spherical correction.

Cylindrical Correction

The second line on your prescription may specify the amount of cylindrical correction you require. We noted in Chapter 6 that "untrue" shapes or noticeable departures from a true spherical configuration in the case of the cornea can result in astigmatism. If a visual target such as (a) in Fig. 8-7 is viewed with an eye which does not present a true spherical surface to the external world, the result may be an image on the retina like (b) of this figure, an indication of astigmatism. Part (a) of this figure is quite similar to the test target your optometrist uses when he checks you for astigmatism.

Note that there is a directionality to the lack of resolution; the corneal surface is "warped" or "misshapen" in a somewhat systematic way. The obvious correction would be one that would compensate for the corneal

(a) Target   (b) Visual Image

(c) Cylindrical Correction

Fig. 8-7. Cylindrical correction for astigmatism.
To a person with astigmatism the target shown in
part (a) appears as shown in part (b). Corrective
lenses with cylindrical curvature, as shown in part
(c), are used to correct this problem.

distortion, thus restoring an overall, total spherical aspect to the incoming
light.

Part (c) of Fig. 8-7 shows schematically the sort of cylinder correction required to counteract the structural distortion. The eye doctor tries
various types of cylinders, rotating them until you report the spokes of the
figure are clear and free from blur. Your prescription would, then, include
both the amount of correction, again in diopters, and also the angle for the
straight dimension of the cylinder section.

Prismatic Correction

The third and last entry on your spectacle prescription is that for
prismatic correction. As you must know by now, the relation between
the eyes and with the central nervous system processor is exceedingly
complex. The existence of two eyes which see almost but not quite the
same thing requires a combining at the level of the brain which is indeed
impressive. Presumably, there are "corresponding points" in the two retinas, such that when one looks at a point of light with both eyes, the
stimulus will activate neurologically analogous loci in the brain. When
the images to the two eyes differ slightly, and in the proper manner, the

experience of depth or stereopsis results. If the images to the two eyes are quite different, the brain may have trouble in combining the two pictures. You may experience *retinal rivalry*, in which the two images are seen alternately, or in some cases one image may be repressed and the other accepted as "reality."

Under some pathological conditions the eyes themselves may have difficulty in achieving this "corresponding point" alignment, even though the images to the two eyes are essentially the same. There are imbalances, both muscular and functional, which result in the images to the two eyes being slightly misaligned. In the case of severe muscular problems resulting in *strabismus,* or cross-eye, surgery may correct the cosmetic problem as we mentioned earlier, but the functional problem of combining the images from the two eyes may still remain.

Look at (a) of Fig. 8-8, a sample stereogram for testing vertical phoria. When viewed through a suitable binocular device, if the eyes function properly the horizontal broken line will pass through the note marked "4." If such is not the case, then the eyes are functionally mis-

(a) Vertical Phoria

(b) Lateral Phoria

FIG. 8-8. Test material for detecting phoria. Illustration (a) is used for determining the presence of vertical phoria, illustration (b) for lateral phoria. (Courtesy Titmus Optical Company.)

aligned. In this case it is referred to as *vertical phoria*. If the orientation of the test material is changed, as in (b) of this figure, we can measure *lateral phoria*. While the true nature of *heterophoria* is not fully understood, one point can be made: it is not simply strabismus or muscular imbalance. It is a functional, image misalignment, and not due merely to the direction the eye points.

The presence of a vertical phoria is particularly disturbing. Remember, we have lateral eye movements of convergence and divergence which can compensate somewhat (with effort) for lateral phoria. But vertical phoria? The muscles which move the eyes in the vertical direction do not work well except in unison. We cannot easily elevate one eye and lower the other. The result, then, of vertical phoria is a blurred image, eye strain, or perhaps even a learned practice of suppressing the image from one eye and relying for all intents and purposes, on monocular vision.

After your eye doctor has determined that you have a phoria problem he then proceeds to measure it. As you can see from Fig. 8-9, the

Fig. 8-9. Bending of light by a prism. Light enters prism by way of A and leaves by way of A'.

effect of a prism is to bend all the rays of light entering a flat side. The effect of a prism in front of your eyes would be to shift the image slightly up or down or to the left or right, depending upon its orientation. By manipulating prisms in the form of trial lenses, for example, the optometrist determines what prismatic correction is required in order for you to align the images of the stereograms. This is then written into your spectacle prescription as degrees prism and the direction of the required correction, such as "base down 1.0 degrees" or "base left 0.5 degrees" for vertical or lateral phoria respectively. Prism correction may also be expressed in diopters; in this case a one-diopter prism is one that will deviate an image one centimeter at a distance of one meter. He may place half of the correction in each lens, as for example "base up" in one lens and "base down" in the other, in order to correct for vertical phoria.

These are the three basic corrections for your eyeglasses—spherical, cylindrical, and prismatic. If you wear contact lenses, your prescription may be somewhat different. Contact lenses replace the cornea with perfect, precisely shaped surfaces, thereby automatically correcting for corneal induced astigmatism without the need for separate cylindrical correction. Indeed, for one eye disorder, known as *keratoconus,* the severe bulging of the cornea can be adequately corrected *only* by means of contact lenses. Due to their unanchored position on the eye, contact lenses are quite free to move about (at least rotate) so that the direction of cylindrical correction would be meaningless, even if such correction were included. For the same reason, prismatic correction in contact lenses is difficult if not impossible to achieve unless some means for assuring non rotation of the lens is employed.

One approach to this problem is to use larger contact lenses which cover more than merely the cornea. Such lenses can indeed have tops and bottoms, but in many cases they are uncomfortable and not worth the additional cost. For severe cases of prismatic imbalance the conventional eyeglasses are probably superior.

Additional Corrections

While the preceding three corrections take care of most visual problems of an optical nature, there are a few isolated exceptions. As suggested earlier in the matter of lenticular removal, the patient may wear trifocals. In this case he needs the basic refraction no longer supplied by the lens as well as a fixed accommodative adjustment for both far and near vision.

For patients who have had their lenses removed, ultraviolet absorbing glass may also be prescribed, as was mentioned earlier in our discussion of optical aberration. Patients with high sensitivity due to lack of pigment (albinism) may be required to wear dark lenses to limit the amount of light entering the eye.

In some instances, the image produced by the two eyes may differ substantially in size. In these relatively rare cases the patient may wear eyeglasses, one lens of which serves to magnify or reduce the size of the retinal image without changing the focal length of the total combination. Thus the patient has images of comparable size and, presumably, correspounding retinal points for the two eyes. For some even rarer cases, the patient may wear magnifying lenses over both eyes, to simply enlarge the image and thereby counteract severe opacities in the optic media, for example.

In the case of children with slight strabismus, doctors may occasionally prescribe prismatic correction, with the hope that forced turning of the eye may eventually result in elimination of the strabismatic condition. For severe cases surgery, followed by visual training, is indicated.

SUMMARY

In this chapter we discussed briefly the meaning of acuity and described three classes of factors which can influence it. We considered optical factors, retinal factors, and the contribution of higher order neural processing. We then discussed various approaches to the measurement of acuity, beginning with the basic visibility acuity and progressing through the use of gratings and vernier devices, and finally the conventional resolution acuity. With respect to the latter we consider three measurement approaches: König bars, Landolt rings, and the Snellen chart. Finally, we described three basic forms of correction for optical defects: spherical correction for refractive errors, cylindrical correction for astigmatism, and prismatic correction for problems involving phorias and ocular imbalance.

SUGGESTED READINGS

1. Lewison, L., *You and Your Eyes* (New York: Trinity Publishing Corp., 1960). This is an excellent reference for the material on visual correction. The 235 pages are quite easy to read, well illustrated, and to some extent, have a message to deliver. The author emphasizes the importance of the eyes and the importance of taking care of them. His presentation on the use of contact lenses is excellent, as well as his emphasis on the possible value of visual training as a way of perhaps eliminating spectacles in many cases. The book is easy to read, interesting, and highly recommended.
2. From S. H. Bartley, *Principles of Perception* (New York: Harper, 1969). This is the same source recommended for the previous chapter. Chapter 3, however, is quite closely related to the material just covered and includes several topics not included in our Chapter 8. The 30 pages of this reference are relatively easy to read, and certainly worthwhile.
3. Boynton, R. M., "Some Temporal Factors in Vision," in R. N. Habor (ed.), *Contemporary Theory and Research in Visual Perception* (New York: Holt, 1968). This is a good reading with a rather restricted content. Although its content include little more than time-intensity relations, it is an excellent example of contemporary research. For the individual with a particular interest in such relations, this article is recommended. Its eleven pages are of generally moderate difficulty.
4. Bartley, S. H., "The Psychophysiology of Vision," in S. S. Stevens (ed.), *Handbook of Experimental Psychology* (New York: J. Wiley, 1951). This is the same reference included in the last chapter. Chapter 24, consisting of 61 pages, probably includes more technical material than any other single

reference I can think of. It is recommended as a reference source, and for general reading by the interested student.

5. Kennedy, D., "Inhibition in Visual Systems," *Scientific American,* July 1963. This short (7-page) article describes the inhibitory action of sensory impulses, and how the existence of "off-receptors" adds in the improvement of light-dark discrimination and the perception of contours. It is a short article, easy to read, and worthwhile for the interested student.

9

VISUAL FLICKER AND MOVEMENT

So far we have been describing relatively static relations between the visual experience and the outside world. More often than not the outside world is in a state of change: lights are alternately on and off, or changing in level, and most visual stimuli move. When objects in the field do not move, the eyes and head move. Movement in some form is central to vision. Some animals are to all intents and purposes "form blind." They can see only moving objects, and presumably respond only to movement. As high as it is in the phylogenetic scale, one might expect the frog to have good pattern or form vision. Evidence, however, indicates that the frog responds primarily to movement in its visual field.

We know too that a visual stimulus remaining absolutely stationary with respect to the retina will actually disappear, as the retinal elements reach a state of complete adaptation. Such an experiment requires a highly sophisticated optical system in order that the test object will remain stationary and not be "scanned" by the very minute, rapid eye movements such as we mentioned before.

INTERMITTENT LIGHT, FLICKER

Research on the effects of intermittent or interrupted visual stimulation has provided considerable insight into the functioning of the visual mechanism. As we learned earlier, the visual response is not an instantaneous event, independent of the temporal and amplitude characteristics of the stimulus. Rather there is a relationship as described by the Bunsen-Roscoe law in which time and intensity of the stimulus tend to summate in producing an experience. The response of the retinal elements themselves occurs over time, and can vary as a function of both the stimulus and the state of the organism (for example, dark adaptation). It is therefore not unexpected, that the exeprience of an intermittent stimulation need not follow precisely the temporal course of the external event.

In lights or other visual targets that flash on and off at relatively slow rates (under 20 per second) the experience of flicker is obvious, and the activity of the retinal elements must indeed follow closely the alternation of the stimuli. But unlike the ear which can sense intermittencies of as great as 20,000 per second, the eye functions in such a manner that intermittency rates over 50 or 60 per second are rarely observable. As we increase the rate of alternation from 20 per second to 60, the experience becomes one of a "steady" visual stimulus. For a specified set of conditions, a point, known as the *critical flicker frequency* or critical fusion

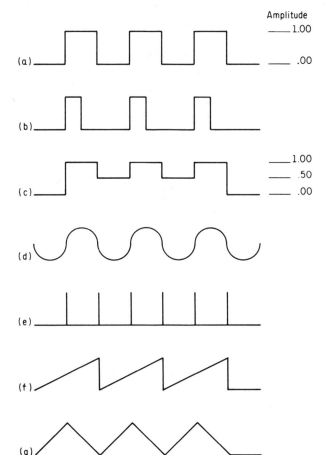

FIG. 9-1. Amplitude and temporal patterns for flicker. (a), (b), and (c) are rectangular waves. (a) is a square wave, (b) has a 25 percent duty cycle, and (c) has a .50 modulation ratio. (d) is a periodic sinusoidal wave and (e) is the result of pulses. (f) and (g) are sawtooth waves, (f) having a slow build-up and rapid decay, while (g) is symmetrical.

frequency (cff) is reached, often quite abruptly, and the flickering light becomes steady. For a specified set of conditions, the cff is remarkably consistent for a single individual.

Wave Patterns for Studying cff

Figure 9-1 shows seven forms of intermittent light presentation which might be used in studying flicker. To be sure, an infinite variety of patterns might be explored, but these seven should serve as general examples.

The first three examples each include three complete cycles. If the total length of the figure represents one second, we should have flicker frequencies of three cycles per second. For rather obvious reasons, these examples are known as *rectangular waves*. Note that they have an instantaneous (comparative, to be sure) rise time and decay time, with an output steady over time. The first example, (a), illustrates a 50 percent duty cycle—that is, it is "on" 50 percent of the time and "off" 50 percent of the time, and is known as a *square wave*. The second pattern is similar, except it has a duty cycle of only 25 percent, since 25 percent of each cycle represents the time light is "on."

Pattern (c) shows a somewhat different situation. It too has a 50 percent duty cycle, but note the height of the "off" portion of the curve. While (a) and (b) vary in amplitude from .00 (no light) to 1.00 (full light), (c) varies from .50 to 1.00. This is expressed as *modulation*. The lights for (a) and (b) have 100 percent modulation, while (c) exhibits a 50 percent modulation, since the total intensity range is only one-half the potential range. The light has been modulated only one-half as much as it might have been.

Rectangular modulation is perhaps of more academic than practical interest in the study of flicker. Few natural, or even man-made sources of light exhibit such near-instantaneous rise and decay times, and such steady light output. One example, however, might be an *episcotister disk*, a segmented disk which when rotated at a nodal point of an optical system chops the light in such a fashion as to produce very nearly rectangular modulation. (See Fig. 9-2.) If the opaque sections of the disk are replaced by filters, variable modulation percentages are obtainable since the "off" cycle will not be the complete absence of light.

If an episcotister disk or other type of moving shutter is placed in an optical system at a nonnodal point it will result in a noninstantaneous build-up and decay of the light being passed. When properly designed it may produce a light wave of a sinusoidal nature such as illustrated by Fig. 9-1d.

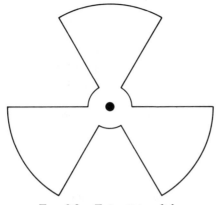

FIG. 9-2. Episcotister disk.

Many simple experimental setups in laboratories involve sinusoidal or near-sinusoidal modulation. An incandescent light bulb, since it is basically a thermal device, requires a finite time for the filament to heat up and a finite time for it to cool. Thus when it is powered by an alternating current it follows, in approximately sinusoidal form, the output force (voltage) of the electrical current. Since the filament probably does not cool down completely between cycles, it may result in less than 100 percent modulation as shown in Fig. 9-1c, but with a sinusoidal, rather than rectangular form. Only if the alternation rate is quite slow can an incandescent lamp bulb be expected to follow faithfully the alternations in a-c current.

Figure 9-1e illustrates a form of intermittency produced by pulses of light. Using gas-discharge tubes, neon glow lamps, and such devices as stroboscopes and automobile timing lights, trains of pulses that are variable in frequency and amplitude may be produced. Since pulses of exceedingly short duration (micro-seconds) are generally involved, any further shaping of the light wave must be produced by the chemical/neural action of the visual mechanism. Hence pulsed light is very useful in studying the activity of the chemical/neurological mechanisms of the eye. As both an advantage and a disadvantage, depending on the purpose of the research, such devices usually emit light of a single wavelength, or perhaps several wavelengths, but rarely of continuous spectrum white light.

The last two patterns of Fig. 9-1 are examples of sawtooth patterns. Generated by electronic circuits or specially designed episcotister disks, they can be of almost infinite variety. Figure 9-1f, for example, illustrates a wave with a gradual build-up and rapid decay, while the last pattern exemplifies a symmetrical sawtooth pattern.

Factors Influencing Flicker

Many factors influence the cff and determine whether flicker can be seen or not.

Intensity and Wavelength. One of the most important determinants of cff is the intensity of the light stimulation. Figure 9-3 shows the relation between the cff and the intensity of the intermittent light. Notice that the curve appears to level off at around 60 cycles per second; no matter how intense the light is made, the normal human eye cannot detect flicker appreciably beyond 60 cycles per second. Note too, that except for lower levels of light, the relationship betwen the cff and the log intensity of the light is basically linear, and is to all intents and purposes the same for all wavelengths. The curve for lower levels of light (peripheral rod vision was used here) does show differences in cff as a function of wavelength, but when vision is limited to the cones no significant differences due to wavelength are found.

The independence of the photopic cff to wavelength provides the researcher in vision with a very useful tool. Matching two lights of different hue (or wavelength) for luminosity by simple judgments is a very difficult task, producing widely disparate results and a singular lack of consistency. But the cff of a light (all other things being held equal) is solely a function of its intensity, and is not confounded by its wavelength. Hence in a technique known as *flicker photometry* it is possible

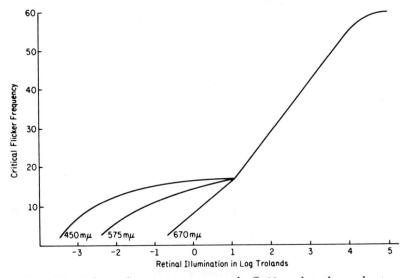

Fig. 9-3. Relation between intensity and cff. Note that above about 1 log troland (10 trolands), cff is independent of the wavelength of the light. (Modified from Hecht, Shlaer, and Pirenne, 1942.)

to match a colored stimulus of unknown brightness with a white stimulus of known brightness. If we know the cff of a colored light we can adjust the level of a white light until its cff is identical. Then, since their fusion frequencies are the same, their luminosities or brightness must be the same, that is the brightness of the colored light is identical to that of the white light. A principle known as the *Talbot-Plateau law* tells us further that the brightness of a light is due to its total energy, that a light with a 50 percent duty cycle will have the same brightness as a steady light of one half the intensity. If the standard white light is flickering with a 50 percent duty cycle, then its brightness is one-half its originally known steady-state level. It is this principle which enables us to apply the cff technique to luminosity or brightness measurement of nonwhite light with surprising precision and repeatability.

Size and Location of Stimulus. Both the size and location of the retinal area stimulated influence fusion frequency. Generally speaking, larger areas of retinal activity result in higher cff's than do smaller, point sources. The reason for this, presumably, can be attributed to summation effects at retinal levels somewhat higher than the cones or rods themselves. In a similar manner, intermittent stimulation in the periphery requires a higher frequency to achieve fusion, or freedom from flicker, than similar stimulation of the foveal area. This is probably not due to differences in cff between the rods and the cones, since the rods when stimulated by very small point sources may show lower cff's than the cones. But for larger patterns and most practical situations, spatial summation in the periphery may result in a higher critical fusion frequency.

It is significant too that simultaneous stimulation of peripheral areas with steady patterns can have a marked influence on foveal cff. This effect must be attributed to interaction and summation effects, in some cases perhaps at levels much higher than the retina.

Other Factors. There are numerous, almost unlimited, additional factors that can influence fusion frequency. One of these, the modulation pattern of the light, has already been implicitly mentioned, and seemingly owes its effect to its interaction with the chemical-neural functioning of the sensory elements and their interconnections.

As an example of still another factor, if one adapts to a light flashing above the cff (appearing as a steady light) the cff obtained in an immediately subsequent test will be elevated above the normally obtained frequence limit. Thus adaptation is a factor in determining critical flicker frequency.

The size of the pupil has an influence on cff, as does such unlikely conditions as body temperature, fatigue, breathing rate and even intelligence. Age appears to be a factor, and may be related to normal changes in pupil size which accompany the aging process, as well as systemic or metabolic influences. It is also well known that drugs can have noticeable effects on cff.

Application of cff Data

But is flicker and fusion frequency only of laboratory interest? Indeed not. Let us look briefly at several instances in our everyday experience where a knowledge of flicker phenomena might be of use. In each case we start out with the tacit assumption that flicker is undesirable, annoying, or in some cases downright harmful. Let us see how our knowledge of flicker and the cff can lead to better designs in light-emitting devices.

As a first example, commercial motion-picture projectors present 24 frames per second with a dark interval in between; home projectors commonly operate at 16 frames per second. Should we not then see highly undesirable flicker, since we are well below the 50 or 60 cycles per second required for fusion? Indeed we should, if special steps were not taken. Most projectors have a small round shutter, similar to the episcotister disk of Fig. 9-2, which rotates in the optical path once per frame, thus providing three exposures or flashes for each frame. The total of 72 (3×24) or 48 (3×16) flashes per second is high enough that flicker is not likely to be a serious problem. For home movies, lower light output also tends to result in less flicker (lower cff), even though the 48 flashes per second might otherwise be expected to result in an unacceptable amount of flicker.

The 50-cycle current supplied by some power companies, especially in foreign countries, can result in noticeable flicker if conditions such as brightness, size, and direction of view are optimum. Some of you may have perhaps noticed flicker in some lights in Canada, where the 50-cycle alternating current is more widely used. The 60-cycle current used in the United States tends to result in much less flicker.

The commonly employed incandescent lamps with their sinusoidal outputs and less than 100 percent modulation tend to reduce flicker appreciably. Flicker is likely to be seen in many gas-discharge tubes, and even in fluorescent lamps. Small neon glow lamps, for example, even with their low light outputs, can be observed to flicker, especially if viewed out of the corner of the eye. Flourescent lights, with their pulse-like outputs, are commonly paired so that when one is on the other is off. The net result then is an overall light made up of 120 pulses per second instead of 60, well beyond the normal cff.

In order to avoid stimulating your retina with flickering light, your optometrist or ophthalmologist might very well use ophthalmoscopes and other light-producing devices powered by direct, rather than alternating current. Note too, if you are going to pass light through a rotating episcotister disk to study flicker, you would have to start out in the first place with unmodulated (continuous) light. Lamps for generating light to be modulated by an episcotister disk would have to be powered by direct current if any high degree of waveform specification were desired.

Another application of cff data is in the design of cathode-ray tubes for such applications as data readouts, radar scopes, oscilloscopes, and television receivers. The choice of the phosphor to be used on the tube is an important consideration, since the response of various phosphors can vary all the way from pulses such as illustrated in Fig. 9-1e to long, extended sawtooth waves with durations in seconds. If a phosphor has the latter characteristics, flicker may not be noticeable, even at relatively low intermittency or refresh rates. While slowly changing signals may level out nicely and result in a minimum of flicker, such a phosphor may be quite inadequate where rapid changes in form and position of the displayed signals are required. Rapid changes can result in multiple images, track lines, ghost images, and generally unsatisfactory image formation due to the slow reaction and/or long persistence of the phosphor. In cases where rapid movement must be depicted, phosphors with fast response times and fast decay times such as in (e) of Fig. 9-1 must be employed. In general, for every application some sort of compromise must be made which often cannot result in completely eliminating the undesirable flicker.

You would probably object if your television picture tube flickered noticeably. Due to the requirements of bandwidth and similar limitations, the maximum refresh rate (frame rate) of your picture is 30 per second. Yet you do not often see flicker. An ingeneous technique known as an "interlace" is utilized to avoid 30-cycle flicker. Every $\frac{1}{30}$ seconds you do indeed get a new frame, but to avoid flicker your set is so designed that you get an half-frame every $\frac{1}{60}$ second. The half-frames are made up alternately of the even and the odd scan lines which interlace to form the total picture. You get just 30 *different* pictures each second (analogous to the movie's 24 frames), but you get a total of 60 images per second, adequate enough to eliminate most flicker. In color television some parameters are changed, but the principle of interlace is still used to reduce the likelihood of flicker.

III Effects of Flicker

While annoyance may be the most common effect and the principle reason for avoiding flicker, it is not the only possible ill effect. There are several electrical waves moving along the surface of the brain (reflecting internal activity) which can be detected and recorded from outside the skull with a sensitive device known as an *electroencephalogram* (EEG). Diagnosis of some forms of brain damage and malfunction can often be made from careful study and analysis of these recordings. One of the well identified components of the complex EEG is the alpha rhythm. It is known to be associated in some manner with vision and has a frequency of 10–12 cycles per second.

When a flashing light is varied in frequency to equal that of the alpha rhythm, a remarkable "locking in" effect, known as *photic driving,* sometimes takes place; as the frequency of the flickering light is changed, the frequency of the alpha rhythm follows along. One might say "so what —so the alpha rhythm does follow the frequency of the flickering light. Does it have any ill effects on the individual?" In most cases the answer would have to be "no, at least not that we know of." Unfortunately, there does seem to be a glaring exception. For reasons that we do not understand, persons subject to epileptic seizures may be forced into a seizure as a result of such photic driving of the alpha rhythm. Since we do not understand the phenomenon and are really not sure that photic driving in the normal individual is completely harmless, the best policy is to avoid flickering lights within the general range of 8 to perhaps 16 cycles per second, regardless of whether the viewer is known to be subject to epileptic seizures or not.

REAL MOVEMENT

It might have occurred to you that animals see form and shapes naturally, and when these forms move across their retinas, they "learn" to interpret the moving images as physical movement. If you believed this, you were wrong. Evidence based on phylogenetic analysis indicates that the reverse probably happened: perception of movement is the basic, original visual capability, while form or pattern vision represents a higher level of development.

Note that the earthworm responds to moving shadows and light patterns, and the frog is for all practical purposes blind, except for moving objects. Reflexive responses from the eye are largely based on the perception of movement. A small infant can follow a moving light with his eyes (clumsily at first) long before he gives evidence of anything approaching pattern vision. Even in adults reflexive eye movements result from movement in the visual field. Notice too that the more primitive peripheral portions of the retina are quite lacking in form perception and resolving ability, yet highly sensitive to movement. You can detect the presence of movement out of the corner of your eye, but in order to see what is moving you must direct your gaze in the appropriate direction.

Eyes which can move in the head appear to have two systems for seeing movement, the more primitive *image/retina* system and a more sophisticated *eye/head* movement system. While an arthropod, with its compound eye, can detect movement only when a shadow moves across the eye's sensitive surface, activating adjacent and successive ommatidia, the eyes of higher animals can detect movement when the image is steady and the eye is moving. When your eye follows a moving object in the field, you rarely think that the object is stationary and the background is moving. While you might attribute this discrimination to learning, I suspect the ability to recognize movement as a result of the moving or tracking eye is somewhat more basic. As evidence, if the background is made quite homogeneous, movement is still perceived as a result of the eye following a moving target.

The more primitive image/retina system is probably based on the fact that all eyes are originally detectors of movement. Since the retina contains elements that fire at the onset of a light, and others that fire at its termination, it is relatively easy to see how contours (leading and trailing edges) or shadows of images can activate retinal receptors as they pass over the surface.

The perception of movement as a result of a moving eye (the eye/head movement system) is not so easy to explain. One explanation, still popular with the modern cybernetic or feedback proponents, holds that impulses arising from sensory endings in the eye muscles and other non-visual portions of the eye signal the existence of eye movement to the brain, and this complex computer makes the necessary interpretation. Known as the *inflow* theory, and espoused by no less an authority than Sir Charles Sherrington, this explanation is now believed inadequate. Based on research involving afterimages and studies of time lags in response, an alternative explanation, originally advanced by Helmholtz and known as an *outflow* theory, appears more clearly consistent with the observed facts. According to this theory, as the signal from reflexive centers is sent to the eye muscles a comparable signal is also sent to the central nervous system computer. While the brain may indeed receive after-the-fact information from the stretch receptors extrinsic to the eyeball, it is the impulses *directing* the movement that are interpreted at the higher neural centers of the brain.

In effect, one important function of this higher-center interpretation is to cancel the impulses arising from the surround, so that when one views an object moving across a complex background, the background can be effectively ignored and does not appear to rush across the visual field in the opposite direction.

ILLUSORY MOVEMENT

The movement we have been discussing to this point has been real, objects actually moving in the visual field, or static objects viewed with a moving eye. But what about movement that appears to exist when no physical change of position occurs, or movement perception which does not truly reflect the antecedent physical movement? Let us examine some instances of movement wherein the experience does not accurately mirror the external world. We can examine only a few of the many forms of illusory movement that have been documented, and we can examine these only at a relatively superficial level.

Autokinetic Movement

We will spend more time on this first example of illusory movement for several reasons, mostly of an academic or scientific-curiosity nature. It is not the most important example of illusory movement, it has no commercial value, the government will not pay you to study it. If you do study it, you do so out of curiosity, "because it's there." It is one of those simple, almost silly phenomena which everyone has seen and no one understands; the most widely accepted explanations still leaving much to be desired. Yet, like Tennyson's flower in the crannied wall, if we understood this simple-appearing phenomenon in its entirety we would be able to explain far more complicated phenomena which do have psychological significance.

Also known as the *autokinetic* phenomenon, or autokinetic streaming (AKS), the apparently random wandering of a point source of light when viewed in an homogeneous field has long been recognized. If you place a glowing cigarette in an ash tray and view it from across a darkened room, and if there are no other visible objects in your field of vision, the point of light will appear to move, first to the right, perhaps, then up, down, to the left, all about, and yet not change its position! Sailors and astronomers peering at points of light in black space were intrigued as well as sometimes disturbed by the apparent erratic wandering of a solitary star or a point of light on a distant shore. It is an eerie, disturbing experience, especially the paradoxical existence of movement without a change in position, and it demands some sort of explanation.

Despite the fact that dozens of explanations have been offered since the phenomenon was first recognized, AKS still remains something of a mystery. One explanation (many early theories were based on psychologists' introspective reports) suggested that small particles floating about in the intraocular media can be seen. Furthermore, as in the case of a stationary moon appearing to move as wind-blown clouds scud by, the point of light seems to move rather than the intraocular debris. There are several weaknesses to such a theory: for one thing, you cannot see the minute particles floating about in your eye; they are too small and incorrectly located with respect to any focal plane of your visual system. Furthermore, optical examination of the eye while AKS is in progress does not indicate any directionality to the movements of the particles which can be related to the direction of the AKS experience.

A similar explanation, based on fluids moving on the external surface of the cornea, suffers from the same difficulties.

A more plausible theory, still held by some persons, contends that the eye cannot hold a steady fixation for long periods of time. Consequently it drifts away from its original line of regard, the experiential misinterpretation being that it is the point of light that drifts away. Such an explanation is untenable. Over 40 years ago Guilford and Dallenbach photographed the eyes while AKS was in progress and found no eye movements to correspond to the subjective reports. What eye movements they did detect were of the small, rapid type we referred to earlier, and could in no way account for the relatively large, subjectively reported autokinetic movements with estimated angular distances of 30 degrees or more.

The Gestalt psychologist had an "explanation" for the effect, couched in terms of a pervading spatial framework into which the experience must fit. The quotation marks are intentional, since such a theory seems to be little more than a rephrasing of the problem and not an explanation at all.

In a similar vein, some modern psychologists explain away the phenomenon by saying "It's a matter of suggestion." In support of the viewpoint, some investigators have shown that when several individuals of a group reports seeing a particular form of movement, others will tend to see the same type of movement. Still other persons have had difficulty in demonstrating the efficacy of suggestibility or social pressure. Any such theory tends to beg the issue. Even if suggestion effects were unequivocally demonstrated, the physiological basis for the effect would remain undisclosed. We do not explain behavior by calling it, for example, an "instinct"; we merely give it a name.

Be that as it may, the writer once tried a perhaps even more ill-conceived approach to the study of AKS. Having a vague, poorly formulated idea that the direction of movement might have something to do with "directionality" established in the central nervous system, I tried to see whether this "directionality" condition might not be experimentally manipulated before presentation of the AKS stimulation, thus making direction and perhaps rate of AKS movement predictable. Before presenting the point of light, subjects were required to stare at stationary figures (satiation targets) with dynamic qualities, such as aircraft silhouettes, or arrows. I anticipated that neural background activity would form a substrate that would determine the direction of movement. The experiment was a failure: subjects would see afterimages of the satiation figures, and the afterimages apparently served as anchoring points, so that no movement of the observed point of light could occur until the afterimages had disappeared. Had there been a central nervous system directionality effect, it probably would have faded away by then too.

Although it has never been clearly demonstrated many investigators still feel that there may be something valid in an explanation based on some sort of dynamic directionality in the underlying neural substrate. Such an explanation will be referred to later in the chapter on visual perception when some of the so-called illusions are discussed.

Perhaps a better explanation in one advanced by E. von Holst, R. L. Gregory of Cambridge (Gregory, 1958), and others. It is basically, a muscle-fatigue theory and involves the eye solidus head visual system. According to the theory we see movement when the muscles of the eye are fatigued, the erratic movements of the AKS effect being due to the command signals required to maintain fixation despite a tendency for the fatigued muscles to permit the line of regard to wander. There is evidence for this explanation, based on experiments in which the eyes were strained in various directions before the AKS observation. In these experiments the predominant direction of movement of the point of light was predictable as a function of the direction of prior eye strain.

Waterfall Effect

If the striped design of Fig. 9-4 is caused to move toward the right for a minute or two, then stopped, the pattern will appear to reverse its direction of movement and move to the left. Similarly, if the spiral design

Fig. 9-4. The waterfall effect. When the spiral is rotated it seems to shrink or expand, depending on the direction of rotation. When stopped, it continues to shrink or expand in the opposite direction. The left-hand figure appears to turn in the opposite direction when it is stopped.

in the same figure is rotated, it will appear to move in the opposite direction when stopped. Even more curious is the fact that, as the spiral design is rotated, it will appear to expand or shrink, depending on the direction of rotation. The experience of reversed rotation which follows the cessation of the physical movement will also be accompanied by the appropriate, and now reversed, expansion or shrinkage. The movement has intriguing paradoxical characteristics. Like the moving point in AKS which constantly moves yet gets nowhere, the constant shrinking or expanding of the spiral results in no change in its size. It constantly gets bigger, yet it is no larger at the end than it was when it started to "grow."

The effect can have a surprisingly long aftereffect. Masland (1969) has recently shown that, with properly controlled observation, the reverse motion can be obtained as long as twenty-four hours after the original exposure to the rotating spiral.

This type of illusory movement is as difficult to explain as autokinetic movement. It cannot be adequately described in terms of the eye/head visual system as was done for the AKS movement. If the eye is permitted to follow the movement, the effect is considerably reduced, but when the eye is held stationary and the retina is stimulated differentially, particularly when the stimulus occupies only a part of the retina, the waterfall illusion is at its maximum, thus indicating the importance of the image/retina system in producing this effect.

We referred earlier to the possibility that the sensing of movement may be a primary neurobiological capability, and not simply the result of an inference based on spatial sequentiality. As with insects and frogs, movement per se may be a basic attribute of all visual systems, and, like most attributes, capable of being evoked by a normally "inadequate" stimulus. Just as very cold water may be erroneously perceived as "hot," or a bump on the head may cause you to "see stars," a combination of visual stimuli such as produced by the targets in Fig. 9-4 may result in the erroneous eliciting of the experience of movement: the reverse movement when the real movement is halted, and the shrinking and expanding without accompanying change in size.

Beta Movement and the Phi Phenomenon

The most commonly encountered illusory movement is that based on the *phi phenomenon* and sometimes referred to as *beta movement*. If two similar lights (or any pair of targets, for that matter) with a moderate separation in the visual field are alternated at the proper rate, the experience may be not of two lights alternately flashing, but rather a single light moving back and forth. If the alternation is too slow, you may simply see the two lights alternately flashing; if the rate of alternation is so rapid that the second light occurs before the image of the first has decayed, then you will see both lights simultaneously, flickering if the repetition rate is below the cff. With optimum alternation rate, however, the apparent movement is quite convincing. Note the effectiveness of motion pictures and television. Both present series of still pictures; you supply the smooth movement by virtue of the phi phenomenon.

The entire field of Gestalt psychology owed its very existence to the monumental work of Max Wertheimer and his 1912 article, *Experimentelle Studien über das Sehen von Bewegung.* Appearing in the journal, *Zeitschrift für Psychologie,* this article spurred on an entire generation, led by such figures as Kurt Koffka, Wolfgang Köhler, and Kurt Lewin, to investigate molar processes of behavior. While most investigators today (the writer is not one of them) reject the Wertheimer-Köhler explanation of phi and similar phenomena, it is to your advantage to at least be familiar with their field-theory approach as summarized below.

Localization of visual functions has been pretty well worked out, and while finer details are still unknown, the principle of spatial localization is generally accepted. It is probably safe to say that every spatioretinal point has a corresponding locus at a higher neuroanatomical level. The locus of a given point may be in the cortex, at a lower brain level, or at a higher retinal level (perhaps at all these levels, with varying complexity). While Köhler seemed to imply that it should be in the cortex, the specific location of the effect is of less importance than the manner in which it behaves.

At some place in this "neural substrate" a locus representing a point on the retina exists, and it will be adjacent to another point representing an adjacent point in the retina. A light activated in visual space will invoke neural activity at some point in the neural substrate. For purpose of expostulation, let us say that a visual figure at point A in space, will produce a response in the neural substrate at point A' and a visual figure at point B in space will evoke a response at point B' in the neural substrate. (See Fig. 9-5.)

But the neural substrate is, in Köhler's terms, like a *volume electrolyte.* The activation of point A' will result in a general spreading of the electrical activity through the electrolytic medium or the "field." If we activate a second light which has its neural projection at B' (see Fig. 9-5a) it will appear to the subject that the image from A has simply moved to a new location, B. Note too that if the stimulus had physically moved from point A to point B, the physiological event would have also been an energy movement from A' to B'. Thus, apparent movement, according to the Wertheimer theory, is physiologically identical (or very nearly so) to real movement. This is the concept of *isomorphism,* so much a part of the Gestalt approach. According to psychophysical isomorphism there is a relationship, almost one-to-one, between the physical event and the physiological event within the organism. No wonder the movies look so real!

To backtrack a bit: as it was originally conceived by Wertheimer,

(a) Condition for Phi

(b) Condition for Succession

(c) Condition for Simultaneity

FIG. 9-5.   Apparent movement. In (a) the temporal condition for optimal movement is shown. In (b) the time interval between the successive stimuli is too great, resulting in successive, nonmoving images. In (c) the time interval is too short, the result being two lights appearing simultaneously and, probably, flickering.

the term *phi* did not refer to simply the movement of the figures from A to B. Rather, it included a vague, difficult to express, concept of movement. It was, if you can imagine it, movement with nothing moving! Movement in the abstract, perhaps movement as a primary experience. In one introspective form, the figures were reported to remain stationary and something (?) moved between them, such as a colorless, amorphous film, obliterating first one, then the other figure. This effect was known as "pure phi" and was at one time the subject of considerable introspective research. Modern usage, however, accepts the term *phi* for the general apparent movement we have been describing, and which has been called *beta movement,* and not just the "pure phi" of Wertheimer.

Time relations for optimum phi movement have been worked out in some detail and are not inconsistent with the Wertheimer explanation. In order for good phi movement to occur, the time relation between the stimulus points (e.g., A' and B') must be consistent with theoretical time requirements for the normal spreading effect in the electrolytic neural substrate. What happens if these time patterns are not met? The second illustration of Fig. 9-5 describes the effect for the situation where the repetition rate of the two figures is quite low. The spreading from A' reaches the location of B' before the latter is activated. When B' *does* become active, the spreading effect from A' has long gone, faded away perhaps, so that the subject simply sees the two lights, in different positions, and alternating, not one light moving to a new position. In Fig. 9-5c, the alternation rate is too fast. Before the wave from A' can reach point B', the latter has been activated. Hence, both light stimuli are seen simultaneously, and no movement between them will occur. Rather, the two lights will appear to blink or to flicker.

Specific alternation rates required to produce optimal apparent movement cannot be stated in the absolute. Rates for phi movement depend on a number of factors. In 1915 Korte presented a series of laws showing that optimal movement depends upon: (1) the distance between the stimuli, (2) the time interval between them, and (3) their intensity. We might also include adaptation level, and point out that there are large individual differences in the experiencing of the effect. With respect to this last matter, it is curious that when a person has adjusted an alternating pattern to achieve optimum apparent movement, comparatively large changes in the alternation rate can be tolerated before the experience of movement is replaced by one of simultaneity or alternation. There appears to be some sort of "locking-in" effect.

There are several other aspects of the phi phenomenon which make it as interesting to study as the AKS phenomenon. For example, if an arrow in the veritical orientation is alternated with one in the horizontal direction, the image may appear not only to move back and forth but also to rotate 90 degrees. In some rare cases the movement will appear in the *y*-axis—that is, the dimension of depth—rather than remaining in the frontal plane.

In another curious example, if a vertical line is replaced by a horizontal line, the visual effect may be one in which the vertical line splits down the middle, the two halves seeming to topple to either side, forming the horizontal line.

While it is not always easy to achieve, targets presented independently, one to each eye, can result in phi if the spatial separations are ideal. Such evidence would militate against an explanation of the effect being located in the retina, at least at the rod/cone level. The possibility of interaction at the ganglion-cell level is not completely eliminated, since recent evidence does indicate that there are connections between the two retinae, presumably by way of the optic chiasma.

The study of the phi phenomenon is extremely fascinating. If you set up even a simple experiment, you will probably observe something that no one in the literature has ever mentioned. Introspect a little the next time you see a simple advertising sign employing the phi phenomenon. You may be surprised at the experience; you may even see the "pure phi" the nineteenth-century introspectionists observed.

Bow Movement

An interesting form of movement, often encountered along with phi movement, is that of *bow movement*, which takes a curved trajectory rather than the presumably straight, shortest distance between two points that might be expected. It comes about presumably as the result of some "interference" in the space between the two stimuli, such that the apparent movement has to "go around."

When I was a graduate student, we once set up an interesting experiment such as shown in Fig. 9-6. If we alternate lights at the opposite extremes of a cross as shown in Fig. 9-6a, while it is difficult, it is possible to find time patterns that will result in simultaneous left-right and up-down apparent movement. But what happens at the intersection?

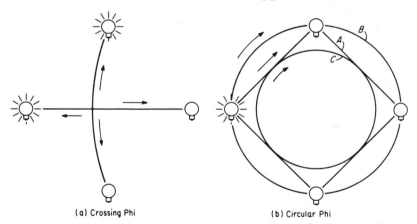

(a) Crossing Phi (b) Circular Phi

Fig. 9-6. Bow movement. Figure (a) shows the result of alternating four lights in such a manner that their apparent movements cross. Figure (b) shows the result of presenting four lights successively to produce a circular movement. See text for details.

In every case where we were able to get the antagonistic movements, we found that one of the two movements would assume a third-dimensional aspect, taking a path either in front of or behind, the straight, flat movement of the other pair.

Another form of bow movement is illustrated in Fig. 9-6b. If we alternate the four lamps at the proper rate we might expect that the light would appear to move from one corner to the next, forming a nice clean square. (Path A) But that is not what happens. At the beginning the movement may be similar to B, a light moving progressively through the four corners and assuming a circular path. But as we observe the illusory "circle of light," it will appear to shrink in size until it has the path labeled C. Notice that the path of the apparently moving light does not even pass through the actual stimuli points!

Gamma Movement

Another illusory movement, *gamma movement,* appears somewhat easier to understand. As the intensity level of a figure is increased, its size seems to undergo an increase as well as its brightness. The figure seems to "grow." Conversely, a decrease in intensity may result in a shrinking, or decrease in the apparent size of the stimulus. When we are aware of the complexities of the retina network, the lateral connections, and the relatively slow, chemical nature of the physiological response, such size-brightness dependency does not seem too unusual.

A somewhat similar, possibly analogous form of movement may occur at the onset and/or termination of a visual signal. A stimulus when suddenly applied seems to "grow" to its full size, and conversely, when a visible stimulus is turned off suddenly, there is a tendency to see a shrinking or size reduction concomitant with the cessation of the light. I suspect a similar process is at work in both examples.

Delta Movement

The last type of movement worthy of mention is that of delta or reverse movement. It is rather unusual, but occasionally a reversal in direction of the usual beta movement occurs, if the second stimulus is appreciably brighter than the first. If in Fig. 9-5 we activate A slightly before B, but the stimulus at B is much brighter than at A, the movement may appear to go from B to A, rather than in the expected A-to-B direction. It would appear that, in spite of the temporal priority of A, the neural signal for B occurred first due to its greater brightness and the resultant increase in rate of the neuro/chemical reaction.

The reader may exclaim "Aha, that's why wagon wheels sometimes seem to go backward in Western movies?" Such an effect is *not* an example of illusory movements—the wheels really do go backward in the projected image. Note that the camera takes 24 pictures per second. If the wheel is turning at 23 revolutions per second (or some multiple thereof) each successive frame of the film will catch the wheel slightly before it has completed a full revolution ($\frac{1}{24}$ of a revolution compared to $\frac{1}{23}$), so that when the film is projected the wheel will appear to be turning in reverse at the rate of one complete revolution each second. The reverse effect has nothing to do with the functioning of the eye: if the wheel were actually rotating at 24 revolutions per second, it would appear stationary; if it were turning at 25 revolutions per second the projected result would be a wheel rotating in the same direction, but at the rate of one turn per second.

SUMMARY

In this chapter we examined various types of moving stimuli and their phenomenological results. We discussed, first of all, the results of intermittent light stimulation, including factors such as wave patterns of the light, its intensity and other factors that influence the critical fusion frequency. We mentioned briefly some practical implications concerning knowledge of cff. We dealt briefly with real movement and spent considerable time describing six forms of illusory movement: the autokinetic phenomenon (AKS), the waterfall effect, beta or phi movement, bow movement, gamma movement, and delta movement.

SUGGESTED READINGS

1. From E. G. Boring, *Sensation and Perception in the History of Experimental Psychology* (New York: Appleton, 1942). Pages 588–602 of this volume represent the best presentation of background relative to perceived movement that I know of. It is historical in nature and should be familiar to the serious student. Its ease of reading and brevity make it highly recommended for anyone reading this book.
2. From R. L. Gregory, *Eye and Brain, The Psychology of Seeing* (New York: McGraw-Hill, 1966). Chapter 7 consists of 24 pages covering the same general material we included in the preceding chapter. It is quite easy to read and provides a theoretical approach quite different from that of the present text. Well worth reading.
3. From S. H. Bartley, *Principles of Perception* (New York: Harper, 1969). Pages 241–258 discuss the perception of visual movement. Both real and apparent movement are described, with a somewhat different approach than that

used in the present book. This reading is well referenced, providing numerous primary sources for the interested student. In addition, pages 104–111 provide some additional information on intermittent stimulation and the cff.

Chapter 2 of Haber's *Contemporary Theory and Research in Visual Perception* includes eight articles on the subject of movement perception which are all worthwhile reading. The following three articles are representative and particularly useful.

4. Spiegel, I. M., "Problems in the Study of Visually Perceived Movement: An Introduction," in R. N. Haber (ed.), *Contemporary Theory and Research in Visual Perception* (New York: Holt, 1968). A brief survey of visual movement, including real movement, induced movement, and apparent movement. Bases for the experience of movement are discussed with extremely liberal use of references. An excellent article of 16 pages, providing many primary references for the serious student.

5. Kolers, P. A., "Some Differences Between Real and Apparent Visual Movement," same source as (4) above. Consisting of 13 well-referenced pages, this is an excellent thought-provoking article which purports to show that the underlying mechanisms for real and apparent visual movement are *not* the same.

6. McFarland, J. H., "The Influence of Eye Movement on a New Type of Apparent Visual Movement," same reference as (4) above. These three pages describe a form of apparent movement resulting from successive presentation of the three sides of an equilateral triangle. The author shows that eye movements may be a factor in this type of apparent movement.

10

BINOCULAR VISION AND DEPTH PERCEPTION

Up to this point we have been considering the functioning of the eye primarily as a unique sensory device, and what might be said for one of our two eyes should apply equally to the other. But we do have two eyes, not one, and they normally function not independently but as a well-coordinated team. Let us consider in this chapter situations wherein two eyes are used, and where meaningful integration of the images from the two eyes occurs and subsequent spatial perception may result. Moreover, the extent to which a single eye can provide satisfactory and adequate depth perception must be examined.

NATURE-NURTURE QUESTION

As we concluded in the last chapter, it would appear that the perception of movement is based on fundamental physiological and anatomical properties of the organism, and is not simply an inference based on learning or experience. What about the experience of depth or three-dimensionality? Is it learned, or the result simply of maturation?

The emphasis of the behavioristic theories of psychology, which arose as a reaction against early structuralism, was on the importance of learning, the development of stimulus-response relations as a function of experience. Behaviorists emphasized that the infant "learns" to see depth, largely by manipulating his environment. The Gestalt psychologists, on the other hand, tended to consider depth as a primary attribute, rather than something inferred as the result of learning or experience. To some extent both proponents have been proven right.

The problem has been under investigation by numerous persons for many years, with somewhat varying results, but with the broad, general conclusion that at least some recognition of depth is a basic capability of the visual mechanism and is not entirely the result of learning.

In 1913 Shepard and Breed published the results of their research on the pecking ability of newly hatched chicks. They showed, for example, that chicks kept from pecking for 5 days subsequent to hatching required only one day "practice" to achieve the same pecking accuracy achieved with 2 to 5 days practice by chicks that had been kept from pecking for only 3 days. Because of the small size of their samples and their general inadequate controls, the experiment has been repeated, with modifications, by numerous other persons including, Moseley, Bird, and Cruze. On the basis of Cruze's most definitive study it can be concluded that the pecking response in chicks includes both learned and unlearned behavior, and that some perception of spatial relations exists purely as a function of maturation, and is not dependent (except for refinements) upon learning.

In 1934 Lashley and Russell showed that young rats, previously deprived of normal visual experience, could make crude distance judgments. These experimenters placed rats on a small platform and forced them to jump to a second platform at varying distances from the first. A spring arrangement measured the force exerted by the rat when he leaped from the first to the second platform. While in truth the rats did not jump very accurately, of greater significance was the fact that the farther the distance to the opposite platform, the harder the rats tended to jump.

A few years later Arnold Riesen of Yale University and later of the University of Chicago was to demonstrate the need for visual stimulation, and indeed actual pattern vision experience, if adequate development of form and spatial vision are to occur in the primate. Riesen's evidence indicated that when young animals have been reared in the darkness some visual reflexes may develop, but prolonged withholding of visual stimulation can have profound effects on the subsequent development of visual skills. In the chick-pecking experiments referred to earlier Bird found that some few chicks, when reared in the dark for greatly extended periods, never did "learn" to peck!

Recent experiments on the nature-nurture issue have focused on the use of a device known as the Visual Cliff. Pioneered by Eleanor J. Gibson (Gibson, 1960) and others at Cornell University, use of this device purports to show that all species of animals seem able to perceive and avoid a sharp drop-off or cliff, as soon as they are able to move about. Using an apparatus such as shown in Fig. 10-1, Gibson and Walk showed that human infants (6 to 14 months of age), kids, lambs, and baby chicks when first placed on the device refuse to crawl onto the glass and over the imaginary cliff. These same authors found that species which apparently do not rely on visual depth perception for their everyday behavior (rats, turtles) are not disturbed by the visual cliff, and will crawl out on the glass with no alarm at the chasm below. A slight physical displacement however, will prevent the rat with his vibrissae-moderated spatial sense from crossing over.

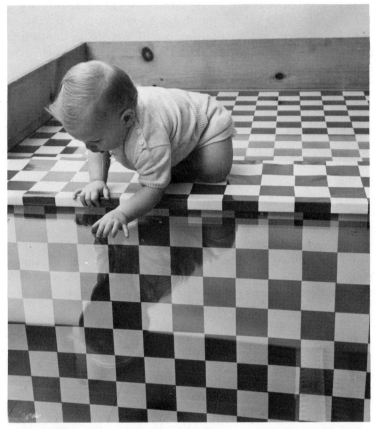

FIG. 10-1. The visual cliff. The child is being tested on the visual cliff. A sheet of glass rests directly over the checkered pattern at one end, and at a distance of several feet above the pattern at the other end. (From Scientific American, Inc., 1960, courtesy William Vandivert.)

If one can accept the premise that these young animals have had no prior opportunity to "learn" depth (admittedly a somewhat dangerous assumption) then the conclusion is clear: depth perception is an unlearned, natural attribute of higher-order animals. Whether it should be attributed to factors of motion parallax (as suggested by Gibson and Walk, and to be described later) or other innate capabilities, is a matter for further conjecture and, hopefully, subject to additional research.

Primary and Secondary Determinants of Depth

With all this smoke there must be some fire. Some aspects of depth perception must be unlearned, a result of the physiology and anatomy of the organism. I should like to refer to these effects as *primary* as contrasted with *secondary* "cues" for distance. Our catagorization may be proven to be in error, but for the purpose of classifying depth determinants let us consider those with a definite, known physiological basis as primary, and those that appear to be learned as secondary. For example, we probably have to learn that of two images of people differing greatly in size, the smaller is probably farther away, or that when one object covers (obscures) another, the former is probably the nearer of the two. We may have to "learn" that railroad tracks converge in the distance, and that colors viewed from a distance tend to lose much of their brightness and saturation.

On the other hand, it may be that those effects shown to result in demonstrable physiological changes are interpreted as distance without a prolonged learning process. The difference in images to the two eyes, the activation of receptors in the muscles of the eye when we accommodate to a near object or when our eyes converge, are perhaps direct cues which require no lengthy learning process. It is probably such primary cues which enabled Cruze's chicks to develop pecking skill so quickly, or Lashley's rats to jump with a degree of skill not consonant with their past experiences.

MONOCULAR CUES FOR DEPTH

While it is indeed true that two eyes provide a richer, more natural appreciation of the three-dimensional world, persons who have the use of only one eye are by no means devoid of depth perception. There are many ways, using monocular vision, that the three-dimensional world can be recognized and spatial orientation maintained.

Primary Cues

Accommodation or the adjusting of the lens for varying distances is perhaps the only primary cue provided by monocular vision.* When one adjusts (reflexively) the lens for varying distances, stretch receptors in the ciliary body and the suspensory ligaments presumably send "messages" to the higher centers indicating the degree and direction of the adjustment. This point of view is quite old, having been advanced as early as 1709 by George Berkeley, Bishop of Cloyne, in his *A New Theory of Vision*. Bishop Berkeley, however, did not presume that convergence

---

* Persons who have lost the sight of one eye may still, in effect, converge the two eyes, thus providing a primary cue of convergence. This of course is actually a binocular cue, since the relative position of the two eyes and the resultant activation of stretch receptors in the extrinsic eye muscles and ligaments are involved.

resulted in an unlearned, primary cue for depth. Rather he felt that it had to be learned, integrated into the tactual/physical perception of depth.

Even today the efficacy of receptors in the accommodative muscles for indicating distance is in doubt. There is even some evidence to indicate that the *apparent* distance of the object rather than the real distance may determine the degree of accommodation.

In any event it is clear that feedback from the accommodative mechanism cannot be effective except for very restricted limits. For all intents and purposes the lens does not change shape for distances beyond 15 or 20 feet, and depth perception beyond such distances must be mediated by other means.

It has been further suggested (originally by the same Bishop Berkeley) that the "blur" arising from inadequate accommodation may serve not only to activate reflexively the accommodative mechanism, but also as an indirect cue for distance. This again must be a relatively restricted cue, serving if at all, for distances of less than 20 feet.

Secondary Cues

In contradistinction to the primary, or unlearned cues, most visual cues which do not require binocular vision are probably learned, hence, secondary cues. (Note the Gibson and Walk reading for a somewhat divergent point of view.) Let us examine some of the visual effects which might be interpreted as depth.

Size. When one has learned the normal, expected size of a familiar object one can presumably estimate the distance of the object as a function of its apparent size or its size on his retina. A man has a known size. When two men are in the visual field and one is distinctly smaller than the other the smaller figure is assumed to be farther away. Indeed, in visual illusion demonstrations, this effect of size can be shown to be more important than most other cues. We are familiar with the relative size of people, and if a man towers over, for example, a locomotive, we rarely see a "large man" and a "small locomotive." We tend to see a man nearby and a locomotive far away. Size differences were among the first cues for distance successfully employed by early artists. Before its use to depict distance, however, size difference was employed to indicate the relative importance of the various characters. The dominantly large figure in early Egyptian drawings, for example, indicated the importance of the character, rather than distance, which was apparently not recognized by these early artists.

Texture. A comparison of near and distant objects may also be observed as gradients in *texture*, as emphasized by James J. Gibson, and illustrated in Fig. 10-2. For example, as a pilot brings an aircraft in for a landing, the closer terrain exhibits considerably more variety or texture,

Texture

Perspective

FIG. 10-2.   Texture and perspective as cues for distance. (Top
figure, showing texture, is from Gibson, *Perception of the Visual
World,* courtesy Houghton Mifflin Company; the bottom figure,
showing perspective, from the same source, reproduced courtesy
of Herbert Gehr, *Life* Magazine © Time, Inc.)

which gradually disappears in the textureless (relatively speaking) distance. As the texture builds up in front of him it must be clear that he is approaching the ground and moving in a forward direction. Note, too, that for the upright individual texture tends to decrease in an upward direction in the visual image. If the visual image were to be reversed 180° (with lenses, for example) texture gradients might very well provide confusing information as to distance.

Linear Perspective. Also related to size differences, parallel lines tend to decrease their separation as they recede into the distance, thus converging at some point known as the *vanishing point*, which may or may not be visible in the scene. The construction of satisfactory perspectived drawings for use in architecture, for example, is highly dependent on the location and use of various vanishing points, frequently positioned on the draftsman's drawing board, well beyond the limits of his actual drawing. Note in Fig. 10-2 how all the parallel lines in the third dimension tend to converge. Linear perspective is one of the most convincing and most resistant to misinterpretation of the large number of distance cues.

Partial Overlap. When one object appears to overlap a second object, it is generally assumed that the former is closer than the latter. While this is most surely a learned cue, it is again subject to error. If what appears to be the distant object is actually closer, but with a portion removed to fit the contour of the nearer but seemingly more distant object, perception of the true relationship is indeed difficult. Note in Fig. 10-3 that the image seen (top) could result from either of the two stimulus situations below.

Shadowing. Both attached shadows—that is, where the shadow is part of the object—and cast shadows, in which the object produces the

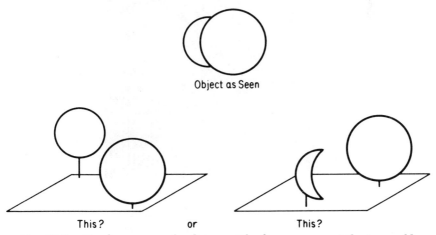

Object as Seen

This?   or   This?

FIG. 10-3. Overlap as a cue for distance. The figure as seen at the top could be produced by either of the two bottom arrangements.

shadow, provide important cues for depth. Figure 10-4 illustrates these two forms of shadowing. The renowned Leonardo da Vinci recognized the efficacy of both attached and cast shadows as cues for distance, and used them profusely and with remarkable success in his paintings. They indeed present a convincing indication of distance.

In the lower part of the illustration of Fig. 10-4 the quonset huts turn into towers when the picture is inverted. This must be a learned relationship. We recognize unconsciously that light normally comes from above, and we interpret our visual images in light of this anticipation. A metal tank with rivet heads protruding will normally have attached shadows on the bottom surface of the rivet heads. Were we to invert such a picture, the rivet heads would now look like dents in the surface, the shadow being on the upper surface of the dents where they logically belong.

Aerial Perspective. This cue for distance is in no way similar to the linear perspective discussed earlier. "Aerial" is really the key word in this cue for distance. Light from distant objects must pass through a much

FIG. 10-4. Shadows as a cue for distance. Rotate the photograph 180 degrees to see the quonset huts change into towers. (From Gibson, *Perception of the Visual World*, courtesy Houghton Mifflin Company.)

greater amount of the atmospheric medium than light from nearby objects. Consequently that light arriving from a great distance has been subjected to considerable absorption and scattering from molecules of air, water vapor, and the minute solids suspended in the atmosphere. One result of this scattering is a lowering of the saturation or purity of color of distant objects. Pure or nearly pure colors appear to be weakened as if by the addition of white or black, thus resulting in tints or shades, rather than the original pure hues. Such a hue can very easily be incorporated in a painting by the simple expedient of painting distant objects with less saturated colors.

In addition, distant objects tend to take on the color of the ambient light, regardless of their own reflective characteristics. Note that in the daytime, distant objects tend to be bluish like the sky, or in the evening, reddish like the prevailing light at that time.

Movement Perspective. Another cue, also related to size, is that of movement perspective and related monocular parallax. It can be induced both by moving objects in the visual field, and by head and eye movements on the part of the observer. Perhaps in the same way that size indicates distance, relative velocity of moving objects can also indicate distance. If you see a locomotive moving slowly along the horizon, you interpret this as great distance, whereas a locomotive moving across your visual field much more rapidly would be interpreted as being nearer. When you try estimating distances of flying objects such as airplanes or balloons you have a great deal of trouble, largely because the actual speed of the objects is often unknown.

When you drive along in a car, the utility poles which seem to flash rapidly by are recognized as being closer than those that move by at a slower rate.

When you see objects moving by (or you move by them) you see more surface than for a stationary object. To the extent that the object is near, you see part of the leading surface as the object approaches, and the trailing surface as it recedes from view. Thus the degree of monocular parallax depends largely on distance. Near objects may even appear to "rotate" as you move past them, viewing them with an ever-changing line of regard. The fact that you can see some of the side of solid object as you move past it is a strong indication of proximity.

Height in Visual Field. This is a cue often overlooked by investigators in the field. For terrestrial-bound animals, nearby objects are usually located near the bottom of the visual field, while distant objects occupy a higher position. In many cases the gradation goes from bottom to center (horizon) and from directly above to center (horizon). Such cues have long been recognized. Indeed, the vanishing point we referred to earlier is frequently located on such an imaginary horizon. In early examples of prehistoric art the artist did not recognize the significance of a horizon or vanishing points; the relative vertical position of objects on the drawing is frequently the only indication of depth provided. The artist who wished to show objects farther away would simply place them higher in the picture.

Height in the visual field may also be related to the cue of cast shadows referred to earlier. Most vertical objects cast shadows, and in almost all cases the shadows are at the base of the object, or, generally speaking, in the lower part of the visual field.

Such a cue, like most others, is subject to misinterpretation. For example, the illusion in which the moon appears to be larger when near the horizon has been attributed to a misinterpretation of this cue. The explanation goes something like this: Being near the horizon, the moon is presumed to be at maximum distance. But, since it subtends the same visual angle, regardless of where it is, the size-distance confusion produces an erroneous perception of large size.

BINOCULAR CUES FOR DEPTH

While the preceding so-called monocular cues can be and surely are employed with binocular as well as monocular vision, the following cues owe their existence to the presence of two eyes—located spatially apart which might, under normal circumstances, not be expected to view identical scenes. Our classification of primary and secondary cues is particularly tenuous in binocular vision. Perhaps all binocular cues are primary, perhaps they are all the result of learning; the matter is not settled. Let us, however, take the approach that convergence and retinal disparity serve as primary cues, the result of inborn structure and maturation, while binocular parallax as a cue for distance must be learned. The writer tends to lean in this direction, although the evidence is still quite controversial.

Primary Cues

The two most commonly recognized unlearned cues are those of convergence (the eyes either converging or diverging as a function of distance) and retinal disparity (the fact that the two eyes receive different images from the same stimulus object).

Convergence. The theory that distance is indicated by sensations from receptors located in the extrinsic muscles of the eye employed in convergence was also a product of Bishop Berkeley's fertile mind. As with accommodation, he felt that cues based on convergence are learned, associated with body movements involved in reaching, positioning, etc.

But as in the case of accommodation, the efficacy of feedback from the extrinsic muscles as a cue for distance is still a moot question.

In line with Gregory's theory concerning the sensing of eye movements referred to in the last chapter, it may be that the cue is not impulses arising from the stretched or constricted muscles, but rather a parallel ouput from the effector nerves which evoke the convergence.

In any event, it is doubtful that convergence is a very important cue for distance. At distances of 15 or 20 feet or so the lines of regard for the two eyes are in effect parallel, so the effect can at best be useful only at comparatively short distances. Perhaps, as in the case of accommodation, the blur due to lack of registration of the two images may be as important as the muscular-evoked impulses, and may be the true basis for convergence as a cue for depth perception.

Retinal Disparity. What happens when the two eyes do not "see" the same thing? Any one of three effects can result from such a situation. As we noted in Chapter 8, ocular imbalance and phorias can be detected and measured by using a pair of stereograms such as shown in Fig. 8-7. In this case the different views to the two eyes are *fused* into one picture containing the elements from both the right-eye and the left-eye view. In anoher demonstration often seen, an outline of a bird is presented to one eye and an empty bird cage to the other. The result, for the individual with normal vision, is a bird in a cage. In general, if the views are such the they can be meaningfully combined, fusion of the two images will result and the ultimate experience will be a combination of the two views. The key word for this effect is *fusion;* the organism must fuse the two images into a meaningful third image.

But what if the combination is not as logical as a bird in a cage, or an arrow under a row of numerals; then what happens? In effect, the eyes simply refuse to function as a coordinated pair, and revert to independent operation, each on its own. If figures such as shown in the stereogram of Fig. 10-7 are employed, the eyes "take turns" seeing. Known as retinal rivalry, and to be discussed later in this chapter, the result is an alternation between the left- and right-eye views. Sometimes there may be partial fusion and part of the scene may be of a checkerboard pattern; sometimes one eye's view may predominate, but generally, the result is an alternating of the two views.

In normal binocular vision, however, neither of the above predominate. The images to the two eyes are, indeed, slightly different. The slight difference is due to the location of the eyes in the head, and results in images, which while slightly different are capable of being fused.

The most significant feature of binocular vision which leads to depth perception is probably that of retinal disparity. The eyes are separated some three or four inches. As a result, they do not "see" the same thing.

The right eye sees a little of one side of an object while the left eye tends to see a portion of the other side. As early as 1838 the physicist Charles Wheatstone pointed out the importance of disparate images to the two eyes for the production of depth. As a result of his development of the stereoscope it was possible to show that a strong depth effect (*stereopsis*) can be produced when disparate images are presented to the two eyes. He further showed that the effect is destroyed if identical views are presented to the two eyes, or if the views are reversed—that is, the right-eye view presented to the left eye, and the left-eye view to the right eye. He was also able to demonstrate that if the disparity is increased (as if the interpupillary distance was greater than three or four inches) the illusion of depth is correspondingly enhanced.

The manner in which disparate images arrive at the retina can be seen from Fig. 10-5. In this figure the observer is looking down on the truncated surface of the pyramid. Note the direction taken by the rays of light proceeding from the object to the eye. The right eye sees some what more of the right surface of the pyramid, while the left eye sees more of the left surface. The images on the retina would be much like the view drawn as (c). Indeed, if a stereogram were prepared like (c), with the correct images being presented to the left and right eyes, the visual experience would be identical to that obtained by looking directly down at the truncated surface.

While this is all there is to the construction of stereograms and the experimental evocation of depth by means of disparate images, the underlying physiological mechanism for the effect is much more illusive. As indicated in an earlier chapter, fibers from the retina do not appear to terminate in the brain in a manner replicating the retinal surface. Rather, if anything, they tend to replicate visual space. Note from Fig. 6-4 that fibers to the left side of the brain arise from these portions of both retinas representing the right half of visual space. Conversely, potentials arising from stimuli in the left visual field are combined in the right side of the brain. This is a highly simplified description, but in general, it is about what happens.

Looking at both Figs. 6-4 and 10-5 we can see then that points represented by 2, 4, 6, and 8 in Fig. 10-5 will fall in the left half of each retina, and hence project to the left side of the brain. But if we assume that points 2 and 8 are the same for both eyes, then points 4 and 6 will stimulate slightly disparate loci in the brain-projection area. It is this disparity in the brain which presumably results in the most convincing stereoscopic or three-dimensional vision.

Indeed, it appears to be the fusion of corresponding points on the retina that makes retinal disparity work. If we present the top drawings

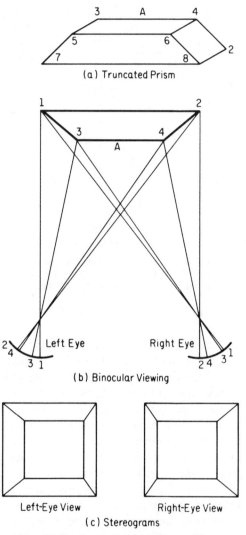

(a) Truncated Prism

(b) Binocular Viewing

Left-Eye View   Right-Eye View
(c) Stereograms

FIG. 10-5. Stereoscopic vision. Figure (b) shows the results of observing the truncated prism from a point directly opposite the surface A. Figure (c), when viewed in a suitable stereoscope, would produce the same visual effect of depth.

of Fig. 10-6 to the eyes by means of a stereoscope we can see depth. The left figure will be that of a bar tilted in the third dimension; the right figure will be of two circles, lying at slightly different distances from the viewer. If we supply anchoring points such as shown in the lower

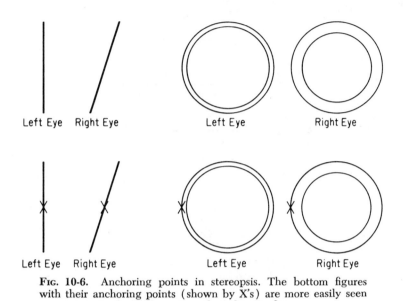

Fig. 10-6.   Anchoring points in stereopsis. The bottom figures
with their anchoring points (shown by X's) are more easily seen
in three dimensions than the top figures.

figures, fusion will occur with less effort and the effect of depth will be
easier to obtain.

While we can create an illusion of depth at will, and while we
understand many of the factors related to such hypothetical constructs as
"corresponding points" on the retina, the underlying physiological mechanism in the brain remains quite an enigma. In some manner or other it
works. One would be hard put to design a computer that would carry
out the operations accomplished so quickly and efficiently by the brain.

Utilization of disparate imagery to test an individual's depth perception or stereopsis is an important laboratory and clinical procedure. Your
optometrist may, for example, give you tests with stereograms which will
result in a score in terms of percent stereopsis—a measure of how well
you can utilize retinal disparity as a cue for distance. Another mensuration technique, somewhat more precise and more useful in research,
determines the amount of disparity in angular distance required to
produce stereopsis.

Persons to whom depth perception is of particular importance, such
as athletes and airplane pilots, may be studied to determine their degree
of depth perception. Most devices used to screen persons for inadequate
depth perception are based on the ability to perceive depth as a
function of disparate images.

When depth is utilized to enhance the realism of visual presentations,
retinal disparity is the technique most often employed. You have all had

some experience with the common stereoscope and the stereo camera which simultaneously takes two pictures from slightly different angles. Means of presenting the results of such stereo photography to the respective eyes varies. One technique employs polarizing filters over the two projectors, and similar polarizing lenses in front of the eyes, so that the image meant for the left eye is delivered to that eye and the right-eye image finds its way to the right eye. In some cases colored filters are used, one image red and the other green. With appropriate red and green filters over the eyes an illusion of depth can be created.

In many instances the depth effect can be enhanced by increasing (effectively) the interpupillary distance. Most binoculars have a somewhat wider separation than the human eye alone. In photography for stereo effects the cameras (or lenses) are often separated by a distance somewhat greater than the normal interpupillary distance, thus increasing the disparity between the left- and right-eye images.

Secondary Cues

The only secondary cue that depends on binocular vision for its existence is that of binocular parallax.

Binocular Parallax. We discussed, under the heading Movement Perspective a form of parallax that presumably contributes to depth perception. With monocular vision, we can see some of the sides of objects as a function of time if either the object or the viewer is in motion. With binocular vision we can see a bit of the sides of objects without time or movement, since the separation of the eyes permits us to in effect "see around" the object, at least if the distance is not great. It is quite possible that we learn to infer distance partially as a result of the amount of binocular parallax available—that is, the amount of the sides we can see.

Note too that objects at distances other than the fixation distance will not be optically superposed. Objects closer than the fixation point will result in crossed images, while objects at a distance will be separated on the retinal surface. Such an effect was hinted at when we were describing the effects of covergence, but probably should be included with binocular parallax effects.

RETINAL RIVALRY

We have discussed two of the effects that can result from the presentation of different images to the two eyes: (1) a combination of the two images to form a third, as illustrated by Fig. 6-4; and (2) the perception of depth as a result of the neurological combining of the disparate images.

The third possibility was also mentioned briefly, the alternation phenomenon known as retinal rivalry.*

If patterns such as illustrated by Fig 10-7 are presented to the

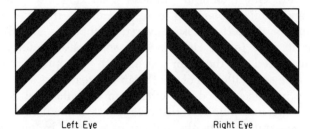

Left Eye   Right Eye

FIG. 10-7. Retinal rivalry targets. When the targets are exposed to the respective eyes the result is alternate impressions of the two figures.

respective eyes, the result will be the alternate perception of the left-eye image and the right-eye image, with quite limited fusion and combination. The alternations may vary from several a minute to 50 or 60 a minute, depending on the nature of the pattern and factors inherent in the observer. What causes this alternation, and of what significance is it?

An answer to the first question is not possible in light of our present knowledge of the visual system. Presumably there is some physicochemical process, perhaps a metabolic-supression cycle that requires refreshing at frequent intervals. Just what it is eludes discovery.

We are fairly sure, however, that rivalry *does* have significance for depth perception. It would appear likely that the fusion of disparate images is in effect not a simultaneous perception of the combined images, but rather, at some neurological level, an alternation of the impulses from the two retinas. It is a known fact that persons with rapid rivalry rates tend to have better stereopsis than those with slower rates. The more rapid suppression of the image from one eye and subsequent replacement with the image from the other goes along with superior depth perception.

Which is cause and which is effect is not entirely clear. Does high rivalry rate produce improved stereopsis, or does good stereopsis result in high rivalry rate? In some severe clinical cases where the two eyes are markedly different optically, thus preventing normal fusion, no rivalry may exist. The patient, while he has two eyes providing two images, uses the image from only one eye, effectively suppressing the image from the other. To be sure, such people tend to have poor depth perception,

---

* Actually the term *retinal* rivalry is probably a misnomer, since it is quite likely that the basis for the rivalry is to be found at a higher neural center.

since they must rely largely on such secondary cues as partial overlap, shadowing, etc. We might also wonder if the permanent suppression of one eye by such people is physiologically the same as the alternate suppression by normal individuals.

With respect to the cause and effect question, many experts in the field feel that good stereopsis is the result of high rivalry rate. Consequently, they use devices which present conflicting images alternately to the two eyes, slowly at first, and gradually increasing in alternation rate until the "normal" rivalry rate is simulated. As a result of such training, patients, it is said, increase their own true rivalry rates and at the same time their depth preception is appreciably improved. In the case of people with severe defects, resulting in complete monocular suppression, it would be necessary to first correct the physical defect, in order that fusion of disparate images would be optically possible.

While they do not really understand the basis for retinal rivalry, most practitioneers *do* recognize its significance for adequate vision.

SUMMARY

We have discussed in this chapter, the recognition of depth and the use of binocular vision. We suggested that depth perception is both a matter of learning, as well as a fundamental property of the visual mechanism. We described numerous indicators or cues for distance, some of which are presumably primary and some of which appear to be learned. Cues that do not require binocular vision include accommodation and blurring, size, texture, linear perspective, partial overlap, shadowing, aerial perspective, movement perspective, and height in the visual field. Cues based upon the coordinated performance of two eyes included convergence, binocular parallax, and retinal disparity. In addition to describing the use of two eyes in producing depth, we also discussed binocular vision which does not result in depth, such as fusion of paired images and retinal rivalry.

SUGGESTED READINGS

1. Gibson, E. J., and R. D. Walk, "The 'Visual Cliff'," *Scientific American,* April 1960. A short (9-page) article which summarizes the recent literature on the nature-nurture issue with respect to visual depth perception employing the "visual cliff." It is an easy-to-read, interesting summary which concludes that all animals seem able to avoid the drop as soon as they can move about.
2. From D. J. Weintraub and E. L. Walker, *Perception* (Belmont, Calif.: Brooks/Cole, 1966). Chapter 4 (18 pages) of this paperback is the best

short summary and description of visual depth of which I am aware. It discusses depth perception from the philosophical and artist's approach as well as from the physio-psychological approach. It is well illustrated and makes quite interesting reading. It is not highly technical, but rather takes a "you are there" point of view.

3. Riesen, A. H., "Arrested Vision," *Scientific American*, July 1950. This is the shortest (5 pages), most concise summary of the early work on the influence of arrested vision on the development of form and spatial vision in the primate that I know of. It is certainly worthwhile reading and is highly recommended.

4. Berkeley, G., "An Essay Toward a New Theory of Vision," from W. Dennis, *Readings in the History of Psychology* (New York: Appleton, 1948). These 12 pages represent merely a short excerpt from the original essay, but do include much of the flavor of Bishop Berkeley's empirical approach to the theory of vision. It is worth reading for historical reasons.

5. From J. J. Gibson, *The Perception of the Visual World*, Boston: Houghton, 1950). Chapter 3 of this book, "The Visual Field and the Visual World" (18 pages) is relevant to the present chapter. Chapters 6 and 7 which consider the stimulus variables for visual depth and distance are particularly germane and are highly recommended. These 68 pages include many excellent illustrations of the cues we discussed, as well as a large number of variations. This entire book (230 pages) is highly recommended for the serious student.

11

COLOR VISION

NATURE OF COLOR

Lights, paints, filters, etc. are *not* colored. They merely produce, reflect, or transmit visible radiation in a selective manner, generating or passing some wavelengths, reflecting some, and absorbing others. Color, like beauty, is in the eye of the beholder. It is an experience that depends primarily, although not exclusively, upon the wavelength of the light which stimulates the eye, light being simply electromagnetic radiation within a highly restricted range, as indicated earlier, from about 400 to 700 mμ. (See Fig. 1-1.) Light can be measured physically in terms of its dominant wavelength, its overall composition, and its intensity. The eye and its associated computer see the combination of these physical parameters as "color." In addition to the attribute which varies as a function of the wavelength and is identified as hue, there may also be an attribute of saturation as a function of the purity of the light, and one of brightness as a result of its intensity. These three psychological attributes —hue, saturation, and brightness (sometimes called lightness)—serve to identify *any* color, and in this sense both black and white must be considered to be colors. Hues other than black and white (and of course, gray) are considered to be *chromatic* colors, while those in the white through black range are *achromatic*. Let us examine these three attributes of color with the intent of relating the psychological experience to the physical characteristics of the light.

Hue

The most obvious characteristic of any color is its hue. Is it red, yellow, green, blue, or some intermediate hue? Or is it achromatic—that is, lacking in hue, such as black, white, or some shade of gray? If a color has a recognizable hue it may be located on the visible spectrum of Fig. 11-1. Note that a light consisting of a single wavelength of 510 mμ will be seen as green; one of 520 mμ will also be green, but a slightly different green, while orange will result from a wavelength of roughly 600

195

Fig. 11-1. Approximate spectral colors.

$m\mu$, the precise location depending on the rather arbitrary standard of the individual. As a matter of fact, the number of discriminable hues which can be identified on the scale of Fig. 11-1 is in the hundreds for the average, noncolor-blind person.

Colors as normally observed in nature, however, are rarely produced by a single wavelength such as in these examples. While sunlight and incandescent light are made up of a continuous spectrum, that is, energy continuous throughout most of the visible spectrum, there are a few sources of monochromatic, or near monochromatic light. Sodium-vapor lamps, often employed as street lights, produce visible energy of a single wavelength in the yellow portion of the spectrum, while mercury lamps, often employed for the same purpose, produce energy in the blue. Ordinary fluourescent lamps produce light of several wavelengths, depending on the nature of the chemical deposition on the inside surface of the tube, but not continuous throughout the spectrum. Known as a *line spectrum,* the output of this common light source is seen as white, since the eye performs an integrative function on the various independent wavelengths.

Most colors are combinations of many wavelengths, and the resultant experience of hue arises from complex activity of the visual mechanism. We refer, then, in the case of complex patterns of wavelengths, to the apparent hue, or the dominant wavelength of the color. If, for example, a color is made up of wavelengths from, say, 560 to 640 $m\mu$ (yellow to red), unless the intensities of the components are greatly diverse, the color will look like the general center of the wavelength distribution. In this case the result would be much like that produced by a 600-$m\mu$ stimulus, and we would refer to the experience as orange. We would say the color has a dominant wavelength of 600 $m\mu$ and an orange hue.

Suppose we have only two equally intense wavelengths, one of 560 $m\mu$ (yellow) and one of 640 $m\mu$ (red). Will we see orange now, even though no 600 $m\mu$ orange light is present? Indeed we will. In this case the apparent or dominant hue will be orange, the midpoint of the distribution, even though no wavelengths normally associated with orange are present. We can generalize: for wavelengths relatively close in the visible spectrum, the visual experience will be equivalent (in hue) to some "balance" point within the range of the individual components. If the yellow hue in our example were much more intense than the red, then the apparent hue would shift toward a yellowish orange (equivalent to 590 $m\mu$, perhaps) and conversely, if the red component were more intense the experience might be one of reddish orange.

Note too that the same orange could be produced by many different pairs of reds and yellows. Pairs of colors which produce the same apparent third color are known as *metameric* pairs. The combinations look alike but the composition differs.

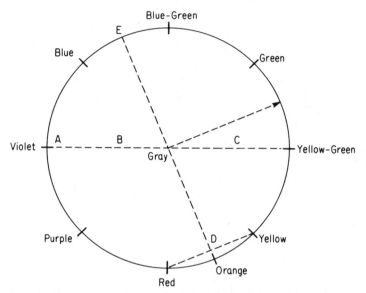

Fig. 11-2. The color circle. The circumference represents saturated, pure colors. Broken lines shown as diameters of the circle represent variations in saturation. Note that the orange indicated at D could be produced either with a mixture of red and yellow or orange plus gray.

What happens if the component hues are *not* nearby in the spectrum? In order to understand and predict the results of such combinations we need a so-called color circle, such as shown in Fig. 11-2.

Saturation

Figure 11-2 shows the influence of the second psychological attribute, saturation, as determined by the purity of a color. When we obtained an orange by combining red and yellow light we did indeed obtain an orange of the same hue as we could have produced with a pure wavelength. But it was not the same orange. The orange of 600 mμ apparent wavelength would be less pure, less saturated, than a similar orange produced by an actual wavelength of 600 mμ. We can explain this in terms of the complementary nature of colors.

The circumference of the color circle of Fig. 11-2 shows the relative location of pure spectral colors from red at one extreme to violet at the other.* A unique feature of many hues is that, when paired, they produce

* What about the purple, shown between the red and the violet in Fig. 11-2? Purple is a nonspectral color. It does not exist in the spectrum and therefore cannot be extracted from white light by means of prismatic refraction. It can be created by mixing spectral red and violet and is necessary to an understanding of the complete color cycle. Hence its inclusion.

achromatic colors. As the color circle is drawn, any diameter of the circle will connect complementary colors, colors which when combined produce white or gray. Specifically, as examples, red and blue-green when combined in the proper ratio produce an achromatic gray or white, as will violet and yellow-green, or blue and yellow.

But blue and yellow make green, don't they? The answer to this question is both yes and no. When we combine blue and yellow pigments, we do indeed get green, but when we combine blue and yellow light (of the proper wavelength and intensity) we get gray or white. The former is called *subtractive* color mixing, the latter, *additive* color mixing. Note the schematic illustration of additive and subtractive color mixing shown in Fig. 11-3. The colors are not genuine in this example, but the principle of color mixing should be apparent.

In the case of subtractive color mixing, a surface, or filter is yellow not because it produces yellow light but because it absorbs the blue end of the white ambient spectrum. The blue pigment is blue because it absorbs the red portion of the ambient light. If we remove both the red and blue ends of the spectrum what is left? Only the center, or green portion of the spectrum remains. Hence blue and yellow pigments result in green, not white, as with additive mixtures. Note too that when we additively combine all colors we produce white. But when we systematically remove all colors, in subtractive color mixing, what is left? Nothing —or in terms of the visual experience, black.

Let us return to Fig. 11-2 and the concept of saturation. As just mentioned, if we combine a violet light and a yellow-green light in the

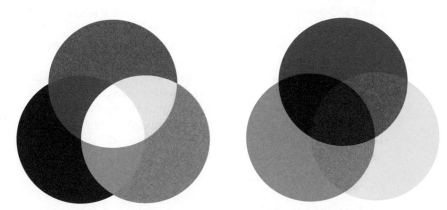

Additive Mixture   Subtractive Mixture

Fig. 11-3. Color mixture. The figure on the left illustrates the results of combining lights of three colors. The figure on the right indicates what may happen when pigments or colored filters are combined. The figures are merely illustrative, and the actual colors shown in the figure would probably not be obtained in practice.

proper proportions (depending on the relative spectral sensitivity of the eye) we will get a gray, indicated by the center of the color circle. But with any thing other than perfect proportions, the result will be a location on a line between the two primaries—not at the center of the circle—resulting in either a violet of less than perfect saturation ($<$ 1.00) or a yellow-green of a saturation less than 1.00. If for example our mixture is predominately violet, resulting in a color at A, the experience will be almost pure violet; if we have only slightly more violet than yellow-green, the result may be found to occur at B. This experience would be of a very low saturation of violet, perhaps just gray with a violet cast to it. If our proportions were such that the composite fell at C the result would be a yellow-green of intermediate saturation, perhaps 0.50. In a similar manner, any hue can be "desaturated" by adding to it its complementary. Remember the hue does not change, only the saturation or purity.

With respect to our example of combining spectral red and yellow: assuming equal effective intensities, the resultant hue will be orange, halfway between the red and the yellow at a point indicated by D. But this point has a saturation of less than 1.00. It is no longer on the circumference of the circle where the spectral hues must be located. It could have been produced by adding a bit of the blue hue between blue and blue-green (E) to the pure, spectral orange. The metameric colors would have been indistinguishable to the normal human eye.

An important fact may be observed. While any hue can be obtained by combining two noncomplementary hues, resultant saturations must *always* be less than 1.00. Note that we could produce violet by combining red and the spectral color indicated by E. But, note too, the line for violet would cross the red-greenish blue line at about B, where we have already indicated the experience would be little more than gray with a violet cast to it. The hue would indeed be violet, but the saturation would be so low as to make the color useless.

This limitation poses a problem to those who deal in color-mixing applications. When one is limited to three primaries, such as in color films or color television, only three hues can have maximum saturation, and all other hues must be tints or shades of the resultant composite colors. We will discuss this problem again when we consider methods for specifying colors for commercial application.

Brightness

Terms such as "white," "gray," "black," "tint," and "shade" have been used without adequately defining them. In order to understand the concept of brightness we must add a third dimension to our circle. The result, shown in Fig. 11-4, is a color solid, a double-ended cone with *brightness* (the psychological correlate of intensity,) running along the

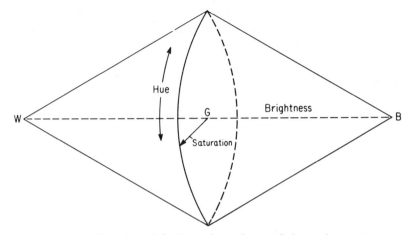

Fɪɢ. 11-4. The color solid. Hue is located around the circle, saturation is the distance from the central line to the surface, and brightness or lightness is shown as the longitudinal axis.

longitudinal axis. In this figure the center axis represents achromatic colors from white at one end to black at the other. All pure colors are located on the surface, with saturation diminishing as the center axis is approached. Thus any color can be located in the three dimensions of the solid by simply stating its apparent hue, saturation, and brightness.

Those colors found to the left of the midpoint—that is, of higher brightness—and approaching the gray center line, are called *tints*. Pastel colors are colors of relatively low saturation and high brightness. *Shades* are simply darker colors lying to the right of the midline of Fig. 11-4.

COLOR SPECIFICATION

The utilization of the color experience can range all the way from the prosaic matching of pastel colors in milady's boudoir to the spectral analysis of radiation from distant stars. While many primitive tribes may have gotten along quite nicely with only three or four words to describe color, our complex civilization utilizes literally millions of color differences describable by words. While the number of actual color words is far less, the possible visual experiences and compound verbal expressions are surely tremendous. Deane Judd, for example, has estimated that there are ten million distinguishable color differences describable by words.

How do we go about identifying and specifying such a proliferation of experience? In addition to the physicists' pure spectral analysis, several other approaches to the specification of color are available. Based on the experience of colors, and including therefore the behavior of the normal human eye, these approaches are of great value in commercial applications from color television to the design of textiles.

The Munsell System

The Munsell system utilizes sample "chips" of color, varying in hue, chroma, and value. The sample plate included as Fig. 11-5 is one page

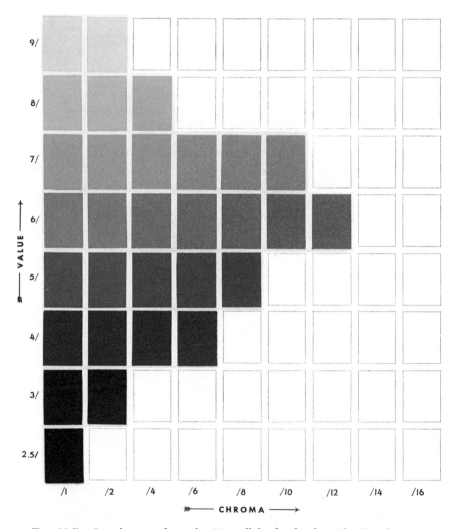

FIG. 11-5. Sample page from the Munsell book of color. The hue for this sample is 5YR, the 5 representing a Munsell code and the YR for yellowish red. (Courtesy Munsell Color Company, Inc.)

from the Munsell Book of Colors and is for a hue defined as 5YR, with a dominant wavelength of 589 mμ.

The Munsell and similar systems plot the *appearance* of the color, not its composition. Munsell reasoned that the appearance of color is apparent in objects, so the result is a series of surface colors varying in appearance, with a well-notated nomenclature. Any color found in the Munsell series is defined in terms of hue, chroma, and value, corresponding roughly to hue, saturation, and lightness. In Fig. 11-5 value (or lightness) is shown on the vertical dimension with values from 2.5 to 9.0, while chroma (or saturation) is represented by the horizontal dimension. As can be seen from this figure, any surface color which can be matched to a chip of the standard can be specified in terms of hue, chroma, and value, and will represent a unique color experience. The color farthest to the right, is notated 5YR 6/12. While Munsell chips are available in both matte and glossy standards, some additional parameters such as texture cannot be adequately accounted for in such a system. This is not the purpose of the system, which emphasizes its relationship to the ICI System (which see), locating points in color space.

The Ostwald System

The Ostwald system of color specification is in many respects similar to the Munsell approach. It, however, is based more directly on the double-cone depiction of Fig. 11-4 with, for example, equal numbers of steps in the saturation dimension for all hues. It is, presumably, based more on psychophysical than psychological variables. Its variables appear to be more like dominant wavelength, purity, and relative luminosity, rather than hue, saturation, and brightness. As a result, its forced symmetry, in contradistinction to the assymmetry of the Munsell system, leaves it somewhat vulnerable to the accusation that it does not truly depict color experience.

ICI System

The system of specifying color developed by the previously mentioned International Commission on Illumination is probably the most useful and flexible approach to color specification available. It is *not* based on psychological, experiential data, such as the Munsell system. Rather it is based on a series of international agreements defining a luminosity curve for a standard eye (see Chapter 7), color-mixture curves for three imaginary standard lights, energy distributions for three basic ambient light sources, and other necessary appurtenances.

The system is quite precise and exceedingly useful for defining and describing such things as filters, pigments, color combinations, and ambient lighting, and their ultimate visual result for the hypothetical standard observer. The system can predict the appearance of various pigment mixtures under differing ambient conditions. Three sources of light known as illuminants A, B, and C ranging from the red incandescent to the bluish north sky are defined, and can be used in the diagram to predict their visual result. It is an excellent, well-developed technique for indicating the psychophysical results of visible energy.

We cannot, within the limits of this chapter, go into the ICI system in any great detail. The interested reader is encouraged to consult the pertinent sources at the end of the chapter.

Let us examine briefly how the system defines color. The ICI chromaticity diagram, as utilized for several purposes, is shown in Figs. 11-6 and 11-7.

If we look back at Fig. 11-2, we can see that we can define a hue by

FIG. 11-6. ICI chromaticity diagram showing approximate location of colors. The abscissa x is the ratio of the tristimulus value X to the sum of all three $(X + Y + Z)$, the ordinate y is the ratio of Y to this sum. (Taken from NBS Circular 478, courtesy National Bureau of Standards.)

two primaries; in our earlier example of producing orange, we used red and yellow. But if we wish to locate a color anywhere within the circle we must utilize a third primary. Again returning to Figure 11-2, in order to produce lower saturations of orange, with the same red and yellow primaries, we would have to add some of the primary indicated as E. Hence, three primaries are needed in order to make any possibly desired color.

The three hues selected by the ICI for universal primaries were previously referred to as "standard lights" and their proportions needed to match a given sample are known as "tristimulus values." The numerals

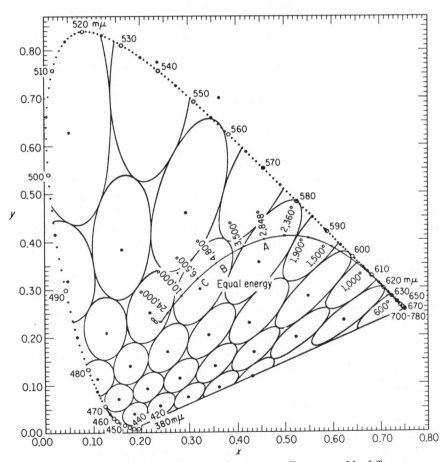

FIG. 11-7.   ICI chromaticity diagram showing equally perceptible differences. The distance from points on the boundary of each ellipse to the indicated point within it all correspond, approximately, to one hundred times the just perceptible chromaticity difference under certain specific viewing conditions. (Taken from NBS Circular 478, courtesy National Bureau of Standards.)

along the side of the figure and identified as x and y are the tristimulus values for x and y respectively. But what about the value of z? The total light can be defined as the sum of the x, y, and z-components. In proportional units, the value of any one is, obviously, one minus the sum of the other two. Hence if we know the values of x and y (the red and green primaries respectively) the value of z is determined and need not be plotted separately.

The numerals on the curved portion of the perimeter represent spectral hues, while nonspectral purples and magentas fall on the straight-line portion at the base.

Approximate location for various colors and the location of the ICI illuminant C are shown on Fig. 11-6. While this specific diagram is based on work by Kelly, involving the description of colored lights on a dark background, it is generally acceptable as an aid to the understanding of the general ICI diagram. Note that the wavelength we referred to as orange (600 mμ) is classed as "reddish orange" in this diagram. Notice too, the tints, or pastel colors (pink, etc.) as one moves in a direction of lower saturation and approaches the "white" center of the ICI diagram.

Figure 11-7 illustrates several different additional properties of the diagram. Note the curved line passing through the three illuminants. This line shows equivalent chromaticities for various color temperatures. If you know the color temperature of your camera flashbulbs or your movie lights, you could locate their chromaticity on this line. Would this be of value to you? If you knew, further, the tristimulus values of your subject, you would know just how the subject would look under your own special illuminant. Manufacturers can predict how a given enamel surface on a refrigerator will look under a known form of illumination in the purchaser's kitchen.

Notice, too, the location of the three standard illuminants and the point of equal energy. At this latter point the tristimulus values are all .33—in other words, equal amounts of the red, green, and blue primaries are indicated for this point. Illuminant A, as indicated earlier, is representative of incandescent light, heavily weighted with red (roughly 45 percent) while illuminant C, corresponding in a general way to light from the northern sky, is made up of only a little more than 30 percent of the red primary.

The oval areas represent another useful application of the ICI chromaticity diagram. They show, in pictorial fashion, equally perceptible differences in color or chromaticity. Actually the distance from each point to the circumference of the respective oval represents 100 times the just perceptible chromaticity difference; in our earlier language, 100 jnd's in chromaticity or color.

COLOR-VISION THEORY

Any theory of how the eye resolves color must take into account the phenomenological experience of color. Most people have agreed on the existence of fundamental hues. Red, green, blue, and yellow "appear" to be basic hues, and all color theories attempt to account for the basic color experience of these so-called primaries.

There are two basically antagonistic groups of theories to explain color vision. One of these, the *opponent* theory, first advanced by Ewald Hering in 1874, holds that there are antagonistic systems at work; thus, white and black are opposites, red is the opposite of green, and blue is the opposite of yellow. According to these theories, there must be some antagonistic sort of neurochemical behavior at the basis of the experience.

The *component* theories, first advanced by Thomas Young in 1801 and elaborated by Helmholtz, Ladd-Franklin, and others, considers that there are individual components—cones, if you will—"tuned" for different wavelengths, and that the chemical-neural response is basically the same for all hue experiences.

Let us examine these two approaches in somewhat more detail, noting some of the evidence for both.

The Opponent Theories

In the opponent theory, paired colors are said to elicit opposing responses. Thus the sensation of red is, chemically and neurologically, the opposite of the green experience. Presumably one might be considered to be a metabolic process, while the other is essentially catabolic. They are not unlike the reversible reactions of chemistry.

Evidence in support of such theories was once largely phenomenological, or in the language of our courts, circumstantial. For example, negative afterimages and simultaneous-contrast effects can both be explained quite nicely with an opponent-type theory. When one gazes at a red figure for some time and then looks away at a gray surface, he sees a negative afterimage of the red figure. The afterimage will be green, the complementary color for red as plotted on the conventional color circle. Similarly, gazing at a yellow figure will result in a blue afterimage. Such an effect can be very nicely explained in terms of an opponent theory. When the "red" process is active one sees red, when the red stimulus is removed the process reverses itself and the effect is a green afterimage produced by the reverse chemical reaction.

Simultaneous-contrast effects, such as when one gazes at a green figure on a gray background and the latter tends to appear reddish, can also be accounted for by the theory. The only requirement is the presence of lateral connections in the retina, and these have been long known to exist.

Historically, there has been a quite severe weakness in the opponent theories. Like my ophthalmologist acquaintance who could find no tubules between the ciliary body and the lens, early researchers were unable to identify, or even conceive of any physiological mechanism by which such color effects might be achieved. With the advent of micro-electrode technology in recent years, however, evidence for an opponent theory has somewhat greater support. DeValois (1965), for example, has shown antagonistic wave patterns from a single nerve cell in the lateral geniculate nucleus as a function of the color of a stimulating light. Red and green result in opposite reactions, as do yellow and blue. Too, responses of the cells in the lateral geniculate are greatly influenced by prior adaptation of the retina. After a prolonged adaptation to a green light, the "red" neural response can be evoked by a much wider range of spectral stimuli than before.

Subjective Color. An interesting phenomenon which can best be explained by an opponent theory and the temporal factors of DeValois is that of subjective color.* It has long been recognized that the viewing of certain patterns consisting of high-contrast stripes, herringbone designs, etc., may result in the sensation of color, especially if the patterns are moving. It is indeed difficult to conceive how "tuned'" receptors in the retina could be activated differentially to such monochromatic stimuli.

A well known example of subjective colors is that produced by the Benham disk, illustrated in Fig. 11-8. If the disk is retated at optimum speed (on the order of 8 to 12 per second) the four sets of thick lines will take on four different hues. The outside set may be blue, the inside set red, with the other two sets taking on intermediate hues. If the direction of rotation is reversed, the location of the hues is reversed, the outside set being red and the innermost lines blue. Paradoxically, it makes little difference what sort of light is used to illuminate the rotating disk. Even with red light the lines appear colored from red through blue. Saturation is poor, and some practice may be necessary in order to identify the colors. But with practice in the effect, the appearance of the "subjective" colors is quite astonishing.

The only explanation which seems reasonable is that when the "on/off" responses of the retinal elements are such as to produce pulse trains in the neural fibers which duplicate those of colored stimuli (note the work of DeValois), the experience is one of color.

---

* The interested reader is directed to the Cohen and Gordon reading at the end of the chapter for numerous examples of subjective color, their history, and possible explanations.

Fig. 11-8. The Benham disk. When the
disk is rotated at the proper speed, the
sets of segmented lines will be seen in
color, ranging from an unsaturated red
to a deep blue.

An entrepreneur in California with a scientific bent recently adopted
the Benham top principle to black-and-white television. In a commercial
for a well-known soft drink, he produced an alternating or flashing signal,
presumably duplicating the time relations of the lines on the Benham disk.
The result was supposed to be the soft drink trademark in color, and all
on black-and-white television. In spite of the fact that the signal flickering
at 10 to 12 cycles per second proved to be rather distracting, a few
astonished viewers did notice the "color" and wrote or called their respective television stations.

Component Theories

As a class, component theories all hold that there are different kinds
of receptors in the retina. Some cones are "tuned" to one color, some to
another, the finer nuances in the ultimate color experience being mediated
through stimulation of combinations of these "tuned" receptors. Until
quite recently the nature of structural or chemical differences in the
receptors was unknown and presented the greatest difficulty for the component theory adherents.

The Young-Helmholtz Theory. Traditionally the most popular theories
for color were those based on the original work of Thomas Young and
developed by Hermann Helmholtz (a contemporary and rival of Ewald
Hering), Christine Ladd-Franklin, James Clerk Maxwell, and others.

Young's original primaries of red, yellow, and blue were replaced by red, green, and blue, but the original theory of Young remained essentially unchanged.

Phenomenological results of color mixing agree closely with the hypothesis of individual receptors in the retina for red, green, and blue. Moreover, the phenomena of color adaptation and afterimages mentioned before do not disprove the theory. Whatever color vision may be, it *is* trichromatic. There are three fundamental hues, and whether their recognition depends on constructs of a component theory or an opponent theory, their existence cannot be denied.

Recent work on the chemistry of vision tends to support a component theory. Just as rhodopsin was demonstrated to be the substance of importance for rod vision, so was *iodopsin* identified as the chemical ingredient of the cones. Wald first isolated this substance from cones of the chicken eye, gave it its name, and showed that it underwent a bleaching action similar to that of rhodopsin. Iodopsin, was shown to have an absorption spectrum with its maximum at 565 mμ as contrasted with rhodopsin's 500 mμ maximum. In light of the Purkinje shift, such a difference was just about what might have been expected.

Wald, Rushton, and others proceeded to further analyze iodopsin, breaking it down into two constituents, one known as *chlorolabe* ("catch the green"), the other, *erythrolabe* ("catch the red"). Rushton found that persons unable to perceive red were lacking in erythrolabe while persons with green color-blindness has an insufficiency of chlorolabe. Persons with normal color vision, on the other hand, had both of these substances in their iodopsin.

There still remained the identification of a "blue catcher" to be named *cyanolabe*. It was not until 1964 that several workers independently were able to demonstrate conclusively the existence of a "catch the blue" substance. The substance finally demonstrated by Marks, Dobelle, and MacNichol at Johns Hopkins and Brown and Wald at Harvard had an absorption maximum at 450 mμ, most definitely in the blue region. These researchers also showed that the three substances were not mixed indiscriminately within a single cone. They found that one and only one of the three substances was present in a single cone. Thus after 160 years the original hypothesis of Thomas Young that three types of "tuned" receptors exist was finally proven.

The Ladd-Franklin Theory. Both phylogenetic and (to some extent) evolutionary evidence tend to support the component theory. The theory of Christine Ladd-Franklin is especially interesting. She reasoned that when vision first developed it was little more than sensitivity to light, and primitive eyes were essentially scotopic devices, probably limited to the elements we now recognize as rods. To creatures with such eyes, light was simply light, and color did not exist.

However, by a mutation (more likely very many mutations) some animals developed the ability to distinguish not only light from darkness, but the extremes of the visible spectrum. That is, they could distinguish between the high and low ends, or what we might refer to loosely as "blue" and "yellow" light. Presumably some organisms developed two kinds of "cones" while still retaining their rods; others (e.g., birds) did not retain their rod vision, their retinas containing only cones.

Still later in evolution the elements which were sensitive to yellow underwent a further division, making possible a discrimination between "red" at one end and "green" at the other. Thus the animal had three kinds of cones, those sensitive to blue, those sensitive to green, and those sensitive to red. Any intermediate colors (including yellow) could, of course, arise from the simultaneous stimulation of more than one of these three types of receptors.

There is at least a modicum of evidence in support of the evolutionary theory. Evidence in general supports the notion that color discrimination improves as one goes up the phylogenetic scale. Man, in contrast with many lower animals, has excellent color vision. The relationship between position on the phylogenetic scale and color vision sophistication is not perfect: mammals other than man appear to be lacking in color vision, in general possessing no cones; some insects appear to have excellent color vision; and birds, as indicated previously, have retinal elements consisting exclusively of cones. Nevertheless, there is a general trend of increased color discrimination ability with higher position in the phylogenetic scale. The possibility of discontinuities in the evolutionary process, and the branching out and specializing by lower species can account for the lack of a simple linear progression from the simple one-celled animals to man. No one has ever claimed that evolution must follow an orderly, single path from simple to complex.

If color vision did indeed develop through evolution in this manner, would there not be additional evidence? There should be and there is. One might expect that the first mutations from scotopic to photopic vision would take place at the fovea of the eye, with further development proceding in a radial direction. Later mutuations would likewise start in the center, developing outward from the fovea. In support of this supposition, we find, that the more highly developed cones are indeed located in the fovea, while rods are more peripherally located.

If we map the color sensitive areas of the eye with a device known as a perimeter (Fig. 11-9) we can determine the areas of the retina sensitive to different spectral radiation. In line with the theory we would

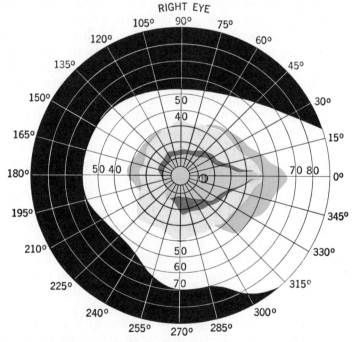

RIGHT EYE

Fig. 11·9. Perimetry. The top figure shows an instrument (perimeter) used to determine color zones of the retina. The bottom figure illustrates the results of such a determination, with the four color zones and the rod-mediated achromatic zone identified by the appropriate colors. (Top photo courtesy Lafayette Instrument Company, bottom figure from Norman L. Munn, *Psychology*, Houghton Mifflin Company.)

expect that the "older" color zones would have migrated out from the fovea, while the "newer "areas, those sensitive to red and green, should be smaller. Results of such experiments are also shown in Fig. 11-9. Note that the area sensitive to blue is much larger than that for red or green, as if it perhaps has been developing for many more eons than the johnny-come-lately red-green vision. The area sensitive to yellow is approximately the same as the blue-sensitive area.

As in the case of most theories, there are weaknesses in the original Ladd-Franklin approach. The specific wavelengths for the primaries as originally defined have since been proven unsatisfactory, and some data based on knowledge of color-blindness fail to support the theory in its details. As a general approach, however, the emphasis on evolutionary development seems to me to be quite useful. But some details and discrepancies in the theory must be worked out and/or eliminated before it can receive universal acceptance.

What about color-blindness? Can this condition be accounted for with the constructs and language of component theory? The answer to this question is, in general, yes. In fact, its ability to account for color-blindness and color weakness is one of the theory's greatest strengths.

DEFECTS IN COLOR VISION

Color vision is commonly evaluated by means of a simple screening device employing *pseudoisochromatic* plates such as illustrated in Fig. 11-10. Subjects with serious color vision deficiencies are unable to discriminate between the dots of a given color and the background color. If plates containing different color schemes are employed, the nature of the color deficiency can be determined as a function of what colors are confused.

A more precise method of detecting and identifying color-blindness involves the use of an *anomaloscope*. With this device the patient adjusts the amounts of two colors in a two-color mixture to match a third color. For example, the subject may adjust the amount of red and green light needed to make a match with a known yellow. The extent to which this is impossible, or the extent to which the subject requires more or less of a given primary than the normal subject, is then a measure of his color-blindness.

Color vision is trichromatic, hence, in theory there might be a weakness or even total absence in any one, two, or all three of the color sensitivities. A classification of color-blindness is shown as Fig. 11-11. While this figure may not be complete, it does show the more common forms of color-blindness. Let us look at this table in more detail.

The most benign form of color vision defect is simply a "weakness"

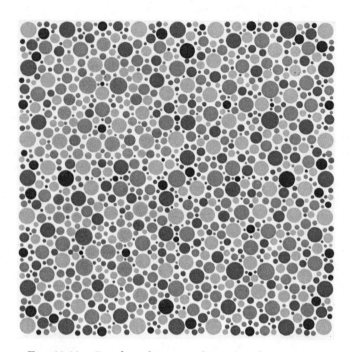

FIG. 11-10. Pseudoisochromatic plate. This plate is an example of the American Optical Company's H-R-R series. The normal individual should see the figures of a circle, a cross, or a triangle located in various quadrants of the square card. In the above figure a cross and triangle should be seen. (Courtesy American Company, Buffalo, N.Y.)

in the ability to see one of the three primary colors. Such people have, like the rest of us, *trichromatic* vision—they can see red, green, and blue, and they require three colors in order to match all the colors in the spectrum. However, in the above example of color mixing, the anomalous trichromat needs more of the one component (for example, red) than the normal individual in order to match a given mixture containing red.

While there is probably a continuum from the normal trichromat through the true color-blind, about 5.6 percent of the male population exhibit enough defect to be classed as *anomalous trichromats*. Most of these cases (4.6 percent) are *deuteranomalous*—that is, they require more green in a red-green mixture to match a specified yellow than the normal person. Deuteranomalous persons are probably deficient in chlorolabe. About 1 percent of the male population is presumed to be deficient in erythrolabe, since they require more red in the red-green mixture. These individuals are classed as *protanomalous*. The third type of trichromatic anomaly, *tritanomalous* vision, should in theory exist as a result of a

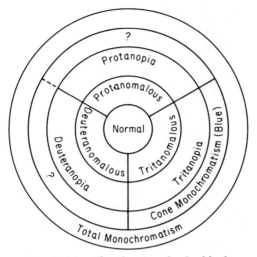

Fig. 11-11. Classification of color-blindness. The inner area of this figure represents normal color vision. The second area includes persons with three-color vision, *but* with some weakness or anomaly. The third level is for persons with two-color vision, while the last two levels represent monochromatism, or one-color vision.

shortage of cyanolabe. As a matter of fact, such cases are exceedingly rare and not at all well documented. Gregory (1966) indicates that the entire theory attributing anomalous color vision to shortages of chlorolabe, erythrolabe, and cyanolabe is in error. He has no alternative explanation, but is most definite in saying that the problem is not simply a pigment shortage.

The second major breakdown of color vision deficiency includes the *dichromats,* persons who can match any color of the spectrum with varying amounts of only two primary colors. As in anomalous trichromats, the condition (at least with respect to the red-green deficiency) appears to be largely of an hereditary nature, specifically a sex-linked recessive characteristic appearing ten times as frequently in males as in females. Three subgroups can also be identified for the dichromats. Known as *protanopes, deuteranopes,* and *tritanopes,* the complete absence of erythrolabe, chlorolabe, and cyanolabe respectively appear as underlying causes. About 1.2 percent of the male population can be classed as protanopes and 1.4 percent as deuteranopes. As a result of a picture-magazine survey in Great Britain, in which a pseudisochromatic chart was included, it has been further estimated that about from 1 in 13,000 to 1 in 65,000 persons in Great Britain are tritanopes.

The most serious, and fortunately most rare, color deficiency is that where no color vision at all exists. *Monochromats* have no color vision; to them, all cats are gray, regardless of the time of day. In theory, of course, four possibilities suggest themselves. A retina could be composed exclusively of cones of a single color sensitivity, red, green, or blue; or a retina could contain no cones at all, providing pure rod vision. Pure rod monochromats have been identified, and one form of cone monochromatism has been documented. Presumably, the other two forms of exclusive cone vision are possible.

—> As a final conclusion in the age-old opponent component theory controversy, we must acknowledge that both approaches have merit. Both theories are needed to adequately explain all color phenomena. Modern investigators tend to feel that a component theory is needed at the cone chemistry level, but for the transmission of the nervous impulse and its higher-level interpretation, some sort of opponent theory demands recognition.

SUMMARY

Chapter 11 has aimed at obtaining an understanding of the manner in which color is experienced. We started out by describing the nature of color and its three attributes: hue, saturation, and brightness or lightness. We then described several approaches to the specification of color, including the Munsell and Ostwald phenomenological techniques and the psychophysically oriented ICI system. In the final half of the chapter we discussed color-vision theory, describing both opponent and component type theories and the experimental evidence in support of each. Such evidence included research results on afterimages and color adaptation, subjective color, the chemistry of cone functioning, color-blindness, and evidence based on evolutionary findings. The ultimate conclusion was that both an opponent and a component theory are required to adequately describe color vision—a component theory at the retinal/cone level and an opponent theory at higher levels.

SUGGESTED READINGS

1. Evans, R. M., *An Introduction to Color* (New York: Wiley, 1948). While relatively old, this is still the best general book on color available. It is well written, beautifully illustrated, and not overly technical. While Chapter II of this reference has already been suggested for reading in support of our Chapter 5, the remainder of the book might very well be read at this time. Most of what has been included in the preceding chapter can

be found in expanded form in the 324 pages of this reference. In addition, interesting chapters on paints and pigments, colorimetry, color photography, and color in art are included. It is the sort of book which can be read at leisure, almost like a novel.

2. Helmholtz, Hermann von, "The Young-Helmholtz Theory of Color," in W. Dennis, *Readings in the History of Psychology* (New York: Appleton, 1948). This reference, included largely for its historical value, presents in six pages a brief description of the popular theory of color vision based on primaries of red, green, and violet. It is a short article, relatively easy to read and understand, and recommended for any student interested in gaining historical perspective.

3. Optical Society of America, Committee on Colorimetry, *The Science of Color* (New York: Crowell, 1953). This reference is the "bible" of color. Much of the book is highly technical in nature and is scarcely to be read like a novel. It presents much of the technical elaboration omitted, for the sake of ease of reading, from the Evans reference. As a reference book it is highly recommended, and every scientist seriously interested in color should have access to this book.

4. Judd, D. B., *Colorimetry*, NBS Circular 478 (Washington, D.C.: Government Printing Office, 1950), or I. Nimeroff, *Colorimetry*, NBS Monograph 104 (same source). Either of these references is suggested for the reader interested in the technical aspects of color production and mensuration. Of minimal interest to the student with a purely biological or psychological interest, the 50 or so pages of either of these pamphlets provide the most nearly complete, yet not extremely complex, explanation of colorimetry and the use of the ICI Chromaticity Diagram.

5. From M. Alpern, "Vision," in M. Alpern, M. Lawrence, and D. Wolsk, *Sensory Processes* (Belmont, Calif.: Brooks/Cole, 1967). While the entire part of this book written by Alpern is worthwhile reading, several pages are particularly useful to an understanding of color vision. Pages 27–48 discuss in an excellent fashion the chemistry of rod and cone vision, color blindness, the component and opponent theories of color, and the present status of color-vision theory. For gaining an understanding of color vision, I know of no better short reference.

6. Cohen, J., and D. A. Gordon, "The Prevost-Fechner-Benham Subjective Colors," *Psychol. Bull.* 46 (1949), 97–136. This is an interesting, even fascinating, history and analysis of subjective color. The reference includes many examples of designs suitable for producing subjective colors. For the student interested in getting at the "root" of the problem, this reference is particularly recommended.

7. MacNichol, E. F., Jr., "Three-Pigment Color Vision," *Scientific American*, December 1964. This is an excellent summary describing the nature and history of the three-pigment theories of cone functioning, written by one of the pioneers in the field.

8. Brindley, G. S., "Afterimages," *Scientific American*, 209, (October 1963). There are eight pages of textual material in this reading which is highly recommended. With demonstrations and examples printed in color, this

short article will supply some of the information on afterimages which had to be omitted from Chapter 11 in the interest of brevity. The relating of the phenomena of afterimages to photochemistry is a particularly valuable contribution to this reading.

9. Teevan, R. C., and R. C. Birney (eds.), *Color Vision* (Princeton, N.J.: Van Nostrand, 1961). An excellent little book of 214 pages, consisting of selected readings from original sources. From Thomas Young to Edwin H. Land, the gamut of information on color vision is sampled. I am not recommending specific readings from this book, but rather its usefulness for general reading. Read what interests you; you will be the better for it.

10. Graham, C. H., "Color Theory," in S. Koch (ed.), *Psychology: A Study of Science*. Volume I (New York: McGraw-Hill, 1959). These 150 or so pages present one of the most nearly complete descriptions of color and color theory that I know of. It describes color mixing in great detail, systems of color notation, and includes detailed analyses of numerous color theories. It is not a particularly simple or elementary article, but worth looking into by the serious student. Its bibliography of 209 entries is especially complete.

12

SOUND WAVES AND HEARING

Let us first examine some terminology and consider the nature of the external stimulus that gives rise to the experience of "sound." Sound is not something that happens "out there." To the contrary, sound is a psychological/behavioral experience. If the proverbial tree were to fall on the deserted island with no one to hear it, there would be no "sound." There would be rapid vibrations in the air which we might call sound waves, but in order to have sound we would have to have an experiencing organism. Similarly, the airborne vibrations would have no loudness, since loudness is also an experience. The sound waves might have amplitude or intensity or power, but they would not have loudness. Loudness is the psychological, experiential correlate of sound amplitude; hence no listener, no loudness. Just as brightness was in the eye of the beholder, so is loudness in the ear of the beholder. Incidentally, the so-called loudness meter used to measure the applause of an audience to an entertainer is not a loudness meter at all; it does not measure loudness; in truth, it measures the amplitude or power of the sound waves produced by the applauding audience. More accurately, the meter in question is, a sound-level meter.

Just as light can be varied in three primary dimensions—intensity leading to the psychological experience of brightness, wavelength with its resultant experience of hue, and purity which is experienced as saturation—so can sound waves vary in three dimensions. For intensity of sound waves the experience is known as *loudness;* the quality or frequency of the sound wave we recognize as *pitch;* and purity evokes the psychological experience of *timbre.* As in vision, we can also recognize temporal variations. Alternating or flickering lights can form temporal patterns not entirely unlike the rhythms and tempos of acoustic stimuli. And finally, to some limited extent, the excellent spatial character of vision can be approximated by the normal, healthy auditory mechanism. The spatial capability of hearing does not match that of vision. In some cases we may even have to "infer" direction of an acoustic source, and often we may be seriously in error. There is however some spatiality in audition which to a limited extent mirrors the three-dimensional world of vision. Let us examine in somewhat more detail the nature of the physical events leading to the experience of "sound."

THE NATURE OF SOUND WAVES

If we imagine a wheel to roll along a flat surface as shown in Fig. 12-1, a point of the circumference will, in effect, follow the path shown by the curve at the right of the wheel. Note that the point will gradually rise to its maximum height or amplitude as indicated by *B* in the adjoining curve. Note too that the rate of vertical climb of the point is gradually decreasing, until at point *B* it is, for an infinitesimally short instant, stationary. For an infinitely short time the point is neither rising nor falling. Then the point returns toward *C*, reaching its maximum downward speed as it passes through its original level, again slowing down and pausing at *D*, and accelerating as it passes its origin, *A'*. The curve generated by such a point on a rolling wheel is known as a *sinusoidal function.*

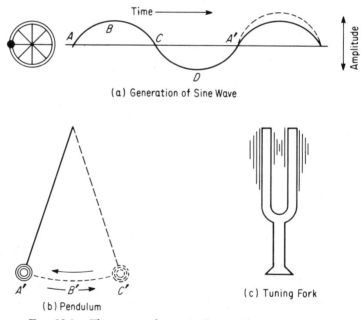

(a) Generation of Sine Wave

(b) Pendulum

(c) Tuning Fork

Fig. 12-1.   The nature of waves. The sound waves generated by the tuning fork are representative of the wave action illustrated by the rotating wheel and the swinging pendulum.

As another example, note the pendulum of Fig. 12-1 which will also generate a sine-wave function. When the pendulum is at point A' it is, for an infinitesimal instant, stationary. It has a velocity and hence, amplitude, of zero (point A on the curve above). But at point B' it reaches its maximum velocity, an amplitude indicated by point B. As a result of gravity, the swinging pendulum will slow down gradually, reaching this time at point C', another instant of motionless or velocity of zero as indicated by C on the sine-wave curve. When the pendulum has returned to point A' it will have completed one complete cycle, or the distance from A to A' on the curve.

As a third example of sine-wave production, a tuning fork vibrates in such a fashion that it alternately compresses and rarefies the adjoining air in a sinusoidal manner. The progressive movement of such alternate compressions and rarefactions through a compressible medium, such as air or water, is known as a sound wave. It is precisely this sort of activity that results from any sound-producing source, be it the vibrating strings of a Stradivarius violin, the reed of a clarinet, the air columns of an organ pipe, or the exceedingly complex vibrations of a cymbal.

Frequency and Pitch

The primary determinant of perceived pitch (high, low) is the frequency of the impinging sound wave. Before examining in detail and in a later chapter, the matter of pitch, let us first consider the physical concept of frequency. If we think of the x-axis (horizontal axis) of the sinusoidal curve of Fig. 12-1 as time, we can see that the time for the wheel to make a complete revolution ($360°$ rotation) is represented by the distance from A to A'. Similarly, the pendulum or tuning-fork action can be shown to complete a single cycle, also represented by the distance from A to A'. (Remember, A to A' is a pictoral representation of time, not distance!)

But, we know that the alternate rarefactions and compressions as produced by the tuning fork do not simply remain alongside the fork's prongs. Like the waves emanating from a pebble dropped in the water, the alternate rarefactions and compressions in the air move steadily away from the tuning fork. They form a progressive wave in all directions.

Happily they move at a known speed. At $0°C$ sound waves travel in air at a velocity of 1,087.5 feet per second. At moderate ambient temperatures, and under certain other specified conditions, their speed is on the order of 1,130 feet per second. While the velocity differs in different media such as water, air, or steel, it is this standard of 1,130 feet per second which is normally specified as the speed of sound. Expressed in miles per hour, instead of feet per second, the number becomes something like 730 miles per hour, the familiar Mach I of jet-airplane interest.

If we know the speed the sound travels and the frequency of the vibrations—that is, the number of complete cycles in a given unit of time (normally taken as one second)—we can calculate an additional parameter of the physical wave, its wavelength. If a source is producing a sound with a frequency of 1,130 cycles per second it is clear that any point on the curve of Fig. 12-1 will repeat itself 1,130 times per second. Furthermore, since the resultant wave is progressing through the medium at a velocity of 1,130 feet per second, the successive points of corresponding amplitude will be exactly one foot apart. The wavelength of an 1,130-Hz tone in air of normal temperature and certain other specified characteristics, is one foot. A 2,260-Hz tone would complete each of its cycles in half the time, hence its wavelength or distance traveled per $\frac{1}{2,260}$ second would be on the order of six inches.

For general application, the relation between wavelength and frequency can be expressed in the following forms:

$$f = \frac{1,130}{\lambda}$$

$$\lambda = -\frac{1,130}{f}$$

and

$$\lambda \times f = 1,130$$

where f is the frequency in cycles per second, λ (the Greek letter, lambda) refers to the wavelength, and 1,130 is the velocity of the transmission. Note too that the time required for each cycle can be expressed as

$$t = \frac{\lambda}{1,130}$$

For media and conditions other than the typically defined air, the velocity figure of 1,130 would have to be replaced by the appropriate value.

The expressions above are general and apply to any wave phenomenon. In Fig. 1-1 we showed the electromagnetic spectrum with both wavelength and frequency identified. But the above formulas when used with electromagnetic radiation involve the tremendous speed of transmission of these waves (about 186,000 miles per second), rather than the relatively slow velocities of sound waves. Note, however, that the *only* similarity between sound waves and electromagnetic waves is the wavelength/velocity/frequency formulations. Sound waves are *not* a part of the electromagnetic spectrum. They simply are alternating compressions and rarefactions in a physical medium. They cannot exist where there is no molecular medium, such as in outer space or in a laboratory-created vacuum.

While most of us have lost much of our hearing ability above 12,000 Hz, the range of 20 to 20,000 Hz is generally recognized as the frequency limits of hearing for man. These limits might also be specified as wavelengths from roughly ¾ inch to 56 feet. The significance of these values will be discussed in later sections of the book.

Frequency of acoustic signals is of importance to us in that the pitch of sounds, from the low hum of the honeybee to the shrill squeak of a rusty hinge, depend largely on the frequency of the physical signal. A low musical note such as C below middle C on the piano has a basic frequency of about 128 Hz, while middle C may be tuned to about 256 Hz, and C above middle C has a frequency of 512 Hz. An octave higher is represented by 1,024 Hz, and so on, each octave representing a doubling of frequency, until the limit of hearing is reached. The manner in which we are able to discriminate different frequencies and their psychological attributes of pitch is a fascinating problem and will be explored in a later chapter.

Purity and Timbre

The sound from the honeybee and the squeaking door may also differ in another important respect. Note that the middle C you strike on the piano does not sound the same as the middle C played on a trombone. While some of the difference may be due to temporal factors such as the rise-and-decay characteristics or the steadiness of the tones, much of the apparent difference between presumably identical notes produced by two different instruments has a much more subtle basis. The sounds produced by the two instruments are not the same, even though they are both producing the same note on the musical scale.

Musical instruments do not produce pure tones like the sinusoidal curve of Fig. 12-1. Rather, they generate a principle wave, known as the fundamental frequency (for instance, the middle C in our example) and numerous variations on this fundamental frequency known as overtones or harmonics.

In Fig. 12-2a the fundamental vibration of a stretched string may be seen. The string bounces back and forth, much like the tines of our tuning fork, alternately compressing and rarefying the air adjoining it. If the string vibrates at a rate of 100 times per second it will produce a tone of 100 Hz. But a string is not as rigid as a tuning fork, it also vibrates in the manner shown in Fig. 12-2b, that is generating an acoustic wave of twice the frequency of the fundamental (2nd harmonic).. If the string in (a) is vibrating at 100 Hz, then the one in (b) will be emitting waves at 200 Hz. Similarly, the string at (c) will be producing a 300-Hz tone. A single string tuned to 100 cps will simultaneously produce all of these frequencies, plus 400, 500, 600 . . . in varying degrees of strength (12-2d). It is the experienced quality of the tone, produced by the relative

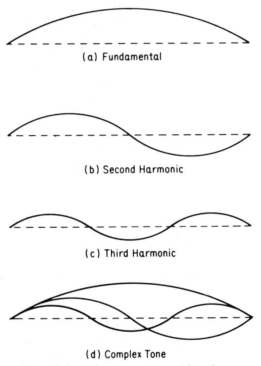

(a) Fundamental

(b) Second Harmonic

(c) Third Harmonic

(d) Complex Tone

Fɪɢ. 12-2. Vibrating strings. This figure shows the nature of the first, second, and third harmonics, and the pattern resulting from their combination.

strengths of the varios harmonic frequencies, that we call *timbre*. Due to differences in absorption, resonance, and other factors, different musical instruments produce patterns of complex waves; thus a cornet sounds different than a French horn. A Stradivarius has a different, presumably more pleasant tone than a less expensive violin. And some voices appear more pleasing due to the richness of their harmonics produced by the resonances of the various cavities of the mouth, larynx, and nasal passages. Timbre, analogous to saturation in vision, is a result of the complexity of the auditory signal.* It is the psychological experience of purity, or perhaps more accurately, the absence of purity that we refer to as timbre.

Random Noise. As an example of a complex sound carried to an extreme, the "whispering" sound, such as produced by the wind, represents a special case in which all (or nearly all) of the audible frequencies are present at the same time. Somewhat analogous to zero-saturated light, or white light, such sounds are, not unreasonably, known as *white noise.* Variously referred to as a Gaussian noise, random noise, or white noise (depending on the actual form and distribution of the tonal components),† such signals are commonly employed in the testing of hearing and in research on the functioning of the ear. When you last had your ears tested, the otologist may very well have "masked" one ear with white noise while he mapped your hearing acuity in the opposite ear with a series of pure tones. Random generators, as used in auditory research, commonly generate frequencies limited to the range of 20 to 20,000 Hz, since these are the general limits of hearing.

Amplitude and Loudness

There is a third primary quality of sound waves which is derived from the amplitude or intensity of the waves, and is experienced as *loudness.* The concept of loudness is not simple, and as suggested before, resides in the experiencing organism. It will be examined in much more detail in Chapter 14. In the meantime, we should gain an understanding of just what amplitude or sound intensity is, how it is measured, and what broad ramifications it may have for our understanding of the auditory function.

Let us look again at the pendulum of Fig. 12-1. It is a law of physics (fortunate for the designers of pendulum-controlled clocks) that a given pendulum will always make a complete cycle in precisely the same time. That is, if the pendulum were to start swinging at a point slightly to the left of A and therefore complete its first half cycle at a point to the right of C, the time required for the extended excursion would be the same as that for the distance A to C. This time, a function of physical parameters

---

* The advanced student may very well recognize the oversimplification of the preceding section. Tones may be produced by both longitudinal and transverse vibrations, the action of columns of air is often quite complex, and in practice the simple harmonic relations we have described do not always obtain. In the interest of brevity and simple exposition, however, it is hoped the serious student of acoustics will find this simplified presentation adequate.

† Strictly speaking, the term *white noise* should be reserved for the situation in which all the frequencies are included in strictly sinusoidal form, such as when one combines a very large number of outputs from differentially tuned audio oscillators. Random noise is truly random, and the outputs of the various components may vary in time from zero to maximum.

such as the weight of the bob and the length of the string from which it is suspended, determines, in accordance with a formulae similar to our last formula on page 222, the primary or fundamental frequency of the oscillation. Note that you change the frequency of a metronome by changing the position of the weight on the vertical shaft. The frequency of the individual waves, and therefore their wavelengths, is determined by the time required for each individual excursion.

A similar situation exists with respect to the tuning fork. As a result of its physical construction it can vibrate (in a given medium) at only one frequency, the one to which it is tuned. If we strike it extra hard the tines will make larger back-and-forth excursions, but always at the same frequency.

What is the difference then, as a result of our starting out the pendulum with a harder push, or striking the tuning fork with a little extra energy? Since the pendulum travels a greater distance in the same time, it must be traveling faster. Similarly, the tuning fork must be alternately compressing and rarefying the adjacent air with increasing amplitude. The movement of the wave through space in the longitudinal direction remains fixed, but the velocity of movement of the individual molecules increases as the excursion distance of the tuning fork's tines is increased.

Such a variation is known as the *amplitude* or *intensity* of the sound wave. It is represented schematically by the height of the wave in Fig. 12-1. The broken line at the right of this figure represents a tone of the same wavelength and frequency, but of a greater amplitude. Psychological loudness, then, is the psychological experience of the amplitude of the sound wave.

Definition of Sound Amplitude. The strength of a sound wave (and many other wave forms as well) is generally specified in terms of power— that is, the amount of work done in a unit of time. In somewhat technical terms we might say that the power of an energy flow through an area one centimeter square (1 cm^2) can be expressed as pressure times velocity. It follows then that the power of a sinusoidal wave is proportional to the pressure caused by the sound wave times the velocity of the air molecules produced by the wave. Can we express this in somewhat simpler language?

The unit known as a *dyne* is a unit of force or pressure, being that force which when acting on a body of one gram mass for one second, will impart in the body a velocity of one centimeter per second. The commonly accepted measure for sound is in terms of dynes per square centimeter (dyne/cm^2). When we express this force over time, we have *power*.

When we use a microphone or similar device for the measurement of sound intensity we take advantage of the fact that a body suspended in space (or of adequate flexibility) will be moved by any alternate compressions or rarefactions in the medium impinging on it. The diaphragm of a microphone will follow the frequency of the impinging molecular vibrations as well as their instantaneous velocity or pressure. If we feed the output of our microphone into an oscilloscope we can see the actual form of the impinging wave. Furthermore, the greater the intensity of the impinging force the greater will be the excursions of our microphone's diaphragm, and hence its output in volts or fractions thereof. In the case of a high-quality microphone, and over a limited frequency range, the output of the microphone will be proportional to the force of the acoustic wave rather than its power. Furthermore, the output of the microphone will be in volts, a pressure unit. We are in no trouble, however, since we know that power varies as the square of the voltage. Thus when the output of the microphone increases from .01 to .02 volt (doubling), we know that the power input to the microphone must have increased by a factor of four. Increasing a sound-pressure level from 1 dyne/cm^2 to 10 dyne/cm^2 is a tenfold increase in pressure but an hundredfold increase in power. It is important to remember that power varies as the square of the force. This is an important concept, necessary for the complete understanding of the decibel scale to be considered in the following section.

Sound Power. When we were discussing the electromagnetic spectrum we noted its tremendous width, and pointed to the necessity for referring to both frequency and wavelength in terms of powers of ten. Indeed, the values shown in Fig. 1-1 are expressed in this form.

While the wavelength and frequency of sound waves in the audible range do not encompass such a great range, variations in amplitude do. The most intense sound that man can tolerate without excessive pain is some 10,000,000,000,000 times more powerful than the weakest sound he can hear—a factor of ten million million to one!

Obviously, handling such long numbers for the various values between the upper and lower limits of sound intensity would be extremely clumsy. As in the case of the electromagnetic spectrum we must resort to a system involving units expressed as powers of ten. For example, 10^0 would equal 1, 10^1 would equal 10, and 10^2 would equal 100, and so on, until the long number referred to earlier describing the most intense sound that can be tolerated would be expressed as 10^{13}.[*]

Also, the concept of zero power with respect to measurement of air-molecule movement is difficult to grasp (Brownian movement occurs

[*] Utilization of a logarithmic form of expression for sound has another basis. Many psychological dimensions of experience vary according to the logarithm of the stimulus rather than its absolute value. Hence a logarithmic nomenclature is more consistent with the experiential world.

constantly in any case), and furthermore there is no way to express zero in a logarithmic form. There is no power to which ten can be raised to equal zero. The solution to this enigma is to adopt a scale which has a starting point, identified as ten to the zero power (equivalent to one), and base all measurements on this anchoring point.

Various anchoring points or scale bases have been used at various times by different disciplines. Engineers commonly use 1 dyne/cm² (also referred to as 1 microbar) as their reference point. Thus 10^0 would refer to the power of a 1 dyne/cm² signal; 10^1 would be a signal of 10 times the power of the 1 microbar standard; and 10^2 would describe a signal of 100 times the power of this reference level. Note again that since power increases as the square of the force, the hundredfold increase in power (10^2) is actually the result of a tenfold increase in pressure (from 1 microbar to 10 microbar, for example).

In the case of auditory work, the commonly used reference level is .0002 dyne/cm², or .0002 microbar. This level has been chosen because it is the approximate absolute threshold for a young, healthy ear over the frequencies of maximum sensitivity.

The Decibel Scale. When you see an auditory signal referred to in print it is not generally referred to as 10^8 or 10^7, etc. Rather, its power is generally expressed in terms of bels,* or more commonly decibels (abbreviated db). This is really just another way of expressing the power in logarithmic terms, simply omitting the base 10 expression and replacing it with the word bel. Thus a signal of 2 bels is one which is ten times as powerful as a signal of 1 bel and 100 times as powerful as one of 0 bels. Since the anchoring point is always identified as zero bels, the comparative power of any signal expressed in bels can be readily calculated.

In practice, however, the distance encompassed by a bel is rather great. The average range of speech power, for example, at a distance of three feet from the speaker, might be something between 6 and 8 bels. We could, of course, indicate intermediate values in the form of 7.5 bels, 8.36 bels, etc. In practice, the procedure is to express powers in terms of *decibels,* or tenths of bels. Thus a six-bel level is almost universally referred to as 60 decibels.

Expressed in technical terms, a bel is the logarithm of the ratio between two powers:

$$\text{bels} = \log_{10} \frac{I_1}{I_2}$$

---

* Named after Alexander Graham Bell, one of the foremost workers in the early development of acoustics and sound research, as well as the inventor of the telephone.

A decibel is defined* in similar terms:

$$db = 10 \log_{10} \frac{I_1}{I_2}$$

Whenever a power is expressed in bels or decibels it is essential that the reference level be known. When we say that one signal is 10 db more powerful than another, the reference is clearly implied. But when we say that a signal has a level of 20 db it is imperative that we define 20 db with respect to what reference level. Therefore, db expressions are always written in the form 20 db re .0002 dyne/cm² or 20 db re 1 dyne/cm² for most auditory and electrical engineering uses respectively.

Table 12-1 shows the relation between various power ratios and their respective values in db.

TABLE 12-1

RELATION OF POWER RATIOS TO DECIBELS

Power Ratio of Two Sounds I_1/I_2	Power or Intensity, db
.001	−30
.01	−20
.10	−10
.50	−3 (approx.)
1.00	0
2.00	3 (approx.)
4.00	6 (approx.)
10.00	10
100.00	20
1000.00	30
2000.00	33 (approx.)

The table can be read in this way: If a signal is .001 as powerful as the reference signal (.0002 dyne/cm² for example) it has a decibel rating of −30 db. Thus db values less than one simply mean that the sound in question is lower in power than the reference level. If a signal is equal to the reference signal we would say that it has a level of 0 db, and if it were 1,000 times as powerful it would be 30 db. Note too that doubling

* One may encounter the last formula in the form:

$$db = 20 \log_{10} \frac{P_1}{P_2}$$

In this case db are calculated as a function of the ratio of the two pressures or forces. In practice, the output of microphones, inputs to amplifiers, etc., are normally expressed in volts, which are units of pressure. Hence the modified formula is necessary to go directly from pressure units to db without the need for calculating power.

(or halving) the power results in a change of approximately 3 db. To get such intermediate values as these, and for values of odd ratios such as 1.643:1, it is necessary to consult a table of decibel equivalents, found in most books dealing with acoustics and electrical phenomena. With slightly more difficulty, one could avail oneself of tables of logarithms to achieve the same purpose.

If one must work with pressure or voltage ratios, a table such as Table 12-2 can be consulted. This table is an extension of Table 12-1, including both pressure or voltage ratios and power ratios. Most available tables do include both voltage and power ratios and are much more like Table 12-2 than Table 12-1.

TABLE 12-2

RELATION OF PRESSURE, POWER, AND DECIBELS

Pressure Ratios P_1/P_2	Power Ratios I_1/I_2	Decibels (some are approx.)
.01	.0001	−40
.1	.01	−20
.5	.25	− 6
1.0	1.0	0
2.0	4.0	6
3.0	9.0	9.5
4.0	16.0	12
10.0	100.0	20
100.0	10,000.	40
1000.0	1,000,000.	60

If you have ever used a tape recorder with a VU (*volume-unit*) meter to maintain recording level you have been employing a decibel scale with a still different reference level. In a VU meter the 0 db you try to maintain (or at least not exceed) is simply some defined level, based on a specified voltage in a circuit of known characteristics. When you record as −6 db your recording voltage is one-half the 0 db optimum; at −20 db your recording voltage is one-tenth the optimum 0 VU, and so on.

THE MEASUREMENT OF SOUND

There are a number of ways in which the physical characteristics of sound are evaluated and described.

Sound-Level Measurement

It should be rather obvious by now that the measurement of sound intensity involves the use of a microphone and the determination of its

(a)

(b)   (c)

FIG. 12-3. Sound-measuring equipment. Examples shown are (a) Type 1551-C
sound-level meter, (b) Type 1558-BP octave-band noise analyzer (shown with
Type 1560-P6 microphone), and (c) Type 1568-A wave analyzer. (Courtesy
General Radio Company, West Concord, Mass.)

Level in db

Level	
140	
	50 hp siren at a distance of 100 feet
	Jet fighter taking off — 80 feet from tail
130	
	Boiler shop
	Air hammer — at position of operator
120	Rock and roll band
	Jet aircraft at 500 feet overhead
	Trumpet automobile horn at 3 feet
110	
	Crosscut saw at operator's position
100	Inside subway car
90	Train whistle at 500 feet
80	Inside automobile in city
70	Downtown city street (Chicago)
	Average traffic
60	
	Restaurant
50	Business office
	Classroom
40	Inside church
	Hospital room
30	Quiet bedroom
	Recording studio
20	
10	Threshold of hearing — young men

FIG. 12-4. Typical sound levels in db re
.0002 dyne/cm². Levels are only approximations and in many cases deviations of
as much as 20 db might be expected.

output as a result of an impinging sound level. A sound-level meter, such as illustrated in Fig. 12-3, measures the level of the sound at the surface of the microphone. A meter of this type measures the total sound-pressure level in decibels with reference to the conventional .0002 dyne/cm² standard. Thus, if it reads 60 db, it indicates that the power is 60 db above the .0002 dyne/cm² reference level. Is it clear that, in this example, the pressure or force would be 0.2 dyne/cm² (that is, $.0002 \times 1000$)? If it is not apparent look again at the last line of Table 12-2.

Sound-level meters can tell us whether the levels are intense enough to interfere with speech or perhaps even damage the ear. Many tables and graphs have been worked out showing the effect on hearing and possible interference with speech as a function of the level and duration of intense sounds. The interested reader should consult the pertinent references at the end of the book.

Most sound-level meters do something else besides simply measure an overall energy level. Since we are interested in the intensity of sound as it affects the human listener, sound level meters are made so that they measure only those sound levels at the frequencies normally heard by humans. Thus most instruments have passbands from 20 to 20,000 Hz, filtering out frequencies beyond these limits. Also, since the ear's sensitivity is partly a function of the level of the overall sound, most meters have different scales for gross differences in level. Thus, A, B, and C scales are often included to provide filtering/shaping capabilities to match the sensitivity curve of the human ear. While sound level meters do not actually measure loudness (no instrument can do this, as we will see in a later chapter) their response in decibels *does* indeed approximate the human experience of loudness.

Figure 12-4 shows some typical sound levels in db as measured with a sound-level meter. In this case the levels represent the total sound-pressure level over the 20-to-20,000-Hz frequency range.

Frequency Analysis

In addition to measuring the overall level of a complex sound, more often than not we are interested in its composition. The ear is not equally sensitive to the entire range from 20 to 20,000 Hz, and potential damage to the ear from excessive sound levels is much less severe for those frequencies far above normal speech frequencies. Intense frequencies at, say, 15,000 Hz might destroy your ability to hear subsequent tones at this frequency, but since most sounds such as speech and music are not concentrated at such high frequencies you might never notice this loss of sensitivity. At least you would not be severely handicapped. But if you were to lose your sensitivity to a band of tones around 400 Hz, your ability to hear and recognize speech might be severely impaired. It is clear that a knowledge of the frequency characteristic of noise or interferring tones is of utmost importance.

Filtering devices known as octave-band and narrow-band analyzers are used to determine the power in different portions of the audio spectrum. (See Fig. 12-3.) Octave-band analyzers determine the power in each of a number of octave bands such as 37.5 to 75 Hz, 75 to 150 Hz, 150 to 300 Hz, all the way to 20,000 Hz. Figure 12-5 shows the octave-

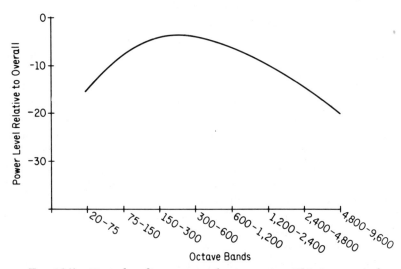

Fig. 12-5. Typical audio spectrum for jet engine. This is a general curve, not representing any specific jet engine, but representative of all.

band composition of a sample of noise, that produced by a jet engine. This typical example has its maximum acoustic power in the 150–300- and 300–600-Hz bands, with a gradual falling off in power beyond these limits. Narrow-band analyzers, on the other hand, determine the total energy in each frequency, or at least in quite narrow bands, often specified as some percent of the total frequency.

When we know the overall levels, and the relative power in the various bands or individual frequencies, we are better able to predict the results of the noise and take remedial steps to reduce the excessive levels if such is indicated.

Probe Microphones

Sound levels or sound intensities can be measured with other variations. Since we are generally interested in the sound level at the ear, or more precisely, at the human eardrum, might we not better measure the level right at that location? For many purposes, such as determining the results of amplitude variations with great precision, that is just what is done. For this purpose a probe microphone is used. A small, tubular arrangement is inserted in the ear canal until it is quite close to the actual eardrum, thus measuring the sound level at the drum itself. This technique, to be sure, requires a delicate touch and is not a method to be employed outside the laboratory. Note, however, that we can also take the output from the inserted microphone and run it through one of the analyzers mentioned earlier, thus determining the actual composition of the sound at the eardrum as well as its overall level.

Coupler Application

A final measurement technique should be mentioned. We may wish to produce a sound-pressure level of known amplitude by means of a headphone. Or perhaps we might wish to know the level at the eardrum produced by a headphone. We could of course insert a probe microphone under the headphone and measure the level directly. More often, however, a device known as a *coupler* is used to calibrate the headphone, such that if the voltage of the signal at the phone is known, the sound-pressure level at the eardrum can be calculated. Figure 12-6 illustrates the use of a coupler in the calibration of a headphone.

To begin with, a calibrated microphone must be used, one for which we know the output in volts for various sound-pressure levels. In practice, an audio signal of a known voltage is fed into the phone

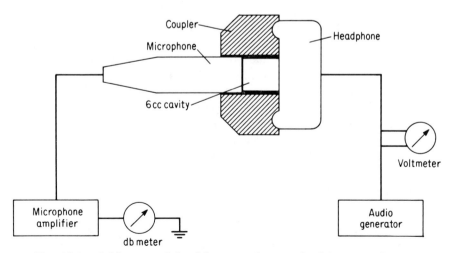

FIG. 12-6. Calibration of headphone. Audio signal of known voltage is fed into headphone. Calibrated microphone assembly indicates sound-pressure level at eardrum.

and the output of the microphone is noted. Since the cavity in the coupler is designed to duplicate the volume of the external ear canal (6 cc) the level impinging on the microphone will be essentially the same as that at the eardrum if the phone were being worn. Thus when the calibrated headphone is worn, levels at the eardrum can be estimated quite precisely as a function of the voltage across the phone terminals.

In the case of insert phones, similar to the ones you get with small transistor radios, a coupler with a volume of 2 cc is used, thus duplicating the unoccupied portion of the external ear canal with this sort of transducer.

CONTROL OF NOISE

Before leaving the realm of the physical nature of the phenomena which produce sound we should at least touch upon the manner in which excessive or unwanted sound is controlled. The broad area of acoustic noise control is quite involved, and we can scarcely scratch the surface of this fascinating and highly technical profession.

Definition of Noise

What is it we wish to control? What is this ubiquitous thing called noise? And why do we need to control it? Noise can be defined in either of two ways, not necessarily mutually exclusive.

1. It is complex sound of an inharmonious nature. Musical instruments are complex resonators, they produce complex sounds containing many sinusoidal components or pure tones. But, as indicated earlier, their components have a simple mathematical relationship to each other and the result (at least to a member of our Western culture) is music. When the components are not harmonically related, or perhaps related in unfamiliar ways, the sound is not harmonious and we refer to it as noise.

2. Noise can also be defined as any unwanted sound. When you are trying to concentrate on studying, sounds that you might otherwise appreciate and perhaps call music are now noise. By this definition, noise is any acoustic activity that interferes in some way with ongoing behavior, or perhaps even results in damage to the subjected organism.

Why Control Noise?

Excessive sound levels can damage the sensitive, delicate receptors in the inner ear. Persons working near jet-aircraft engines frequently suffer hearing loss due to damage of the tiny hair cells in their inner ears. When this hearing loss is in the range normally required to understand speech, the result may be quite serious.

Noise also interferes with ongoing activity. Noise control techniques are employed in hospitals, schoolrooms, recording studios, and countless other places for obvious reasons. One particular development of the acoustic engineers (and psychologists) is the concept of Speech-Interference Level (SIL). Based on the acoustic power in several specified octave bands, the SIL can predict the interference with speech of almost any complex sound if its composition is known. Thus acceptable levels for offices, churches, and similar locations can be determined and necessary control measures instituted to insure adequate speech communication.

Noise Reduction

The manner of controlling noise is not at all simple. One doesn't just install acoustic tile in the ceiling. Actually, all such a simplistic procedure does is to prevent (or reduce) reflection of the sound, thereby reducing potential echoes or reverberations. Any reduction in the actual level in the room rarely exceeds 2 or 3 db.

The ideal method to reduce noise is to control it at the source. Noisy engines can be equipped with mufflers and the volume on the radio can be turned down. In the long run, reducing noise level at the source is the only truly effective technique. Other techniques are merely treatments or ways of circumventing the problem.

Another method is to increase the distance between the noise source and the auditor. Since the sound waves spread out in all directions (not unlike the light rays from a candle), as one increases the distance between the source and the listener, the level at the listeners ear will decrease, not as the distance but as the *square* of the distance. Thus each doubling of the distance results in a 6-db drop in the experienced power. Mechanics working around jet engines, for example, are required to maintain some specified distance from the engine, unless specific and limited duties require greater proximity to the source of the noise.

A third possibility is the placing of a barrier between the source of the noise and the listener. One approach is to isolate the noise-producing source. Noisy machines, for example, are placed in enclosures surrounded by thick concrete or metal walls. Or, as another alternative, the place to be kept quiet can incorporate heavy walls and doors, as in recording studios. Such installations may even have double-layered windows and double doors to help keep out the noise.

A barrier may also be used right at the listener. Earplugs, or (more effectively) heavy protectors covering the entire ear, may be used to keep out much of the unwanted sound. Such devices have a limitation: even if all the sound is prevented from reaching the inner ear by way of the external ear and the auditory canal, one could still suffer irreparable damage to the inner ear as a result of sounds passing directly through the bone of the head. In fact, the transmission of the skull to the inner ear is only some 30 db poorer than that through the normal canal. Thus earplugs or pads can only reduce an intense sound by a maximum factor of 30 db. In practice, the reduction is usually much less.

SUMMARY

In this chapter we considered briefly the nature of the physical changes in our environment that we identify as "sound." We examined first the three principle variations in an acoustic signal which we identified as frequency, purity, and amplitude. We suggested, with reference to later chapters, that the experiences of pitch, timbre, and loudness are related to these three physical variables. In the course of this discussion we examined concepts of force and power, and learned how the decibel system is employed in the measurement of physical quantity. We were also introduced to methods of measuring sound, involving such devices as microphones, couplers, sound-level meters and sound analyzers. Finally, we touched briefly on the methods used to control unwanted sound or noise.

SUGGESTED READINGS

1. Peterson, A. P. G., and L. L. Beranek, *Handbook of Noise Measurement* (Cambridge, Mass.: General Radio Co., 1956). Later editions are of equal value. The second chapter of this manual to General Radio's sound-measuring equipment is one of the clearest and best descriptions of the decibel notation system that I know of. It is short (about four pages), lucid, and as complete as necessary for the beginner in acoustics and auditory measurement. Several of the remaining chapters in this book should also prove of interest to the serious student, providing information on loudness, masking, thresholds, and other topics to be discussed in subsequent chapters.
2. From S. S. Stevens, *Handbook of Experimental Psychology* (New York: Wiley, 1951). Chapter 25, "Basic Correlates of the Auditory Stimulus," by J. C. R. Licklider, is an excellent description of the physical nature of sound and its relation to the experiencing organism. The first fourteen pages of this chapter are particularly relevant to the material just covered. The remainder of the present chapter is germane to the subsequent chapters on hearing in this book, and are recommended for the serious student.
3. Jones, A. T., *Sound* (New York: Van Nostrand, 1937). While quite old and possibly not available in all libraries, this book is one of the best sources for information on an introductory, highly readable level. It presents the subject matter in a highly understandable fashion, avoiding highly technical terminology wherever possible, yet preparing the reader for more advanced study. While recognizing that the last sections on technical

application may be somewhat dated, the remaining 360 pages are well worth selective reading by the serious-minded student who has not yet mastered the highly technical area of sound and acoustics.

4. From W. A. Van Bergeijk, J. R. Pierce, and E. E. David, Jr., *Waves and the Ear* (Garden City, N.Y.: Doubleday, Anchor Books, 1960). The first 66 pages (Chapters I, II, and III) are concerned with the same sort of subject matter we considered in this chapter. This reference is quite easy to read, interesting, and informative. It is a worthwhile adjunct to the material in Chapter 12 and is well worth reading.

5. Stevens, S. S., F. Warshofsky and the editors of *Life, Sound and Hearing* (New York: Time, Inc., 1965). This is another of the excellent little books (about 200 pages) in the *Life* Science Library series. It is beautifully illustrated, written for the intelligent layman, and of considerable value as an introductory survey of the entire field of sound and hearing.

The following two books are recommended for the serious student who has sufficient background to profit from them:

6. Beranek, L. L., *Acoustic Measurement* (New York: Wiley, 1949).

7. Beranek, L. L., *Acoustics* (New York: McGraw-Hill, 1954). These two books do not read like popular novels. While they are relatively difficult reading, I feel that they make a highly complex subject matter just about as simple and readable as is possible. As reference books, these two volumes are musts. Any person with a serious interest in acoustics as related to hearing will at least have access to these two books.

13

THE HUMAN EAR

The development of the human ear makes for as interesting a tale as the development of the eye. And in some respects they are quite similar. Sensitivity (irritability) to mechanical movement or vibratory activity is probably basic to all protoplasm. As in the case of sensitivity to electromagnetic waves, evolutionary development presumably resulted in the creation of specialized tissue and structures more ideally suited for mechanical sensitivity than the undifferentiated protoplasm.

An early example of specialization can be seen in the frog embryo. At a stage of development when one can scarcely tell which end of the embryo is which, a *lateral placode* begins to develop on the dorsolateral surface near the head end. This placode (remember the placode which eventually developed into the eye?) ultimately develops into the inner ear, and in many lower animals such as fish, a remarkable structure known as the *lateral-line* organ.

Most fish have a visible streak running along near the midline of the lateral surface. This is the visible portion of the lateral-line organ, a string of sensitive hair cells imbedded in a gelatinous *cupula*. Any unusual movement of the water alongside of the fish is sensed by the delicate sensory cells, and neural impulses transmitted to the central nervous system of the animal alert it to the untoward event.

Many animals phylogenetically lower than the fishes do not have such a well-developed sense as the lateral-line organ provides. But many do have sensitive cells equipped with delicate hairlike processes that can respond to vibratory movement. In many worms these delicate hairlike transducers are located over a large portion of the body.

Unlike fish, which retain their lateral-line organs while still developing rather complex inner ears, most higher animals such as birds and mammals do not develop lateral-line organs. (Or at least they disappear before birth.) On the contrary, these higher animals develop quite sophisticated inner ears, as well as middle ears, and, in many of the highest-order animals, sophisticated outer or external ears.

240

DEVELOPMENT OF THE INNER EAR

The development of the inner ear parallels the development of the eye in a disarmingly similar manner. The previously mentioned placode develops a dent or pit which becomes deeper and deeper until the surface ectoderm finally closes over it, leaving a little nodule or bubble of placode tissue. This bubble is called the *otic vesicle*. This description sounds like the development of the eye with its optic vesicle, does it not? But there is a difference! The optic placode and optic vesicle were composed of neural tissue, they developed from the wall of the forebrain. Indeed, the retina which developed from the invagination of the forebrain actually included several layers of neural tissue. The inner ear like the lens of the eye, develops from the ectoderm layer of the embryo; hence it is not made up of neural tissue. As we shall see later, the inner ear does not have the multiple neural layers of the retina. Instead, impulses from the inner ear must travel some distance before reaching any ganglionic "switching station."

The otic vesicle, which is at first like a tiny fibrous tumor, continues to grow, becoming larger and more nearly spherical and generally filled with fluid. Rather suddenly, then, it begins to constrict in the center into a dumbbell shape, eventually into two cavities connected by a fine channel. These two halves of the structure develop into the major organs of the inner ear.

The upper of these two cavities develops into the organs of equilibrium or balance, consisting of three semicircular canals, lying in three distinct planes, and their associated structures. We will return to the semicircular canals in a later chapter when we consider the sense of equilibrium.

The lower cavity develops into the inner ear in a manner much too complex to delineate at this time. It is so complex that much of the detailed development is not fully understood. Apparently hair cells, not entirely unlike those in the lateral-line organs of the fish, develop in a membrane known as the *basilar membrane,* buried deeply in the bony, spiral structure called the *cochlea.* This latter structure is so named because it looks like a snail (Latin *cochlea*). We shall look more deeply into the anatomical nature of the cochlea and its basilar membrane when we consider the ear in detail. In the meantime, let us regress a bit and examine the overall auditory organ, starting logically from the outside and working in.

ANATOMY OF THE EAR

For purposes of description, the ear is commonly divided into three rather independent but still closely related parts: the outer ear, the

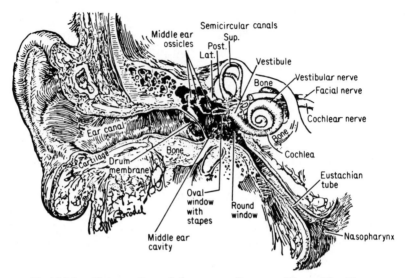

FIG. 13-1. Cross section of the mammalian ear. (From *The Neuro-anatomical Basis for Clinical Neurology*, 2d ed., by T. L. Peale. N.Y.: McGraw-Hill Book Company, 1961, courtesy of McGraw-Hill Book Company.)

middle ear, and the inner ear. Let us examine these three parts of the ear in detail with frequent reference to Fig. 13-1.

The Outer Ear

This is the only part of the ear normally visible. It is totally lacking in many species and is probably the least critical part of the ear. It does have a function, however. The *pinna*, or external portion of the outer ear, works somewhat like a megaphone in reverse, or perhaps like the "snooper" or parabolic microphone the television networks use to pick up the quarterback's instructions in the huddle. Due to its larger area and particular shape, it tends to catch sound waves and "focus" them into the internal ear. While the actual increase in level (amplification) is probably quite small at the inner boundary of the outer ear, the *ear drum* or *tympanic membrane*, the shape of the external ear *does* help provide information as to the direction of the sound source. Animals such as dogs improve their localization ability by moving or aiming their external ears. The directionality provided by man's pinna undoubtedly aids him in localizing the source of sounds as he moves his head about.

External Meatus. The second principal part of the outer ear is the *auditory canal* or *external meatus*. This is simply a tube, about one inch long and with a volume of about 6 cc, connecting the external ear with the eardrum. Many lower animals with no external pinnae likewise have no auditory canal; their eardrums are flush with the surface. It would appear that their hearing sensitivity should suffer a bit due to this lack.

The external meatus and its associated pinna probably provide some amplification due to their resonant frequency.* This canal is in effect an open pipe and presumably resonates according to well-established principles. With a resonant frequency of about 3,400 Hz and a maximum pressure point at the eardrum, this resonating device provides for an amplification of from 5 to 10 db, and, of great significance, largely in the frequency range most essential for hearing of speech. Without this canal and its collecting devices—that is, if our eardrum were flush with the surface of the head—our hearing would be as much as 10 db less acute.

Tympanic Membrane. The eardrum or tympanic membrane, which marks the boundary between the external ear and the middle ear, is a thin, membraneous tissue of a generally circular shape, anchored at its circumference. It is really quite similar to the head of a snare drum. Sound waves produce back-and-forth vibrations in this membrane, not entirely dissimilar to the vibrations in the diaphragm of a headphone, or perhaps the cone of a loudspeaker. At this point acoustical vibrations in the air are transformed into mechanical vibrations. Actually the vibratory movements of the eardrum, which must be transmitted to the inner ear by way of the middle-ear ossicles, are incredibly small. For ordinary conversation, the displacement of the tympanic membrane is something like one one-hundred millionth (1/100,000,000) of a centimeter, or about equal to the diameter of a hydrogen molecule!

How important is this tympanic membrane? What happens if it is torn or punctured? When your doctor lances your ear for a middle-ear infection he simply makes a small, sharp cut through the tympanic membrane, thus allowing undesirable fluids to drain from the middle ear into the outer ear. When the infection is cleared up and the extra fluid has been absorbed, the clean slit in the drum heals with a minimum of scar tissue and your hearing is as good as before.

Even if the drum is slightly torn or punctured, hearing is usually not too severely damaged. Georg von Békésy, winner of the 1961 Nobel prize in medicine and physiology, and probably the foremost authority on the ear in this or any other century, showed that cats with perforations of about one millimeter, while losing hearing below 100 Hz, retained essentially normal hearing for those frequencies over 1,000 Hz (von Békésy, 1957). One millimeter is actually a rather large hole, especially for an animal as small as a cat. Even if the drum is slightly torn or punctured,

---

* We touched on earlier the manner in which musical instruments have resonant frequencies in that they amplify some components of complex tones while suppressing other components.

hearing is usually not severely damaged. The resonant frequency may change somewhat as the result of membrane damage, and some amplification may be lost. In general, however, the drum can still vibrate and transmit most sound waves to the bones of the middle ear. If the damage is extensive, or if large portions of the tympanic membrane have been replaced by relatively stiff scar tissue, hearing may be damaged.

Why then does a punctured eardrum keep a person out of the military service? The problem is not so much due to hearing loss as it is the danger of middle-ear infection by way of the unsanitary opening into the middle ear. Dirt which is normally blocked off at the eardrum can now pass into the middle ear, greatly increasing the likelihood of infection. Indeed, when your punctured eardrum heals—if it does—you might find yourself again a likely prospect for military service.

It is also possible, under extreme conditions, to replace the tympanic membrane surgically if the remaining parts of the ear so warrant.

The Middle Ear

Many species of animals which do not have an outer ear, do indeed have a middle ear. The function of the middle ear seems to be to transform the mechanical vibrations of the tympanic membrane into vibrations in the liquid medium of the inner ear. Many fishes do not have a middle ear. The liquid-borne vibrations in their water milieu are transformed, with a minimum loss, to the liquid medium of their inner ears. In animals surrounded by air, however, the transformation of sound waves from acoustical vibration to mechanical vibration to vibrations in the liquid of the inner ear presents a much more formidable problem.

Without a middle ear the transformation of the airborne sound to vibrations in the liquid medium of the inner ear by way of the skull bones would result in a loss (drop in power) of nearly 30 db. This is roughly the figure we suggested as the theoretical maximum attenuation possible with ear protectors that block all of the sound at the opening of the ear canal. Notice too that the hearing loss in persons who have little or no functioning middle ear is frequently on the order of 30 db. That is, sounds are reduced by 30 db, or to a value of $\frac{1}{1,000}$ that of the normal ear.

Ossicles. While all animals do not have such a complex system of bones or *ossicles,* most land-dwelling animals of reasonably high position in the phylogenetic scale do have some sort of amplification or impedance-matching device in the middle ear. Birds and some reptiles, for example, have a simple, elongated bone known as a *columella,* while some amphibians have an arrangement of two bones.

The origin of these middle-ear bones presents a fascinating example of evolutionary development. As you are probably aware, most vertebrates have the same number of skeletal bones. Some have atrophied to the point where they are barely discernible, and some have taken on rather unusual, even bizarre, forms. The long "finger" or "toe" of the horse is a case in point; the specialized wings of birds and the "wings" of bats are all examples of such modification and specialization. But, basically, the same structures exist in all. Primitive fishes have no middle ears, or at least no bones in their middle ears. They do have gills, however, each with a bony structure known as a *gill arch*. Through the process of evolution, these gill arches have decreased in number, having taken on various other forms, in many cases migrating to loci quite remote from the original gill location. Just as the horse walks on a single toe (cloven-hoofed animals walk on two toes), higher-order animals have developed uses for the no longer needed gill arches. Many of the bones of the face, for example, have been derived from the early gill arches. Of significance to us here is that the ossicles of the middle ear are direct descendants of portions of the early fishes' gill arches. Some success has been achieved in identifying that portion of the gill arch which developed into each of the specific ossicular bones.

How the Ossicles Work. At higher levels of development most mammals have a leverlike arrangement of three bones arranged somewhat as shown in Fig. 13-2. These three bones, or ossicles, called the hammer (*malleus*), anvil (*incus*), and stirrup (*stapes*) serve to transfer the sound from the tympanic membrane to the inner ear by way of the *oval window*. As can be seen from this figure, back-and-forth movements of the tympanic

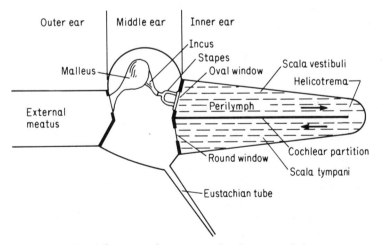

FIG. 13-2. Schematic of ear. Note the direction of the wave movement, down the scala vestibuli, around the helicotrema, and back by way of the scala tympani. Note too that the cochlear partition is quite a complex structure as shown by Figs. 13-4 and 13-5.

membrane produce a movement in the malleus. The rocking movement of the loosely attached incus is then transmitted to the stapes, whose single point of contact with the oval window and pistonlike movement, succeeds in transforming the original acoustic vibrations into vibratory waves in the fluid of the inner ear (*perilymph*).

It has been estimated that these three bones regain about 25.5 db of the 30 db loss that would prevail if sound has to go directly from the air medium into a liquid medium. As mentioned earlier, the pinna and meatus contribute some amplification, but the greater bulk of the excellent impedance matching is provided by the design of the bones of the middle ear.

Amplification is accomplished in at least two ways. First, the lever action results in a smaller amplitude of movement at the output—that is, the oval window. Movements at the eardrum are reduced by a factor of from 1.3 to 3, thus resulting in a mechanical advantage at the oval window. Such a lever action is analogous to the familiar gear changes in an automobile or the lever action of a crowbar.

Secondly, the area of movement at the tympanic membrane (attachment of malleus) is some 14 to 20 times greater than that at the oval window (stapes attachment). Thus a principle analogous to that employed in an hydraulic ram is built into middle-ear functioning. This latter amplification probably reduces the air/liquid transfer loss by as much as 23 db. With a roughly 2.5-db gain by the lever functioning and some contribution of the external meatus resonance, the 30-db loss we referred to earlier is pretty well taken care of. The overall effect is to greatly increase the energy transfer from the light, compressible air to the dense, incompressible fluid of the inner ear—a remarkably well-designed system.

Birds, as suggested earlier, have a much simpler system. In addition to having no pinna, they have only a single columella in their middle ears. Hence they utilize only the areal ratio and hydraulic ram effect to counteract the air to fluid transfer loss and still maintain excellent auditory sensitivity.

The ossicles of the middle ear also provide some protection to the inner ear from unduly intense sounds. Under normal sound levels the ossicles vibrate in a manner to increase the energy at the oval window, as we have just seen. But when sounds are quite intense, the movement of the ossicles changes to an alternate mode; they vibrate in a different fashion, thus transmitting less of the energy to the inner ear.

Also, there are two muscles attached to the ossicles which may tend to damp their movement somewhat. Many persons question the efficacy of these slow-responding *tensor tympani* and *stapedius* muscles as means of protecting the inner ear from intense sounds. It would appear that their function may be somewhat analogous to the function of the iris and its pupil—to set a resting tension to maximize sound transmission, rather than to protect the ear. The existence of autonomic nervous system ennervation of these muscles would tend to support this view.

The Eustachian Tube. A small tube with an inside diameter roughly that of a pencil connects the middle-ear cavity with the back of the mouth. While it plays a minor part in hearing, the *Eustachian tube* is of importance for the well-being of the middle ear. This tube drains undesirable fluids from the middle ear which might result in serious infections and damage to the delicate bones therein. In its normal, healthy state it also insures that air pressures in the middle-ear cavity will be the same as those impinging on the outer surface of the tympanic membrane. You have all experienced the movement of air between the middle ear and the mouth concurrent with sudden changes in elevation, such as when you ascend or descend a mountain, or even in an elevator in a tall office building. For the proper functioning of the ear it is important that the normal resting pressures be the same on both sides of the eardrum.

If the Eustachian tube collapses due to general systemic disorder or gets clogged up with a superabundance of fluids from the middle ear, serious problems may develop. It is even possible to clog the tube with germ-laden mucous as a result of a violent sneeze. Pressures building up in the middle ear as a result of such an occlusion can produce severe pains and the infectious material may damage the delicate contents of the middle ear. Lancing of the eardrum may have to be resorted to in order to drain off excess fluid.

One semimedical organization that I know of attaches particular importance to the functioning of the Eustachian tube. They believe that many cases of hearing loss can be attributed directly to a general failure of the Eustachian tube to maintain a functional opening because of loss of muscular tonus in its walls. Their chiropracticlike treatment consists of massaging the walls of the tube, first with a small tool inserted though the mouth and into the tube, later by actually massaging the interior of the tube with the finger. Can you imagine sticking your finger in your ear through your mouth? Apparently it can be done, since the walls of the Eustachian tube are quite flexible and stretchable. A healthy, well-defined Eustachian tube might be expected to perform its function better than a sickly, flabby one.

Round and Oval Windows. As can be seen from the schematic drawing of Fig. 13-2, not one but two openings (covered by thin diaphragms) connect the middle ear with the cochlea of the inner ear. A portion of the stapes is attached to the *oval window*. Thus as the stapes rocks back and forth it imparts a wave motion to the fluid in the inner ear. The resultant pressure waves move along the path of the inner ear, crossing over a dividing septum at the *helicotrema* and returning to the round window. Without a flexible oval window the pressure waves could not move through the incompressible perilymph of the inner ear and stimulate the sensory elements located there. Thus both the oval window, to introduce the vibratory motion, and the round window, to permit compression of the liquid medium, are essential for hearing.

In a later section we will discuss in more detail how the waves in the inner ear perilymph are converted into nervous impulses. However, when we get to that point we will be dealing somewhat in conjecture, since the nature of cochlear functioning is still not fully understood.

Disorders of the Middle Ear. Since it is a mechanical device of a quite delicate nature, troubles with the bones of the middle ear are to be expected. A large portion of deafness, especially that found as an accompaniment of the aging process, can be attributed to malfunctions of the middle ear. Such disorders are referred to as *conduction deafness,* as distinguished from *nerve deafness* which involves some problem of the inner ear and the sensory organs located there. Fortunately, several methods for relieving deafness due to conduction or middle-ear malfunction are available, and no one should be truly deaf due solely to diseases of the middle ear.

The commonest defect of the middle ear is known as *otosclerosis,* which literally means, "auditory tissue turning to bone." It was once believed that the cartilaginous portions of the middle ear did indeed ossify, thus prohibiting their movement and the conduction of sound waves to the oval window. We now know differently. What *does* appear to happen as a concomitant of aging and the general systemic changes which accompany it, is a depositing of hard, calceous material around the footplate of the stapes. Such a deposit prevents the free movement of this last link in the middle-ear chain, thus greatly reducing or even completely eliminating wave transfer through the oval window and to the inner ear.

Stapes Mobilization. One early approach to the treatment of otosclerosis was to go into the middle ear with a slender probe like a blunt needle and break the footplate loose from its calcified anchor. This was not a highly successful maneuver. Von Békésy suggests that success can be achieved in about 30 percent of the cases. (von Békésy, 1957) He further adds, rather wryly, that he doubts that bone breaking can be improved to a standard procedure. Finding the obstreperous footplate and breaking it loose without danaging other delicate parts of the ear is scarcely a job for the clumsy or the untrained. And too, even if the stapes is made free by the mobilization operation, continuing calcification will ultimately interfere with its motion again, and deafness will recur.

Fenestration. A more successful surgical approach to the problem of conduction deafness is known as *fenestration.* As can be seen from Fig.

13-2, the problem is to get the wave moving in that part of the cochlea known as the *scala vestibuli.* This can be accomplished by simply ignoring the normal conduction mode by way of the middle-ear bones and making a new opening (window, or *fenestra*) into the cochlea. The surgical technique involves boring a small hole (usually with a dental drill) into the scala vestibuli by way of the lateral canal of the *vestibular organ.** When the hole is covered with a flap of skin, sound conduction from the middle ear into the inner ear is again achieved. The operation is straightforward, all steps are well under control, and prognosis, assuming the inner ear is functioning properly, is quite good. Since most of the amplification potential of the middle ear is lost, hearing, while much improved over the severe otosclerotic condition will not be as acute as the normal, healthy, unoperated ear. A hearing aid will in most cases make up for the loss.

Hearing Aids. The last approach we shall mention with respect to alleviating conduction deafness is the use of a hearing aid. The old-fashioned ear trumpet you may have seen in old pictures or museums was an example of a simple hearing aid which did indeed work. The trumpet-shaped affair collected the sound waves and focused them into the auditory canal, not entirely unlike a convex lens that is used as a burning glass, or the parabolic microphone we referred to earlier.

Most conduction deafness, unless it has progressed to an extreme state, is not the result of complete stapes immobilization. If the sound is intense enough it can still force movements in the ossicles and subsequent conduction to the oval window. Modern hearing aids simply amplify the sound electronically so that the reluctant ossicles are forced to conduct the sound vibrations to the inner ear. Note, too, that electronic amplifying devices have "tone" controls, amplifying those parts of the audio spectrum most in need of amplification and not simply *all* sound frequencies equally, irrespective of their importance to hearing and the unique nature of the hearing disorder.

If the ossicles are indeed incapable of conducting sound vibrations, a normal hearing aid may be of little value. Increasing air-conducted vibrations to such a level that they can activate the oval window directly, without the mediation of the middle-ear bones, may result in severe unpleasantness and even pain. For extreme loss of middle-ear functioning a bone-conduction device may be required.

It was suggested earlier that the difference in sensitivity between the normal auditory mechanism and one without an external or middle ear would be about 30 db. It should be apparent then that by amplifying the

---

* The vestibular organ is the nonauditory portion of the inner ear referred to earlier. Due to its primary involvement in equilibrium and balance, it will be treated in a later chapter.

sound some 30 db and introducing it into the inner ear directly by way of the bones of the skull, hearing should approach normalcy. This is precisely what is done in some cases of severe conduction deafness. A bone-conduction device is placed against the mastoid bone, behind the pinna, and sound vibrations are conducted directly to the inner ear with no need for the middle-ear involvement. There are problems inherent in such a technique. Individual differences exist between heads and mastoid bones, and conduction of sound through bone is not the same as conduction through air. Nevertheless, for the almost totally deaf individual who can adapt to it, a bone-conduction hearing aid may be a very great blessing.

If the deafness is due to inner-ear malfunction (discussed in the next section) any hearing aid may be of little value. Von Békésy suggests that an old test, often used by deaf musicians, was to touch one's teeth to a vibrating musical instrument. If one cannot then hear the music, he knows he suffers from nerve deafness and there is no adequate treatment (von Békésy, 1957).

The Inner Ear

As indicated at the beginning of this chapter, the portion of the inner ear involved in hearing is known as the cochlea. The human cochlea is a tube about ⅛ inch in diameter and perhaps 1⅓ inch long. But, it takes up somewhat less space than this because it is severely coiled in the manner of a snail. The number of turns in the cochlea varies with the species: The guinea pig's cochlea, which is frequently studied in the laboratory, has about four and one-half turns; the human cochlea has about three and one-half turns.

Imbedded deep in the bones of the skull, it is a difficult organ to get at, and its function is not completely understood. For much of what we do know about the cochlea and its functioning we are indebted to the pioneering work of the aforementioned von Békésy. Perhaps no man has so dominated his field and achieved such wide recognition as does Georg von Békésy in the area of auditory functioning.

Scala Vestibuli and Scala Tympani. As can be seen from Fig. 13-2, in which it has been "uncoiled," the cochlea is a two-chambered tube, being divided by a very complex structure identified as the *cochlear partition.* One chamber, the *scala vestibuli,* and the second parallel chamber, the *scala tympani,* are connected at the apex of the tube by the *helicotrema.*

Pistonlike movements of the stapes against the flexible oval window set the fluid (perilymph) in the inner ear into motion, reproducing the wave action of the original sound. These wavelike activities in the fluid proceed to travel the length of the scala vestibuli, through the helicotrema, and down the scala tympani, where they spend themselves against the flexible membrane of the round window. On their way through the entwined cochlea they presumably set up activity in the basilar membrane which serves as the stimulus for hearing.

Figure 13-3 shows a cross section taken through a cochlea. Note that several turns of the cochlea have been transected, exposing the interior of the tube in several places. Note too the helicotrema at the extreme left of the figure.

Basilar Membrane. Figure 13-4 shows a schematic drawing of a cross section taken at one point in the cochlear canal. As described earlier the cochlear canal is divided into two channels by a structure known, not unreasonably, as the cochlear partition. The functional portion of the cochlear partition is the basilar membrane, a tapered structure resting on a bony shelf at one side of the tube and apparently suspended from the other side by a ligamentlike contrivance. While the overall width of the cochlear partition remains constant throughout its length, the basilar membrane is

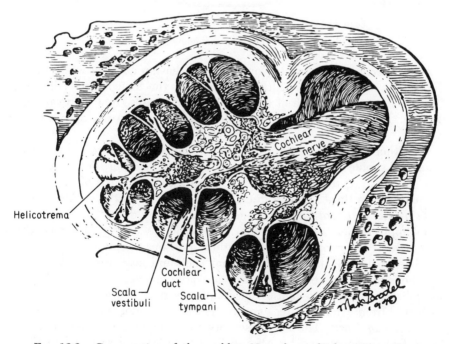

FIG. 13-3. Cross section of the cochlea. Note the multiple cross sections due to the coiling of the organ. Notice too the three ducts and the helicotrema. (From the Otological Research Laboratory and the Department of Art in Medicine, John Hopkins University, *1940 Yearbook of the Eye, Ear, Nose and Throat,* drawn by Max Brodel. Copyright 1940 Yearbook Medical Publishers, Inc. Used by permission.)

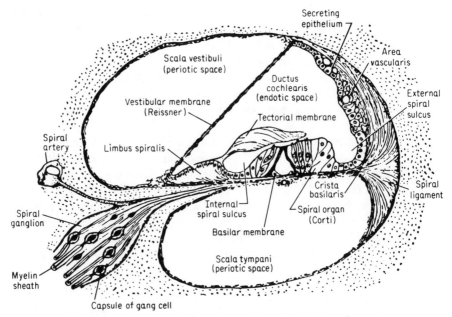

FIG. 13-4.   Cross section of the cochlear canal. (Rasmussen.)

indeed tapered. According to von Békésy, it has an average width of .04 mm at the stapes and a width of 0.5 mm at the helicotrema (Stevens, 1951). Thus, as the width of the membrane increases from the oval window to the helicotrema, the bony shelf on which it rests decreases in width.

Another thin membrane (*Reissner's membrane*) divides the cochlear canal and should be included as a part of the cochlear partition. Anchored near the base of the bony shelf at one side the presence of this membrane creates a third space or duct, known variously as the *cochlear duct, scala media,* or *endotic space.* It gets its last name due to its containing endolymph, rather than perilymph. This basic cavity is continuous with structures of the nonauditory labyrinthine portions of the inner ear.

The basilar membrane, with its bony shelf and suspensory system, and Reissner's membrane team up in a remarkable manner to create a highly specialized chamber to house the delicate, sensitive organs of hearing, protected from external forces and bathed in the endolymphatic fluid.

Organ of Corti. The actual sensory unit in the ear is the organ of Corti, first demonstrated by Alfonso Corti in 1851 and pictured in Figs. 13-4 and 13-5. The organ of Corti is a collection of fleshy cells in the scala media, resting on the basilar membrane and the bony shelf of the cochlear partition. It is, indeed, a remarkable organ. You may recall that the lens of the eye has no blood vessels to interfere with the passage of light.

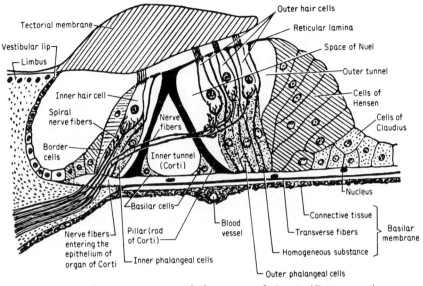

Labels in figure:
Tectorial membrane
Vestibular lip
Limbus
Inner hair cell
Spiral nerve fibers
Border cells
Nerve fibers
Nerve fibers entering the epithelium of organ of Corti
Pillar (rod of Corti)
Inner phalangeal cells
Basilar cells
Inner tunnel (Corti)
Blood vessel
Outer hair cells
Reticular lamina
Space of Nuel
Outer tunnel
Cells of Hensen
Cells of Claudius
Nucleus
Connective tissue
Transverse fibers
Homogeneous substance
Basilar membrane
Outer phalangeal cells

Fig. 13-5. Cross section of the organ of Corti. (Rasmussen.)

Instead, any necessary interchange of nutrient and waste material is accomplished by direct interaction with the intraocular fluid. While there are small blood vessels in the basilar membrane, the organ of Corti has no blood supply. If it had, as sensitive to movement as it is, one would be constantly hearing one's pulse. The amount of movement in even small blood vessels as a result of the pulse would probably be so great as to completely mask out the infinitesimally small movements produced by sound stimuli. Remember that if the ear were any more sensitive you would be hearing the Brownian movement of air molecules. Instead of a vascular supply, the organ of Corti is bathed in the endolymph, a primitive, highly nutritive embryological liquid, thus mitigating the need for any accessory blood supply.

The ultimate end organs in the organ of Corti are the *hair cells*, which are in turn supported by the *phalangeal cells*. There are two distinct groups of hair cells: the outer hair cells, numbering about 20,000, whose phalangeal cells rest on the flexible basilar membrane; and the inner hair cells, numbering about 3,500, whose supporting cells rest on the bony edge of the cochlear partition. These hair cells pass through a perforated layer of cells known as the *reticular lamina* and terminate with their ends imbedded in the *tectorial membrane*. The hair cells are presumably activated as a result of a "shearing" action set up by motion of the fluid of the inner ear. It would appear that the tectorialmembrane, the reticular lamina, and the organ of Corti slide with respect to each other, thus bending the hairs and setting off a neural discharge. Such a "shearing" action in effect serves to greatly amplify the effects of the otherwise insignificant movements in the perilymph.

Von Békésy's efforts with an internal ear removed from a cadaver, as well as his demonstrations with laboratory models were instrumental in our gaining an understanding of just how this remarkable organ of Corti performs its function.*

To complete the anatomical story, individual nerve fibers from the hair cells wend their way through the organ of Corti, meeting near the juncture of the basilar membrane and the bony ledge, from whence they procede, by way of the VIIIth cranial nerve, to the brain.

Disorders of the Inner Ear. Hearing loss due to malfunction of the inner ear is indeed a serious problem. So-called nerve deafness, due to atrophy or disease of the hair cells and their associated neural connections, presents an irreversible condition. Once the neural connections are destroyed nothing can be done; a hearing aid cannot force a nonexistent end organ to fire.

In addition to general circulatory and systemic disease of old age, which may result in "death" of the organ of Corti cells, or the eighth nerve, at least one well-known drug, streptomycin, can produce nerve deafness. When taken to excess over long periods of time, this drug has resulted in numerous cases of deafness due to destruction of neural endings in the inner ear and eighth nerve.

Another cause of deafness attributable to the inner ear can be related to actual damage of the organ of Corti. If the basilar membrane is forced to vibrate violently due to extremely intense acoustic stimulation, hair cells may be physically torn loose from their phalangeal cell roots. Such deafness presents an interesting opportunity, as well as a challenge, to the study of hearing. If the intense sound has a frequency of, say, 1,000 Hz, not all of the hair cells on the basilar membrane will be damaged. Rather, only those in a rather narrowly circumscribed area will be destroyed. Thus the person will be deaf at only 1,000 Hz, and of course, some distance on either side in a more or less graduated manner, depending on the intensity of the sound and the resultant spreading along the basilar membrane.

Such hearing losses are typified by *auditory scotoma,* or "blind" spots in the auditory spectrum. Persons exposed to very intense narrow-band noises such as the compressor whine of a jet engine may lose their hearing over a relatively narrow range of frequencies. If the loss is at a frequency not critical for perceiving speech, the victim may not even know he has sustained inner-ear damage, or that he has a hearing loss.

---

* We will return to the von Békésy explanation when we consider theories of hearing in a later chapter.

A severe ringing sound or a whistling in the ear is a not too uncommon symptom and may or may not herald increasing deafness. Known as *tinnitus,* such symptoms are presumably the result of spontaneous activity, or perhaps hypersensitivity, of the delicate hair cells of the inner ear. There is normally a faint "background" noise anyone can hear if conditions are otherwise sufficiently quiet, but when the condition becomes severe some sort of degeneration is either in progress or has occurred.

As an example, subjection to intense sounds can produce a temporary tinnitus, apparently as a result of mechanical injury to the hair cells of the basilar membrane. It is significant too that the pitch of a tinnitus frequently corresponds to a pitch to which some sensitivity has been lost.

Tinnitus is frequently found in conjunction with Ménière's disease, the vertigo-producing disorder clearly attributable to damage or malfunction of the labyrinthine portion of the auditory nerve. Tumors or other mechanical damage to the auditory nerve also can result in tinnitus.

SUMMARY

In this chapter we first discussed the general development of the ear, with emphasis on the inner ear and its possible evolution from the lateral-line organs of lower animals. We then examined in some detail the three main divisions of the ear: the outer ear, the middle ear, and the inner ear. With respect to the outer ear we considered the pinna, external meatus, and tympanic membrane. For the middle ear we examined the ossicles and how they work; the round and oval windows; the Eustachian tube and its function; and potential disorders of the middle ear. We concluded this section with a discussion of hearing loss due to middle-ear malfunction and the nature of corrective treatment indicated. With respect to the inner ear we described the scala vestibuli, scala tympani, and the interconnecting helicotrema. We described the cochlear partition in some detail, elaborating on the basilar membrane and its organ of Corti with its sensitive hair cells. We concluded the chapter with a discussion of inner-ear disorders.

SUGGESTED READINGS

1. Von Békésy, Georg, "The Ear," *Scientific American,* August 1957. A short article of 10 pages, well worth reading. Professor Békésy points out some of the wonders of the auditory mechanism, describes the structure of the ear, and elaborates on a number of topics such as hearing pitch, hearing speech, vocal feedback, auditory localization, and deafness. It is a short

article that anyone can read, understand, and profit from. It is highly recommended.

2. Von Békésy, Georg and W. A. Rosenblith, "The Mechanical Properties of the Ear," in S. S. Stevens (ed.), *Handbook of Experimental Psychology* (New York: Wiley, 1951). These 38 pages are by far the best detailed descriptions of the human ear of which I am aware. Indeed, this chapter goes into fine detail to an extent not normally required for general understanding of the ear's functioning. However, for an advanced, complete understanding of the manner in which the ear functions, this chapter has no peer. Detailed reading is for the serious, advanced student.

3. From W. A. Van Bergeijk, J. R. Pierce, and E. E. David, Jr., *Waves and the Ear* (Garden City, N.Y.: Doubleday Anchor Books, 1960). Chapter V of this excellent little book is a fine, highly readable presentation of the development and structure of the mammalian ear. In addition, this chapter contains much of the information related to theories of hearing which we will cover in a later chapter. These 40 pages are well worth reading.

4. From C. G. Mueller, *Sensory Psychology* (Englewood Cliffs, N.J.: Prentice-Hall, 1965). Chapter 4 of this paperback is the shortest reference I have included for this chapter (8 pages). It is well worth reading, however, especially the treatment of cochlear partition activity and the neural response.

5. Various authors, from Békésy Commemorative Issue, *J. Acoust. Soc. Am.* 34, (1962), 9 (Part 2). This is a complete issue of the journal dedicated to von Békésy to celebrate his winning of the Nobel prize in physiology and medicine. The original articles by pupils and contemporaries of von Békésy are of considerable value for the serious student.

6. Von Békésy, Georg, *Experiments in Hearing*, trans. E. G. Wever (New York: McGraw-Hill, 1960). This book of some 700 pages represents the collected works of Georg von Békésy. It is well worth reading if you are seriously interested in just how the ear works. Chapters 1 through 6 (205 pages) are particularly germane to the material covered in this chapter. Chapter 1 presents some fascinating historical perspective, while Chapters 1, 2, and 3 delve into the anatomy of the ear and the techniques, apparatus, etc., used for its investigation. Chapters 5 and 6 on middle-ear action and bone conduction are well worth reading. The last four chapters (11–14) provide, by far, the best description of cochlear action available. This is not an easy book. It is comprehensive, and for the serious student it is very important.

14

AUDITORY SENSITIVITY AND LOUDNESS

The attribute of hearing, corresponding to the visual attribute of brightness, is that of loudness. Like brightness, loudness is related to the intensity of the impinging stimulation. Before examining the psychological attribute of loudness, let us start at the beginning—the actual detection and recognition of intensity as a parameter of an auditory stimulus.

THRESHOLD FOR HEARING

The absolute sensitivity of the ear is evaluated in terms of absolute thresholds over a wide range of frequencies. Individual determinations are made of the minimal sound pressure that can be detected for each of a number of pure tones, ranging from perhaps a low of 30 or 40 Hz to a high of 10,000 Hz or higher. When these individual thresholds, expressed in decibels re .0002 dyne/cm^2, are plotted, the result is a curve of sensitivity. (See the solid line of Fig. 14-1 for a curve based on a "normal" ear.)* Any loss of hearing ability will show up as departures from the shape and location of the curve found for the normal or "ideal" individual.

Various psychophysical techniques may be employed in obtaining the data for plotting such a curve, or for clinical applications in which interest is focused on hearing loss, or departure from the "normal."

One common procedure for collecting such data involves a form of the method of limits, in which a signal below threshold is gradually increased in intensity until the subject gives a positive response. Descending series can also be included to "bracket" the threshold or 50 percent detection point. (See Chapter 3, especially Fig. 3-3.) The signal may be a continuous tone, or be presented in discrete pulses of tone, with durations such as one second, for example.

---

* *Normal,* as used here, does not really mean normal in the sense of the average. Rather, it is the "norm" for the ideal ear, based on young, healthy, almost perfect ears. As we will see later, few older persons exhibit hearing that meets this criterion.

Fig. 14-1. Sensitivity curve for the "normal" ear. This figure shows the absolute threshold as a standard for comparison. It is *not* the threshold curve for the average person, rather, it is an agreed upon standard which only a few, young persons attain. Most individuals will not achieve this ideal.

As an alternative, a constant method may be employed in which numerous signals are presented in random order, some above the threshold and some below, the subject simply indicating where he hears the tone. In some cases a light may indicate when the subject should hear the tone. The absolute threshold is then determined in the manner described in Chapter 3 and illustrated by Fig. 3-4.

Finally, a production or adjustment method may be used. In this case the testee physically adjusts the level of the tone until he can just hear it. Bracketing can also be employed in this method, in that the subject might finally set the level to some rather arbitrary point which he considers to be his "threshold."

Equipment used to determine thresholds and ultimately plot sensitivity curves may vary widely. In one approach, loudspeakers driven by audio oscillators and associated amplifiers are used. More often calibrated headphones are employed, the tones being injected directly into the listener's ear. In Chapter 12 we learned how headphones are calibrated, utilizing couplers which simulate the external-ear cavity and headphones with inputs from audio signal generators.

The suggestion that methods employing either loudspeakers or headphones may be used may seem to imply that the choice is simply procedural and the same results will be obtained in either case. This is not so.

Sensitivity curves obtained by the two methods are not directly comparable. We may examine briefly the differences between *minimum audible fields* (MAF), obtained by placing an individual in a previously calibrated sound field, and *minimum audible pressure* (MAP), obtained by measuring the actual level at the eardrum by means of a probe microphone or a coupler-calibrated headphone. Incidentally, Fig. 14-2 shows four "standard" curves obtained by several experimenters, two by the MAF technique and two by the MAP procedure.

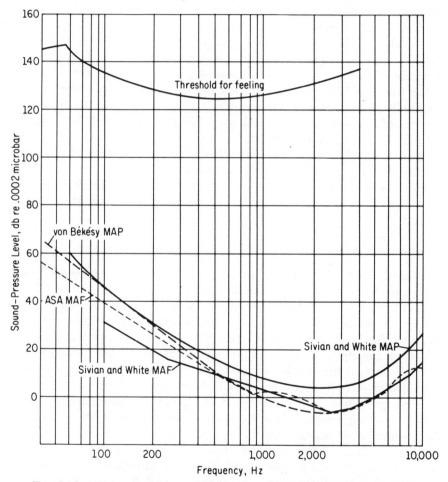

FIG. 14-2. Representative sensitivity curves. Two threshold determinations by each method, minimum audible field and minimum audible pressure, are illustrated. In addition, the curve at the top of the figure is a representation of the approximate threshold for feeling based on several determinations. See text for discussion. (Modified from Stevens 1951.)

Minimum Audible Field

It might seem logical that this technique would be most realistic, determining the sound level at a point in an open space and then placing the listener at this point. When this is done, the plot of thresholds is likely to look somewhat like the two curves of Fig. 14-2 identified as MAF measurements. Note that they are not smooth curves throughout their range. In the vicinity of 1,000 to 3,000 Hz they seem to have perturbations in their otherwise smooth functions. It is unlikely that the physiological response of the ear itself should show such discontinuities. When the head is placed in a free field of sound, the field is no longer a free field. The head (and the rest of the body, for that matter) have an influence on the field due to reflection and absorption which cannot be predicted precisely. Moreover, variations in the configuration of the external portion of the ear would be expected to influence the nature of pure tones in a nonpredictable manner. In some cases this might be just the problem one wishes to investigate. For such purposes a free-field technique would not only be desirable, but necessary.

Note too that facilities for conducting minimum audible field measurements should insure control of echoes and reverberations. A truly anechoic chamber is a must for valid free-field measurements. As a result, free-field measurements are more of academic and scientific than of practical interest.

Minimum Audible Pressure

Thresholds for hearing and subsequent clinical audiograms are more commonly based on minimum audible pressures, in which the threshold level at the eardrum itself is determined. As described in Chapter 12, this can be accomplished by means of a probe microphone which actually measures the level at a point very close to the eardrum, or by means of calibrated headphones the outputs of which have been determined precisely. Actual thresholds can be determined by any of the previously described psychophysical methods which are appropriate.

Perhaps "determined precisely" in the preceding paragraph is somewhat too strong a term. Microphones intended for use with couplers in the calibration of phones may be accurate to 0.1 db. Measurements of hearing sensitivity, however, rarely have precisions greater than two or three db. For practical purposes, and due to uncontrollable variables, any clinical audiogram that reports accuracies beyond 5 db is probably suspect. If you have a hearing loss of 20 db at some frequency this is really a loss someplace in the range of 15 to 25 db. Sensitivity curves vary rather substantially from day to day and from test method to test method, and any more precise statement should not generally be made. For practical purposes, differences of less than 10 db are not particularly significant.

AUDIOMETRY

When the data are to be used for clinical purposes and the interest is in hearing loss, rather than sensitivity, they are not normally plotted in the form of Figs. 14-1 or 14-2. Rather, they are plotted directly in decibels of hearing loss. (See Figs. 14-3 and 14-4.)

While the audiologist may use the equipments and techniques just described, it is more likely that he will employ a commercial audiometer that does much of the routine work automatically. Some, complete with calibrated headphones, vary intensity and frequency automatically, even plotting the final audiogram as a function of the patient's signals (e.g., key depressions). If you have your ears checked by a professional he will in all likelihood use some sort of automatic or semiautomatic audiometer, thus eliminating much of the tedium of manual calculations, frequency adjustments, and output level settings as well as the recording of responses and plotting the data.

Masking Noise

Quite frequently in the application of MAP techniques the audiologist may introduce a simultaneous masking signal in the ear opposite the one being tested. If the sensitivity of one ear is quite low, elevating a signal to the point where it is detectable may very well result in its being heard by the good ear by way of bone conduction. Since the listener cannot always be sure which ear is doing the hearing, determination of thresholds for relatively insensitive ears would be impossible.

In order to avoid this problem, random or white noise may be introduced in the good ear while the test signal is injected into the less sensitive ear. One can utilize a masking signal for the opposite ear in all testing if he so wishes. Of course, the masking noise must not be so intense as to stimulate the ear being tested.

Hearing Loss

The dotted line of Fig. 14-1 shows an audiogram of a person with a mild hearing loss. The individual has normal* hearing for most of the audio spectrum, but at frequencies above about 2,000 Hz the threshold has been elevated. That is, sensitivity has been reduced. While the normal individual can detect a 10,000-Hz tone of about 26 db, the ear identified by the broken line requires that a tone of 10,000 Hz be some 10 db more

* Recall our earlier definition of "normal."

intense in order to be detected. Hearing loss such as this appears to be an inexorable result of the aging process and most individuals of 30 or 40 years of age might be expected to show a loss comparable to that of the broken line in Fig. 14-1. With increasing age the loss can be expected to be greater, both in degree and in that it will spread to somewhat lower frequencies. A loss such as shown here would not be of any great consequence, and the individual would in all likelihood not even be aware of it unless he were quite young, and perhaps a musician.

If a sufficiently large number of points are plotted (measuring the threshold for more pure tones) the curve will take on a less regular form. There may be dips and humps, all indicating minor variations in the sensitivity curve.

If there are severe perturbations in the shape of the curve, indicating sharp losses of hearing sensitivity in relatively restricted frequency ranges, a more serious hearing loss may be indicated. If the curve at, say, 400 Hz suddenly rises to the 60-db level, then a loss of some 42-db for a 400-Hz tone is involved. Such uncommon instances are probably due to localized damage in the basilar membrane of the cochlea, rather than the simple conduction deficiencies leading to the broken line in the figure.

In practice, audiograms are generally plotted in terms of hearing *loss,* rather than sensitivity. Figure 14-3 is an example of how an actual hearing

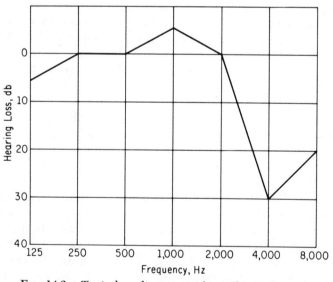

Fig. 14-3. Typical audiogram with moderate hearing loss. Note that the loss of about 30 db is in the vicinity of 4,000 Hz with sensitivity to the 8,000-Hz tone being somewhat better.

loss might be plotted. Notice that it is based on seven pure tones and that measurements are given only to the nearest 5 db, in keeping with our previous observations of precision of audiometric measurements. If more detailed analysis of the 30 db loss at 4,000 Hz were desired, additional pure tones could be employed for detailed exploration. Notice too that this individual has somewhat better than normal sensitivity at 1,000 Hz.

Figure 14-4 shows the manner in which hearing loss develops as a function of age. Included in this figure are differences due to sex. Are sex differences due to genetic characteristics or to the fact that men live somewhat different lives than women? Perhaps men are subjected to more severe noises in their workaday lives than are women, or perhaps the difference is due to biological factors. In Fig. 13-4 it appears that even in the youngest group the males have less sensitivity at the higher frequencies than their female counterparts. At older ages this difference becomes more marked. It may be both genetic and environmental.

FIG. 14-4. Hearing loss as a function of age and sex. Note the sharp fall-off in the case of the 50-59 year group. Notice too that the losses for women tend to be somewhat less than those for men. (Adapted from Steinberg, Montgomery, and Gardner, 1940, copyright, The American Telephone and Telegraph Co., reprinted by permission.)

The data from which this figure was drawn were collected at the New York and San Francisco World's Fairs and might be considered to be representative of people in general. There has been some criticism of the procedures used, and the actual values may be more suggestive than definitive, but I suspect the curves are not too far from the real truth. More recent but less extensive studies tend to bear out these earlier findings.

ADDITIONAL INTENSITY CONSIDERATIONS

A Bit of Terminology

Several terms are frequently encountered with respect to auditory stimulation which might best be clarified at this time. *Monaural* and *binaural* probably need no explanation, they simply refer to the use of one ear or two, and are basically laymen's terms. *Stereophonic*, primarily a hi-fi term, refers to binaural listening in which differences in the signals to the two ears, normally experienced as a result of the location of the ears on the head, are simulated by means of separate speakers, separate headphones, or the like.

You may also encounter the terms *Monotic, diotic,* and *dichotic.* Monotic simply means the stimulation of one ear, and is essentially the same as monaural. Diotic and dichotic both refer to binaural stimulation, but they differ in that diotic refers to situations in which the stimulus signal is the same to both ears and dichotic refers to stimulation which is different to the two ears. If we stimulate both ears with a 300-Hz tone of the same sound-pressure level, we would be employing diotic presentation; if we give a 300-Hz tone to one ear and a 500-Hz tone to the other, we would be employing dichotic stimulation.

Monaural vs. Binaural Thresholds

It has been recognized for some time that the absolute threshold for a pure tone is somewhat better—that is, lower, if two ears are employed, rather than one. The normally encountered advantage for the binaural (diotic) condition is generally on the order of 2 to 4 db with 3 db as the average. It was only natural to attribute such "binaural summation" to the central nervous system.

In the light of recent contributions of those psychophysicists who espouse the signal-detection approach (see Chapter 4) a better explanation appears possible. The threshold for detecting a signal with one ear is defined as the 50 percent point, that signal which can be detected 50 percent of the time.* But look what happens when you use two ears: at a given level (if the two ears have similar sensitivities) each ear will provide a 50-50 chance of detection. Hence the likelihood of a positive report is much greater when two ears are used, purely on a probability basis. It is really not unlike tossing two coins at the same time. The probability of getting "heads" will be appreciably greater than if only one coin were tossed. The advantage of binaural over monaural detection is very nearly what would be predicted on the basis of the increased probability when two ears were used. A concept of binaural summation becomes quite un-unnecessary.

Difference Thresholds for Sound Intensity

One might assume that the determination of minimum detectable differences in the intensity (the experience of loudness) of two tones would be rather straightforward. In practice such a determination is not at all simple and straightforward. We know that DL's in general are influenced by the duration of the stimuli, their temporal separations, and various other experimentally controlled parameters. In the case of sound amplitude and the resultant loudness experience, many of these changes may also change the physical nature of the sound waves. Hence any determination of difference thresholds for sound intensity is highly dependent upon the technique employed; and various investigators may very well get highly divergent results.

Probably the most often cited research on DL's for intensity is the work of Riesz (1928). In order to avoid many of the pitfalls of induced transients, frequency changes, and the like, and having determined the optimum rate for intensity change was three per second, Riesz produced intensity changes by a technique involving *beats*.† A pure tone of a given frequency was paired with a second tone differing from the first by precisely three cycles per second. Thus the two tones interacted, providing augmentation and partial cancellation at a rate of three cycles per second. The resultant experience is one of a tone changing in intensity (or beating) at a rate of three times per second. The difference in level between the partially canceled and the augmented component was the intensity difference being investigated. By changing the intensity levels of the paired tones while holding the frequency difference constant, the threshold for intensity was obtained. When the subject could just hear the beats, he was operating at the threshold for intensity change.

---

* With some techniques, the threshold determination is based on a ratio other than 50/50 in order to allow for chance. Such procedures merely shift the calculated threshold; they do not eliminate the increased probability for two-ear detection.

† The problem of beats is considered in more detail in the following chapter.

Fig. 14-5. Difference thresholds for intensity of pure tones. Increments to various levels, shown on the abscissa, were obtained by a method of beats for four frequencies: 70, 200, 1,000, and 4,000 Hz. (Adapted from Riesz, 1928.)

Some of Riesz's results are shown in Fig. 14-5. The curve for the 4,000-Hz tone shows the highest discriminability. Had we included higher frequencies, their curves would have been similar to those for the lower frequencies, peak discriminabilities being in the 1,000–4,000-Hz range. Note too that for low levels such as 5 and 10 db, increments on the order of 3 db or higher are required in order for the subject to detect a difference. Recall that 3 db is a doubling of power. At a level of 15 db a 70-Hz tone must be doubled in power (3-db increase) in order to be recognized as being louder. At the other extreme a 0.2-db increase, such as required for a 4,000-Hz tone at 90-db sound-pressure level, represents a ratio of 1.05 to 1.00.

Temporary Threshold Shifts (tts)

When we studied the function of the eye and the retina we discovered the existence of remarkable adaptation effects which we likened somewhat to fatigue, based on reversible catabolic/anabolic chemical processes. Does the ear fatigue in the same way? The ear is basically a mechanical transducer rather than a chemical device, as was the case for the rods and cones; hence the same sort of adaptation would not be expected to occur, and indeed does not. There are, however, changes in sensitivity as a result of exposure to sound.

We have already indicated how permanent changes in sensitivity may result from damage to the inner ear as a result of its being subjected to intense sounds. We also indicated that, within limits, such damage to the ear is related to the duration and even lifetime exposure to inordinately intense sounds. In addition to these permanent shifts in threshold, exposure to sounds can also result in temporary changes in sensitivity—known, not unreasonably, as *temporary threshold shifts* (tts).

Figure 14-6 shows one example of the nature and magnitude of such shifts (Lüscher and Zwislocki, 1947). In this experiment the ear was stimulated by a very short, 0.4-second burst of a fatiguing or preconditioning tone, followed after an interval by a determination of the absolute threshold. The different curves in this figure are for various intensities of the preconditioning tone, expressed in conventional decibel units. For time intervals between the fatiguing stimulus and the test stimulus of a duration greater than perhaps 200 milliseconds, only a slight shift still remains, even for the more intense preconditioning tone.

Because of its implications for an understanding of the functioning of the ear, research on tts has been quite widespread in recent years.

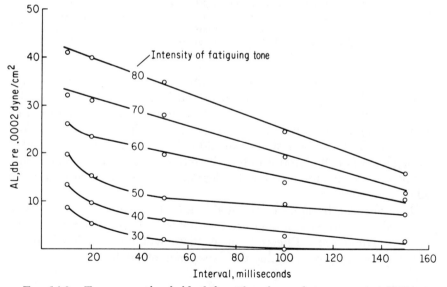

Fig. 14-6. Temporary threshold shifts. The observed increases in absolute threshold were obtained as a result of a short preconditioning exposure to tones ranging from 30- to 80-db sensation level. (From J. J. Zwislocki, *Acta otolaryng.*, 1947, with permission.)

Frequencies, levels, and time intervals have been manipulated and a wealth of recent literature has resulted.

As a recent example of research on tts, Fig. 14-7, based on the work of Bell and Fairbanks (1963), indicates that some shift does indeed remain

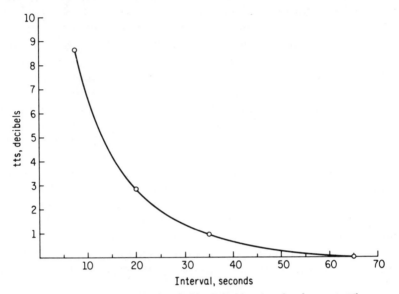

FIG. 14-7. Temporary threshold shifts for low-level tones. The results are based on the pooling of several frequencies and levels. Note the relatively long time intervals and the lower amounts of tts as contrasted with Fig. 14-6. (From Bell and Fairbanks, 1963, with permission.)

for quite an appreciable time, measurable in seconds rather than the millisecond durations found by Lüscher and Zwislocki. The curve in this figure is based on a variety of low-level fatiguing conditions appreciably greater than the 0.4-second bursts explored by Lüscher and Zwislocki. Results shown for both these studies should only be considered as examples, and suggestive of the interest in tts. The interested serious student should consult the recent literature for developments in this fascinating area of auditory research.

It might also be appropriate at this time to point out that shifts in perceived pitch, as well as intensity thresholds, can result from prolonged pure-tone stimulation. Effects such as these will be considered in the next chapter when we examine the experience of pitch.

LOUDNESS

Up to this point we have been dealing predominantly with the physical nature of sound; physiological ramifications, and to some extent the psychophysics of hearing. What about the latter? How is the experience of sound intensity, which we call loudness, related to the amplitude or intensity of the sound waves? We might surmise on the basis of our earlier experiences that the relationship would not be perfect. That is, doubling the intensity of a sound might not be expected to result in doubling of loudness. Let us examine the concept of loudness in some detail.

Equal-Loudness Contours and Phons

It is possible to determine various frequencies and intensities of tones which appear equally loud to a listener. Such a procedure is the basis for the development of the *equal-loudness contours* shown in Figs. 14-8 and

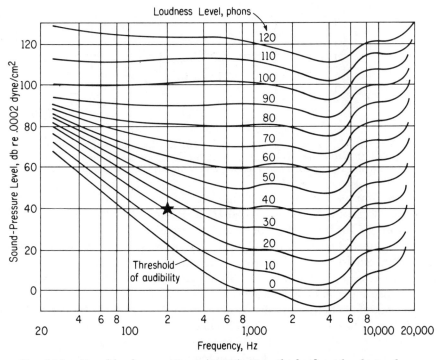

FIG. 14-8. Equal-loudness contours (MAF). Note the loudness levels, in phons, from 0 to 120. (From Fletcher, 1940, with permission.)

14-9. The term *isophonic contours* is used interchangeably with equal-loudness contours, and means exactly the same thing.

Determination of Isophonic Contours. The rationale for the computation of equal-loudness contours is quite straightforward. To begin with, before we can develop a mathematical scale of loudness which has units that can be manipulated we need a scale of the basic psychophysical

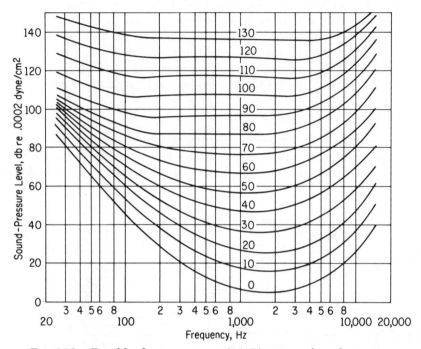

Fig. 14-9. Equal-loudness contours (MAP). Note that the contour labeled 0 is the threshold for hearing for the normal subject. (From Stevens and Davis, 1948 and Fletcher and Munson, 1933, with permission.)

relations. The most obvious starting point for such a scale would be the absolute threshold. And, since 1,000 Hz is a convenient even number and very close to the frequency of maximum sensitivity, what better point could be selected for the starting point of a loudness scale? A tone of 1,000 Hz at threshold was arbitrarily assigned the value of 1, or in the logarithmic scale, 0. A level of 10 db above threshold would therefore be 10 db more intense, or have a loudness level of 10 db. It was a relatively simple matter to determine just how intense, in db above their absolute thresholds, other frequencies would have to be raised in order to be equivalent in loudness to a 1,000-Hz tone of a specified level.

Let us look at Fig. 14-8. Each contour line in this figure represents a single loudness level, with the lowermost contour, labeled 0, being the threshold of audibility. This line is the same line found as an average from Fig. 14-2, and any point on this line will represent the threshold for that particular frequency. Let us examine additional contours—that labeled 40, for example. Any point on this line will have the same loudness level. A 1,000-Hz tone at an intensity level of 40 db has the same loudness level as an 80-Hz tone at an intensity level of about 52 db. Expressed in other words, an 80-Hz tone must be 25 db more intense than a 1,000-Hz tone in order to have the same loudness level, and a 10,000-Hz tone must be 12 db more intense to achieve the same loudness level.

Notice that each of the successive isophonic contours does indeed pass through the 1,000-Hz point with equal increments. That is, the contour labeled 20 passes through the 1,000-Hz line at a level of 20 db, the contour labeled 30 passes through the 1,000-Hz point at a 30-db level, and so on, to the limit of the diagram. This is the basis for the identification and labeling of the contours: the loudness of a 1,000-Hz tone at a given sound-pressure level.

The contours are identified in terms of *phons*. Thus, a 60-phon tone is one that has the same loudness level as a 1,000-Hz tone of 60-db sound-pressure level. A 100-Hz tone with a sound pressure level of 71 db, a 400-Hz tone with a sound-pressure level of 61 db, and a 6,000-Hz tone with a level of 68 db would all have the same loudness level—60 phons.*

Figure 14-9, like Fig. 14-8, also shows equal loudness contours, but for minimum audible pressures rather than minimum audible fields. Most of what has been said concerning minimum audible fields also applies to minimum audible pressure measurements. Indeed, the curious shape of the equal-loudness contours for MAF measurements, especially at the high frequencies, might lead one to the conclusion that MAP techniques might better be employed to assign values for equal-loudness-level contours.

Practical Applications of Isophonic Contours. The concept of equal-loudness contours is of more than simple academic or scientific interest. It has very practical ramifications. Look at Fig. 14-8 again. Suppose you are listening to music from your radio or hi-fi at a relatively high loudness level, say 90 phons. The appropriate curve indicates that your ear has about the same sensitivity throughout the audio spectrum, at least for the frequencies below several thousand Hz, where most musical tones are to be found. What happens if you reduce the volume of your amplifier by 50 db in order to provide simply background music, or to mollify complaining neighbors? If you do this note that a tone of 200 Hz will drop in loudness level from 90 phons to—not 40 phons, but 20 phons (the star on Fig. 13-8)! Considering the ambient noise in the room, the 200-Hz component of the music will in all likelihood be completely inaudible.

If you are a music lover and do not wish to lose the subtle components of the lower-register instruments, you may turn up the bass control of

* Another term frequently encountered in conjunction with loudness level is *sensation level*. The sensation level of any sound is the pressure level of the sound in decibels above its absolute threshold. In Fig. 14-8 a 100-Hz tone of 60 phons would have a sensation level of about 34 db—that is, a sound-pressure level of 72 db compared to the threshold level of 38 db (72 minus 38 equals 34) for the frequency under consideration.

your amplifier, thus compensating for the frequency-sensitivity characteristics of your ear. As can be better seen in Fig. 14-9 some loss of
high-frequency components may also occur, but these are probably of
less interest to you. You might of course increase your separate treble
control to compensate for their loss if you so desired.

Modern hi-fi amplifiers often have a separate control, commonly
called a "loudness" control, which does this shaping of the audio output
automatically. If your loudness control is in the "on" position, reducing the
level simultaneously activates an electronic filtering-shaping circuit which
results in less attenuation of the lower frequencies than those nearer the
center of the spectrum. Thus a reduction in overall sound level does not
result in loss of the lower-frequency components of the complex audio
signal.

You may recall that references were made earlier to the existence of
different modes, commonly called A, B, and C, for use of sound-pressure-
level meters. These modes provide varying amounts of the shaping function for the differential sensitivities of the ear for different overall sound
levels. The A-scale setting, for example, may be used for levels below
40-db sound pressure level. By utilizing these correction positions, readings on the instrument do indeed compare favorably with apparent sound
levels sensed by the human ear.

Subjective Loudness and Sones

As suggested in earlier chapters, the ultimate aim of any sensory/
perceptual researcher is to relate the physical world to the world of experience. The system of phons does indeed relate sound intensities to
loudness level at the psychophysical level. But what about the subjective,
experiential, psychological level? Can we develop a sensory scale which
is indeed a ratio scale, a scale with units that can be added, substracted,
and otherwise manipulated mathematically, like dollars or apples? Expressed another way, can one sensation be twice as great as another? in the
case of loudness, considerable progress has been made.

By means of some of the scaling techniques described in Chapter 4,
such as single-stimulus estimation and fractionation methods, numerous
investigators have attempted to develop ratio scales for loudness. The
ratio scale developed by Fletcher and Munson in 1933, based largely on
fractionation techniques, was a major milestone. Perhaps the greatest
contribution was made by S. S. Stevens, who in 1936 gathered together
and analyzed much of the diverse literature, including some of his own,
developing a loudness scale with units he called *sones*.

A sone, as defined by Stevens, is the loudness of a 1,000-Hz, tone 40 db
above threshold (40 phons). The curve of Fig. 14-10 shows subjective

FIG. 14-10. Subjective loudness in sones. Note the difference in the relationship between phons and sones for the two parts of the curve, as indicated
by the dotted lines.

loudness in sones, plotted against loudness level in phons. While this
curve was based on the addition of two tones, there is evidence that the
relation holds for combinations of more than two tones.*

Note that while a tone of 2 sones is twice as loud (subjectively) as a
tone of one sone, an increase of about 9 db in loudness level is required
to obtain this doubling of subjective loudness. While this general relationship appears to hold for sounds of relatively high intensity, at lower
levels subjective loudness in sones increases somewhat more rapidly than
loudness level in phons.

ADDITIONAL SUBJECTIVE ATTRIBUTES

The reader should be familiar with several other intensity related
attributes of sound, if only to clarify layman-scientist differences in mean-
ings.

Volume is an experience frequently alluded to when what we really

---

* Addition of pure tones in this fashion assumes that the tones are of the same
frequency and do not interact in any complex way. When combining tones of different frequencies (or the same frequency but differing phases), numerous complications such as beats, difference tones or masking greatly complicate the results and
simple additive characteristics do not obtain. Some of the complications encountered
in combining tones with different parameters are considered in the next chapter.

mean is sound intensity, or perhaps loudness. As implied before, the previously mentioned volume control on your amplifier is not a volume control at all, but rather a sound intensity control, or a loudness control, as the case may be. To the psychophysicist, volume is a true attribute of sound, referring to the "size or extensity" of the sound. It is a subjective attribute in the truest sense of the word and may even be related to our knowledge of the source of the sound. The output of a tuba has more volume than that of a flute, and part of this difference may indeed be due to our knowledge of the appearance of the two instruments. Yet some researchers have been able to develop scales of volume, based on subjective judgments of listeners, which seem to be independent of simple loudness or pitch and are not dependent on the identification of specific tonal sources.

Other attributes which have been investigated include *density* and *brightness*. Stevens (1944), for example, was able to obtain contours for equal-density and equal brightness as well as equal-volume contours. Later suggestions indicate that perhaps density and brightness may be simply different words for the same experiential dimension.

SUMMARY

In this chapter we have examined quantitative auditory experience as it relates to the physical world. We examined first the nature of the absolute threshold for hearing, describing techniques involving minimum audible fields and minimum audible pressures. We looked into audiometric procedures and the determination of hearing loss. We then considered several aspects of auditory sensitivity such as difference thresholds, and shifts in sensitivity due to prior tonal subjection. Finally we examined the overall area of loudness, describing the nature of equal-loudness contours and how they are derived, as well as the more subjective scales of loudness based on the unit of loudness, the sone. In addition to describing some applications of loudness data, we concluded with a cursory look at several additional subjective attributes related to the intensity of auditory stimuli.

SUGGESTED READINGS

1. From M. Lawrence, "Hearing," in M. Alpern, M. Lawrence, and D. Wolsk, *Sensory Processes* (Belmont, Calif.: Brooks/Cole, 1967). Pages 65–101 are concerned with hearing. This is a relatively easy reference and well worth reading in detail. The first 20 pages of this chapter are particulary relevant to the material covered in our Chapter 14.

2. Licklider, J. C. R., "Basic Correlates of the Auditory Stimulus," in S. S. Stevens (ed.), *Handbook of Experimental Psychology* (New York: Wiley, 1951). These 50 pages present just about as thorough a description of auditory sensory/perceptual processes as any with which I am familiar. The material included covers both this chapter and the following chapter on pitch perception. As a result, the reader should probably read selectively, since the order of presentation differs from that of this book. The interested student should be familiar with Professor Licklider's excellent chapter in this handbook. It is well worth reading and also invaluable for future reference.

3. Hirsh, I. J., *The Measurement of Hearing* (New York: McGraw-Hill, 1952). An excellent book, somewhat technical, perhaps, but ideally suited for the interested student. With its emphasis on clinical audiology and hearing loss, it is particularly relevant to the preceding chapter. I recommend this reference as a source-book, rather than for general reading. Its wealth of informative material is useful when needed for a particular application.

4. Stevens, S. S., "A Scale for the Measurement of a Psychological Magnitude: Loudness," *Psychol. Rev.* 43 (1936), 405–16. This reference is included to give the reader a "feel" for the general area of scaling psychological attributes. This reading and the two to follow should provide enough background for the interested reader to pursue the problem of sensory scaling to any depth he might desire.

5. Stevens, S. S., "The Attributes of Tones," *Proc. nat. Acad. Sci.* 20, (1934), 467–69. See preceding reference for description of this article.

6. Stevens, S. S., "The Psychophysics of Sensory Function," in W. A. Rosenblith (ed.), *Sensory Communication* (New York: Wiley, 1961). This article, in a large sense, summarizes the work of Stevens and is probably the most significant and important of the three Stevens references included. For the seriously interested student.

15

AUDITORY SENSITIVITY AND PITCH

Just as loudness is the psychological attribute for sound intensity, so is *pitch* the psychological attribute for sound quality. Pitch is related to the frequency of the sound waves much like hue is related to the wavelength (or frequency) of electromagnetic radiation. As can be seen from Fig. 14-1, the human ear can hear sounds produced by mechanical waves from roughly 20 Hz to as rapid as 20,000 Hz, for the young, healthy ear. Some animals, like dogs and bats, are sensitive to sounds with frequencies above 20,000, but man can rarely hear sounds above this limit. Moreover, the bottom cutoff is not always clearly defined. At some low-frequency sound becomes vibration or perhaps pulsation; and the rough "sounds" below 30 Hz, when sensed, might better be called something other than "sound." Indeed, they may owe their being sensed to something akin to a tactual vibratory sense, rather than hearing.

SCALES OF PITCH

There are two historic approaches to the scaling of pitch. The oldest and most widely accepted is the musical scale, which has existed in numerous forms since antiquity.

Musical Scale

The pitch scale with which we are most familiar is that of the musical scale, based on octaves or powers of two. Each "do" of the scale represents a doubling of the frequency. If middle C on the scale is assigned a frequency of 256 Hz, then C above middle C will have a frequency of 512 Hz, the C one octave higher will be 1,024 Hz, etc. With a little practice we can detect a resemblance among the various C's, or any other selected note on the scale.

Aristotle recognized many years ago that the octave is probably "native," in that voices of different register tend to harmonize in octave separations (Boring, 1942). On the other hand, the (to our ears) curious

276

musical scales developed by Oriental cultures and the subjective/psycho-physical scale, described in the next section, do not completely support such a simple explanation.

In a book of this scope we cannot examine in any great detail the development of musical scales, nor indeed, the voluminous history of music. The interested reader is directed to the many excellent descriptions and accounts of the history of musical development. As a starting point, Boring's chapter listed in the suggestive readings is recommended. If you are interested in historical perspective, Boring's references at the end of his Chapter 9 are especially valuable.

The Mel Scale

Perhaps, as Licklider suggests (Stevens, 1952), there are two scales of frequency sensitivity: one based on the quality of tones, called *tone chroma* or *tonality*, and applicable to musical scales, the other based on psychophysical measurements and called *pitch*. It is the latter which concerns us in the following paragraphs.

While we found loudness to be a function of both frequency and sound intensity, the experience of pitch appears to be somewhat more simple, with only slight dependence on intensity. We do know that pure tones below about 500 Hz sound lower in pitch when their intensities are increased, and pure tones above 3,000 Hz sound somewhat sharper when their intensities are increased. The differences are relatively slight, however, and for the middle frequencies of primary interest, pitch is to all intents and purposes a function of frequency.

In 1937 Stevens, Volkmann, and Newman published their scale of pitch, with the unit of pitch being called a *mel*. As a result of additional data collection and refinement, the current form of the scale was published by the first two authors in 1940. (See Fig. 15-1.) For the purposes of the scale, the pitch of a 1,000-Hz tone, 40 db above threshold, was assigned the value of 1,000 mels and the remainder of the points were plotted as a result of many fractionations and bisections of subjective pitch. A frequency which sounded half as high in pitch was given the value 500 mels, and so on, until the entire range was encompassed.

Note that a tone of 400 Hz has a mel value of 500, while a 1,000-Hz tone is 1,000 mels. Thus a 1,000-Hz tone has a pitch twice as high as a 400-Hz tone, not a 500-Hz tone as might be naively expected.

The controversy between the musical scale and the mel scale may not be entirely resolved, but there are some additional findings which appear germane, and seem to indicate that the mel scale is more than a strained attempt to quantify something which cannot in fact be quantified. For example, the DL or just noticeable difference for pitch is almost

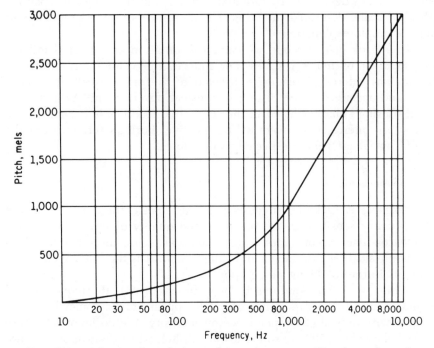

FIG. 15-1.   Relation of pitch (in mels) to frequency. (Based on data of
Stevens and Volkman, 1940, with permission.)

always a constant number of mels, actually about 1/20. The critical bandwidth within which the loudness of tones fails to add (to be considered
later in this chapter) is about one mel. A critical bandwidth for masking
(also to be considered later) is a constant number of mels wide. And,
finally, frequency ranges which contribute equally to speech intelligibility
are very nearly the same width in units of mels. As van Bergeijk et al.
(1960) point out, it is unlikely that such agreement is purely accidental.

DIFFERENCE THRESHOLDS FOR PITCH

When we suggested that the determination of DL's for intensity was
difficult because of unpredictable changes in the tone as a result of temporal manipulations, we were anticipating similar or even greater difficulties in the determination of difference thresholds for frequency. In
order to compare tones differing slightly in pitch or frequency, one must
present successive tones in some way. But any time one turns tones on
and off rapidly, or suddenly shifts an oscillator from, say, 500 Hz to 503
Hz, an infinite number of transient frequencies and variations are pro-

duced which tend to confound any valid judgments with respect to pitch
or frequency.

Work of Shower and Biddulph

Despite or perhaps because of the difficulties involved, many investigators have tried various means to circumvent the switching difficulties
and arrive at valid measures of difference thresholds. After trying numerous approaches, Shower and Biddulph (1931) succeeded in producing what are generally considered to be the most valid measures of
difference threshold. They used a technique involving slow (two per
second) sinusoidal changes from frequency to frequency. Their data are
quite complex, since they varied not only frequency but also intensity, and
included monaural, binaural, and bone-conduction modes.

The curves of Fig. 15-2 illustrate some of the Shower and Biddulph

Fig. 15-2. Difference thresholds for pitch. The curves have been
smoothed to indicate the probable "true" function. They are based
on the original data of Shower and Biddulph (1931) but with considerable modification.

data. Note that for some frequencies, and at optimal levels, DL's approaching one cycle were obtained.

Diplacusis

The clever reader might wonder why the early experimenters did not
deliver one tone to one ear and the comparison tone to the other in order
to determine a DL. Perhaps this method might be useful were it not for

the existence of a little-studied phenomenon known as *diplacusis*. Persons with this condition hear different pitches in the two ears as a result of stimulation with the same frequency. For example, a 600-Hz tone may appear higher in pitch in the left ear than in the right. A moderate amount of such diplacusis is probably quite common. Indeed, Licklider (1952) suggests that it is probably the rule rather than the exception.

Davis et al. (1944) showed experimentally induced diplacusis, using tones of 130 to 150 db as preconditioning or adapting stimuli. (Perhaps "deafening" would be more descriptive.) They obtained pitch shifts as great as one octave as a result of exposures to the fatiguing tone of several minutes. The "adaptation" effects of Davis et al. might indeed be likened to fatigue, a temporary threshold shift (tts) in pitch, rather than in sensitivity such as in the case of conventional tts investigations.

At the other extreme, the writer was able to induce diplacusis with pure tones at a moderate (85-db) level, for preconditioning durations of one minute or less, and in a predictable direction (Christman, 1954, 1963). Figure 15-3 shows the result of one experiment aimed at studying the decay effects of the shifts. In this experiment a 600-Hz tone in one ear

Fig. 15-3. Experimentally induced diplacusis. The ordinate shows the amount and direction of pitch shift, as a result of preconditioning with either 575- or 635-Hz tones, for the time intervals shown on the abscissa. (From Christman and Williams, 1963.)

was followed by a variable tone in the opposite ear, and a match made. The ear receiving the 600-Hz standard was preconditioned, or "satiated" for one minute with either a 575- or 635-Hz tone of the same level as the subsequent test tones. After subjection to the preconditioning tone, the comparison was made. You can see from Fig. 15-3 that with a time interval of 1 second between the preconditioning stimulus and the standard, the apparent pitch is shifted, in the case of the 575 preconditioning tone to 608 Hz, and for the 635-Hz satiation tone to about 596 Hz. Thus a fatiguing tone below the standard raised the pitch of the standard, while a fatiguing tone higher in frequency depressed the pitch of the standard. The remainder of Fig. 15-3 simply shows the course of the effect as it decays with time (up to 30 seconds).

SIMPLE TONAL INTERACTION

In the normal state of affairs one seldom hears pure tones. Rather, most sounds are complex combinations of many pure tones, varying in frequency as well as in temporal characteristics. Let us examine some of the available knowledge bearing on the experiences resulting from combinations of pure tones.

Paired Tones

Two pure tones of precisely the same frequency will, as indicated in Chapter 12, either reinforce or cancel each other, depending on the phase relationship of the two waves. If two waves of the same frequency are exactly in phase—that is, both waves have their peaks at precisely the same time—then the resultant overall wave amplitude will be the sum of the individual amplitudes. (See top drawing of Fig. 15-4.) If the two waves are 180° out of phase (one leads the other by one-half wavelength) as shown in the second and third parts of Fig. 15-4, then the resultant amplitude will be the difference between the individual amplitudes. With equal amplitudes, as shown in the second example in this figure, the two waves will subtract in such fashion as to cancel each other, and there will be in effect no sound. If the amplitudes are different, the result will be a tone represented by the difference between the two constituent tones, as shown in the bottom of the three figures.

Such reinforcement or cancellation effects are of serious consideration in the design of hi-fi audio reproduction equipment. If for example a speaker cabinet is so designed that internal reflections of the sound may differ by half-wavelengths for a given frequency, then tones of this frequency may be canceled and the speaker system may in effect be "dead" to this frequency. Or, at the other extreme, if strong reflections of pure tones tend to reinforce each other, we have a different problem. The sys-

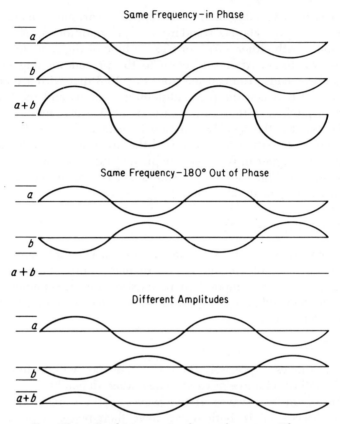

FIG. 15-4. Combining tones of same frequency. The top
drawing illustrates the addition of two tones, in phase.
The middle drawing is the addition of two tones of equal
amplitude, 180° out of phase; while the bottom drawing
shows two tones of unequal amplitude, 180° out of phase.
Note from the middle drawing, that if the phase difference were other than exactly 180°, the resultant tone
would be greater than zero.

tem may "boom," or even resonate at some particular frequency. In practice it is often some frequency near the bottom of the tonal register that
is involved in such unwanted reinforcement or "booming." Expensive
steps are taken to insure that good speaker systems are "flat" and have
outputs that truthfully reflect their input, avoiding both reinforcement
and cancellation effects.

Beats

If pure tones of slightly differing frequency are paired, it is clear from
Fig. 15-4 that the simple addition or subtraction of amplitude will not

occur. A phenomenon known as *beats* may result. If, for example, the two tones differ by one cycle per second (say 200 and 201 Hz), once every second the waves from the two tones will be in phase and reinforce each other; similarly, they will be out of phase, tending to cancel each other, at one instant each second. The result to the auditor will be a 200-Hz tone waxing and waning in loudness once per second. The experience of this waxing and waning is referred to as beating, or beats, and is illustrated schematically by Fig. 15-5.

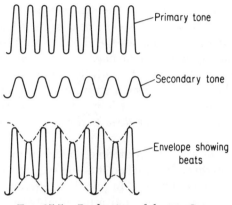

Primary tone

Secondary tone

Envelope showing beats

Fig. 15-5. Production of beats. Combining the primary and secondary tones results in the envelope wave shown at the bottom.

Notice from this figure that what is apparently experienced is an "envelope" of the two tones. If the difference between the two tones is two cycles per second, then the envelope will repeat itself twice per second, and two beats per second will be heard; with a difference of three cycles per second, three beats, and so on. Above six of seven beats per second the successive waxings and wanings produce something like a throbbing or pulsating auditory experience. At about 25 per second the throbbing experience tends to be replaced by something like a low "burr," or perhaps a low-pitched tone.

Combination Tones

Two tones with sufficient separation in frequency will, of course, be heard as two tones. A trained musician can indeed resolve not only two separate pitches, but often many pure tones within a complex pattern. He can detect the presence or absence of various instruments in the orchestra, or the harmonically related frequencies produced by a single instrument.

In some cases, the combination of two tones may produce a third tone, and even additional harmonically related tones. Simultaneous presentation of a 600-Hz and an 800-Hz tone may result in the hearing of a 200-Hz tone and perhaps a 1,400-Hz tone, as well as, in some cases, various combinations of the harmonically related frequencies. Such effects are known as *combination tones*.

While we can understand the production of beats as a simple phenomenon, reproducible, for example, on an oscilloscope, the situation with respect to combination tones is not that simple. Combination tones are not produced in nature unless there is some nonlinearity in the medium or mode of transmission. A linear system is one that reproduces its pure tone input with perfect fidelity. A nonlinear system has an output that contains components not present in the input, consisting mainly of harmonic multiples of the input frequency. It has been demonstrated that the ear is nonlinear, particularly at relatively high sound levels; hence the nonlinearities in the ear mechanism are assumed to be responsible for the production of combination tones. At low sound levels, combination tones cannot be detected, and the ear *does* perform as an optimal analyzing device.

When the tone heard is the difference between the two frequencies, it is known as a *difference tone;* when it is the sum of the two combining frequencies it is a *summation tone.* In practice, difference tones are much easier to produce and recognize, and are probably of more significance than summation tones. If you activate two tuning forks of, say, 850 and 1,000 Hz of sufficient amplitude, the low, 150-Hz difference tone may be immediately apparent; the summation tone of 1,850 Hz may or may not be noticeable. Unless the levels are sufficient to produce nonlinearities, the summation tone of 1,850 may not exist at all in your particular ear.

COMPLEX TONAL INTERACTION

In addition to the simple beats and combination tones, the combining of tones of different frequencies and intensities can produce varied results, results of particular importance in gaining an understanding of just how the auditory mechanism processes and recognizes tonal differences.

Masking with Pure Tones

It has been implied that two different tones—different in frequency to an extent that beats are not distinguishable—will be heard as two tones, that the ear will analyze the aural components and sense each of them. The ear will in a sense perform a Fourier analysis of the complex tone. Within limits this is indeed the case. However, when one tone is of sufficiently greater amplitude than the other, the weaker of the two tones may not be sensed; it may be masked by the louder tone. We can measure the extent of such masking by measuring the threshold of a tone, both by itself and in the presence of a masking tone—the threshold shift, then, being the measure of masking.

Probably the most extensive study of masking with pure tones was made many years ago by Wegel and Lane (1924). One example of their work is shone as Fig. 15-6. In this figure the masking efficacy of a 1,200-Hz tone is shown as the shaded area. In this figure any combination of frequency and intensity found in the shaded area will be below the absolute threshold—it will not be heard. The curve itself shows the combination of frequency and sensation level which can just be detected in the presence of a 1,200-Hz masking tone at 80 db above threshold. Note for example that a 600-Hz tone need only be at about 4-db sensation level in order to be detected, while a 1,000-Hz tone requires a sensation level of above 36 db to be detected.

The nearer the tones are to each other, the greater the masking effect —that is, the more intense the masked tone must be in order to be detected. This phenomenon is known as the *spread of masking*. Masking spreads in both directions, the effect decreasing the farther one gets from the frequency of the masking tone.

You may also have noted that frequencies above the 1,200-Hz masking tone require greater intensities to be heard than do those below the masking tone. In other words, the effect of spread of masking is such as to mask tones higher in pitch better than those lower in pitch. Even a

Fɪɢ. 15-6. Masking of pure tones by 1,200-Hz tone at 80-db sensation level. Combinations of frequency and level in the shaded area are inaudible. (Adapted from Wegel and Lane, 1924 and Fletcher, 1929.)

pitch as high as 3,200 Hz requires a level of 45 db in order to be detected in the presence of an 80-db 1,200-Hz masking tone.

When combining a 1,200-Hz tone with other frequencies, several other phenomena may be observed. Note the presence of beats around the 1,200-Hz tones. Beats may also be observed in the immediate vicinity of the 2,400 and 3,600-Hz tones. In the former, the 1,200-Hz masking tone is beating with the near-1,200-Hz secondary tone; in the latter the 2,400-Hz and 3,600-Hz, second and third harmonics respectively, are apparently beating with the near-2,400 and near-3,600-Hz tones.

On the basis of this and many other examples, several facts concerning masking with pure tones may be stated: (1) masking is greater for tones near the masking tone than for those farther away; (2) low-frequency tones mask higher-frequency tones better than the converse; and (3) the rate at which masking increases, as the intensity of the masking tone is increased, depends upon the frequencies of the tones. The latter finding is based upon many additional measurements by Wegel and Lane, and cannot be deduced from the single example shown.

Wegel and Lane also established that very little masking occurs if the two tones are applied to opposite ears (dichotic stimulation). Any masking that does occur appears to be a matter of sound leakage around the head. The basis of masking must therefore be found in the functioning of the inner ear. This is an important finding, bearing on the theoretical explanation of pitch discrimination to be discussed later.

Masking with White or Random Noise

White noise contains all audible frequencies and should therefore have a profound effect on the detection of pure tones. Since it contains all of Wegel and Lane's pure tones, white noise should mask pure tones with considerable efficiency. Moreover, the masking effect should be less dependent upon the pitch of the masked tone. Experimental evidence does indeed support these expectations. Figure 15-7 shows the threshold for pure tones presented in a background of white noise, based on the work of Hawkins and Stevens (1950). The various curves are for different levels of noise, expressed in decibels per cycle.* Notice from this figure that, except for quite low tones, and with respect to level per cycle, any pure tone must be from about 20 to 30 db more intense than the masking noise in order to be detected. If the masking noise is expressed

---

* Decibels per cycle is a new way of expressing sound pressure or power. The overall sound pressure for a bandwidth of roughly 10,000 Hz would be 10,000 times that for each of the 10,000 components, assuming a flat spectrum. The overall sound pressure would, therefore, be 40 db greater ($10,000 = 10^4$) than the level per cycle, as indicated on the curves of Fig. 15-7.

FIG. 15-7. Masking pure tones with white noise. Note that the level of the masking noise is expressed in db per cycle. Expressed in overall sound-pressure level of the white masking noise, these values would be increased by about 40 db. (From Hawkins and Stevens, 1950, with permission.)

in overall sound-pressure level instead of energy per cycle, the pure-tone signal must be no more than 10 to 20 db less intense than the masking level in order to be detected.

But what about masking with *bands* of noise, rather than the entire audible spectrum? Can we learn anything of value by making such comparisons? We surely can.

If we use two tones to mask a test tone, one on either side of the test tone, we can determine the distance we must move each tone from the test tone, before the masking effect becomes negligible. We can get similar results by using narrow bands of noise, centered on the frequency to be masked.

We find in this case that there is a point on either side of the masking band beyond which tones do not contribute equally to the masking effect. In other words, there is a *critical bandwidth* for masking. The situation in which tones close to a second tone produce greater masking effect appears not to be simply the result of a continuum, but to be rather a discrete locuslike effect.

Figure 15-8 shows critical bands for masking pure-tone signals. This curve tells us, for example: For a tone of 1,000 Hz, the critical band for masking is about 65 cycles. That is, individual frequencies within a band 65 cycles wide, centered at 1,000 Hz, summate to increase the effectiveness of the masking of a 1,000-Hz tone. Low-level tones which individually would not be intense enough to mask the test tone will summate in such a manner that their total effect will be to mask the 1,000-Hz tone if they

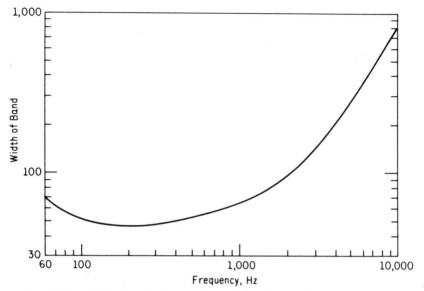

Fig. 15-8. Critical bands for masking. The ordinate shows the width, in cps, of critical bands of noise for masking the frequencies shown on the abscissa. (Adapted, with permission, from Fletcher, 1940.)

lie within this 65 cycle band. Frequencies outside of this 65-cycle band will not summate so as to contribute to the masking. Adding to the frequencies within the band would increase the masking effect in a proportional manner, adding to frequencies beyond the critical band would contribute little to the overall masking effect.

The inclusion of such complex relationships in a book of this scope was not done in order to confuse you. Rather the purpose was first to point out the orderliness of the auditory sensory system, and second to provide the groundwork for later obtaining an understanding of auditory theory.

With respect to the former, note that critical band widths tend to increase with frequency, like the jnd's for pitch discrimination. It is significant that, for frequencies above 100 Hz, the critical bandwidths for masking are almost exactly 20 times the smallest change in frequency (jnd) that can be noticed at that frequency (van Bergeijk, 1960). The implication is that there is a relationship between the frequency discrimination and the masking of one tone by other tones.

It is also worthy of note that the discrimination of speech seems to depend on the presence of bands of frequencies. The articulation index, considered in the next chapter, is based on 20 bands of frequencies, each contributing equally to speech intelligibility. Like critical bands for masking, the widths of each of these 20 bands increases with increasing frequency, and in a fashion not entirely unlike the bands for masking.

We referred in the last chapter to another form of critical band, critical bands for loudness summation. Pure tones, far removed from each other in frequency, summate in an orderly manner. That is, the loudness of two equally loud tones, widely separated in frequency, is twice the loudness of either of the tones alone. But two tones closer together in frequency, within a so-called critical band for loudness, do not summate in such an orderly manner; their total loudness is not the sum of the loudness of the individual components. While they may be based on similar physiological functions, critical bands for loudness summation are found to be some two and a half times as wide as critical bands for masking.

Findings such as those described above are of great importance in gaining an understanding of how the auditory mechanism works. Any theory of hearing must account for such findings.

The Missing Fundamental

There is yet another phenomenon, observable under rather unusual circumstances, that is worthy of mention. This is the case of the *missing fundamental* or *residue phenomenon*. If we listen to a complex tone made up of sinusoids with frequencies of 2,000, 2,100, 2,200, 2,300, . . . Hz we will hear a 100-Hz tone. Indeed, we will report the fundamental of the complex tone as being 100 Hz. Is this not simply a difference tone of 100 cps? Actually it appears to be other than a simple difference tone, as was shown by Schouten in 1940. If we listen to a tone made up of components of 300, 500, 700, 900 . . . Hz we should, if a difference tone is the key, hear a fundamental of 200 Hz. What *is* heard, however, is a fundamental of 100 Hz. This frequency is the largest common denominator of the set of frequencies. The highest frequency tone that could generate the 300, 500 (etc.) components with simple harmonics is a 100-Hz tone. None of the frequencies is a multiple of 200 Hz, but all are multiples of 100 Hz. Hence 100 is the missing fundamental. Since it is generally true that the apparent pitch of any complex tone is the pitch of the fundamental, the perceived pitch of the combinations of 300, 500, 700, 900, etc., would be the pitch of a 100-Hz tone.

Furthermore, this effect appears to be other than the result of difference tones, since it can be observed for quite weak tones. We pointed out earlier that normal difference tones require rather high levels to bring about their generation; presumably levels high enough to induce non-linear distortions in the auditory mechanism.

There is yet another clever bit of evidence militating against the difference-tone explanation. If the missing fundamental, for example

200 Hz, exists in the ear as a result of distortion, it should be possible to mask it in the same way that any 200-Hz tone might be masked. The introduction of low-frequency random noise at a level that would mask a genuine 200-Hz tone does not mask the internally created missing fundamental of 200 Hz.

Another key to the nature of the missing fundamental, and its relation to auditory functioning, arose when many investigators were unable to even generate it. Some even denied its existence. It was then discovered that all of the elemental components of the complex tone must be in phase. If they are arranged randomly, the phenomenon disappears. It would appear from these results that the basis for the missing fundamental lies in the existence of an envelope of frequencies, not entirely unlike our illustration of Fig. 15-5.

A final conclusion based on these and other data is that there are two pitch mechanisms. One is dependent upon the existence of a sinusoidal component and a locus of activity on the basilar membrane (at least for high frequencies); the second is dependent upon a rate of fluctuation and appears to be a less direct analysis of the envelope of the energy. With respect to the latter mechanism, even random noise, when alternated at low frequencies such as 200 per second, will appear to have the pitch of the repetition rate.

Theories of pitch perception, discussed in the next section, must account for these phenomena.

HOW PITCH IS PERCEIVED

Man has long wondered how he was able to perceive pitch—how different frequencies could be heard as different pitches. Even today we do not understand fully just what happens in the inner ear to allow for such fine discriminations and such a range of possible tones and combinations of tones that can be sensed. There have, however, been numerous attempts to make some sense out of the chaos. Let us look at some of the early thinking and trace the development of theories of pitch perception up to the present time. We will have to be highly selective and can hit only the high spots of auditory theory. The reader who wishes really to delve into the matter should consult references at the end of the chapter and in the bibliography.

Resonance Theories

Theories of this type fall into two general categories: place-resonance theories and pattern-resonance theories. The best example and indeed the most thoroughly worked-out place-resonance theory was that of Helmholtz.

Resonance Theory of Helmholtz. According to E. G. Wever, "The year 1857 marks the beginning of modern auditory theory" (Wever, 1949). In that year Hermann von Helmholtz offered the first version of his resonance theory. Six years later his classic *Die Lehre von don Tonempfindungen* appeared, elaborating on his theory, but now quite complete and documented with considerable care.* Helmholtz in effect, tied together current developments involving Ohm's law of auditory analysis, Mueller's doctrine of specific energy of nerves, and the brilliant anatomical work of Corti.

Helmholtz's theory was not entirely original. Many persons anticipated and contributed materially to the development of resonance theories. For example, Du Verney, in 1683, not knowing of the inner-ear fluids, thought that the nerve fibers were spread out on the bony part of the inner ear, and that resonant vibrations of the bony organs (that is, to airborne vibrations) produced the nerve impulses. Du Verney thought that, since the bony shelf (spiral lamina) is wider at the base of the cochlea, this portion must resonate for lower frequencies, and the narrow shelf at the apical end must resonate for higher frequencies. This is just the opposite of the situation as we understand it today. The bony shelf *is* wider at the basal end, but this simply means that the flexible basilar membrane, which occupies the space not taken up by the bony shelf, is narrow at the basal end of the cochlea and wide at the apical end.

Helmholtz proposed that there are specific resonators, tuned for the various audible frequencies, and which respond in a highly selective manner. Presumably, resonators (organs of Corti?) located near the basal end of the basilar membrane respond to high-frequency tones, while resonators near the apical end must be tuned to lower frequencies.

There may be and probably is a resonance effect at work in the inner ear, but it is not as simple as Helmholtz's rather naive theory would indicate. Anatomical evidence does not disclose organs capable of resonating in the manner his theory would require. Furthermore, we know that any sharply tuned resonating body (and Helmholtz's hypothesized resonators would have to be rather sharply tuned) tends to continue resonating after the inducing force has been removed. The ear simply does not act in this manner. If it were indeed highly enough damped so as to eliminate poststimulus resonances, then it would not be as sharply tuned as it clearly is.

To be sure, many aspects of auditory experience seem to fit in quite nicely with a resonance theory. The specific localization of damage as a

---

* The English version of this book, Ellis' translation in 1885 of the 1870 third edition and called by Ellis *Sensations of Tone,* is a true classic in every sense of the word. It has been reprinted right up to the present time, one edition being as recent as 1930.

result of high intensity, pure frequency, or narrow-band noise might lead one to accept a resonance theory. We showed earlier how a single frequency at extreme levels or long durations can be found to produce highly localized lesions in the basilar membrane; higher frequencies producing physical damage nearer the basal end of the basilar membrane and lower frequency tones tearing hair cells away at points nearer the apical end.

Furthermore, results of masking experiments can be quite nicely explained in terms of a physical spreading effect, especially if one allows for somewhat less than maximal sharpness in the tuning of the resonators.

Finally, other recent investigators such as Fletcher and von Békésy have indeed shown that many frequencies *can* be located along the basilar membrane. Helmholtz was not far wrong, but he erred in oversimplifying the effect—in attributing pitch perception to rigidly tuned entities, resonating in response to physical vibrations of the sound.

Pattern-Resonanace Theories. Several early theories followed, either based on or in opposition to the resonance theory of Helmholtz. These theories emphasized the pressure-pattern response of the basilar membrane, rather than the discrete resonances Helmholtz's theory required. Ewald, for example, around 1900, developed a "standing wave" theory. Using a membrane in which standing waves were set up by acoustic stimuli, he photographed from this model patterns of loops and nodes, thus demonstrating (at least for his model) a sort of pattern-resonance effect, and thereby providing evidence against Helmholtz's theory.

Ewald and others like him were anticipating modern traveling-wave theories and the generally accepted explanations of Békésy today.

Before examining what is currently thought to be the true state of affairs, let us look into some additional historical landmarks.

Frequency Theories

A number of earlier theories which placed the analyzing function in the brain might be lumped under the title of "frequency theories."

Rutherford's Telephone Theory. In 1886 W. Rutherford suggested that the ear works like a telephone, merely transmitting simple and compound frequencies, by way of the auditory nerve to the brain. According to Rutherford, the brain then serves as the analyzing instrument to perform, in effect, a Fourier analysis of the compound waveform. Apparently the recency of the invention of the telephone (1877) served to convince Rutherford that known limitations in the rate of firing of neurons were not effective in determining the maximum frequencies which could be transmitted by way of the auditory nerve.

The Volley Theory. Rutherford did indeed overestimate the maximum rate of firing of individual neurons, which is accepted as 1,000 per second, and even that rate for very few fibers. One possible solution to Rutherford's dilemma was proposed by Wever and Bray in 1937. They expounded a "volley theory." They advanced the suggestion that, while individual fibers could not fire at a rate adequate to account for high-frequency tones, there might be a condition wherein fibers would drop out and other fibers would pick up, so that the volleying of fibers with the same or different time constants could cause the auditory nerve, as a whole, to carry the actual frequency of the stimulating tone. Such an effect was proposed, at least for frequencies too high for individual neuron response.

Wever-Bray Effect. One reason perhaps for believing that the auditory nerve could indeed carry the complex, high-frequency signals to the brain for analysis was based on early electrical recordings. It was found that when electrodes were inserted into the auditory nerve, the same signal that entered the ear could be recorded from the nerve. One could, for example, talk into a cat's ear, take the recordings from its auditory nerve, amplify them, and hear the output from a loudspeaker. It looked like the nerve was, indeed, carrying the complex, high-frequency signals to the brain. Wever and Bray (1930) however, showed that what was being picked up and amplified was not the neural impulses at all, but rather an alternating electrical field, arising not in the auditory nerve but in the cochlea itself. These authors showed that there are two types of electrical energy which can be recorded: (1) that arising from the hair cells of the basilar membrane, mirroring the acoustical input, and (2) that from the neurons which is indeed like all other neural impulses, with the same chemical/physical constraints of any neural response. Variations in neural response indicate magnitude, with intense stimuli forcing the neuron to fire more rapidly, and probably bringing in additional neurons with higher thresholds. Frequency, on the other hand, must be determined by *which* fiber is activated, not *how* it is activated.

Modern Theory

Modern theory, really an elaboration of the early traveling-wave theories, might properly be called the von Békésy theory. In 1928 Georg von Békésy pointed out that the essential difference among the various theories lay in their assumptions concerning the nature of the basilar membrane, its elasticity, friction, mass, etc. Since that time, von Békésy has been working, with models and preparations, to determine the precise nature and function of the basilar membrane. In 1956 he was able to review the entire history of the theories and show that by manipulating only two physical variables of the basilar membrane—the absolute stiffness and the coupling of adjacent parts—he could produce all of the necessary vibratory patterns to account for the physical data. In fact, he did such a good job that in 1961 he was awarded the Nobel prize in medicine and physiology.*

Békésy showed the existence of traveling-wave patterns on the basilar membranes of various animals, and demonstrated that resonance was not the requisite factor. Thus location on the basilar membrane à la Helmholtz was indeed the key, but the resonances of Helmholtz was contraindicated.

There is also, as indicated earlier in this chapter, a possible second basis for pitch perception. The sensing of pitch for low-frequency tones appears to be a matter of the direct analysis of the fluctuations or the envelope of the pattern, as distinguished from the basilar membrane involvement for higher frequencies. The entire question of just how the ear produces the experience of pitch has not yet been completely resolved.

Moreover, there is yet another paradox to be accounted for: discriminations as good as one to three cycles per second can be made. The traveling-wave theory of von Békésy is not entirely up to resolving this question. With respect to this limitation of the traveling-wave theory, he *has* suggested a function called "funneling," in which the broad response of the basilar membrane is narrowed down by means of the individual fibers leading to the brain. It has been shown, for example, that recordings from individual fibers show sharper tuning as one progresses from the cochlea to the cortex. A cell in the medial geniculate shows a narrower, sharper response than a cell in the cochlear nucleus. That is, it responds to a narrower range of frequencies than a comparable cell in the cochlear nucleus. Do you recall the inhibitory effects postulated for the retina which presumably result in greatly enhanced contrast? One example of such an effect was demonstrated by Mach bands (see Chapter 7) and generally attributed to the retinal bipolar cells. There are indeed cells in the auditory chain which resemble the retinal bipolar cells and could conceivably produce just such an effect of gradient enhancement, increasing auditory contrast rather than brightness contrast. Perhaps someday von Békésy may receive another Nobel prize for demonstrating an auditory "Mach band" effect and settling once and for all the problem of how such a general wave action of the basilar membrane can ultimately result in such fine-pitch discrimination.

SUMMARY

In this chapter we examined the perception of pitch, the experiential correlate of frequency. First we considered scales of pitch, namely musical

---

* The interested reader is highly encouraged to read the short (about 8 pages) description of von Békésy's experiments from the Lawrence reference at the end of the chapter.

scales and the psychological mel scale. We then examined knowledge concerning differential thresholds for pitch, and the nature of diplacusis. Both simple and complex tonal interactions were considered, including such phenomena as beats, summation tones, difference tones, and the result of combinations whose effect includes the masking of other tones. With respect to masking we discussed masking with pure tones, broadband white noise, and bands of noise. Concepts of critical masking band and the elusive missing fundamental were described. Finally, we described past and present theories of pitch perception, beginning with the early Helmholtz resonance theory, progressing through telephone theories, and concluding with an all too brief account of von Békésy's traveling-wave theory.

SUGGESTED READINGS

There are not many available readings which limit themselves specifically to the material covered in this chapter. Most of the readings suggested for Chapter 14 are also applicable to this chapter. Furthermore, while several have been included which appear somewhat more appropriate for the material covered in this chapter, most of the following readings contain material appropriate for both the preceding and following chapters.

1. From E. G. Boring, *Sensation and Perception in the History of Experimental Psychology* (New York: Appleton, 1942). Chapter 9, consisting of 39 easy-to-read pages, is recommended for its historical value. The first nine pages present one of the best, short histories of the development of musical scales that I know of. This reference is particularly recommended if for no other reason than the excellent bibliography at the end of the chapter. Chapter 11 is also recommended. In 32 pages Professor Boring presents an excellent summary of the history of auditory theory. The serious student, will want to go beyond the history of Boring and learn more of the more recent investigators, such as von Békésy, Rosenblith, etc. For early history, however, this chapter from Boring is excellent.
2. Licklider, J. C. R. "Basic Correlates of the Auditory Stimulus," in S. S. Stevens (ed.), *Handbook of Experimental Psychology* (New York: Wiley, 1951). This is the same reference included in the last chapter. It is simply repeated here, since it is equally applicable to the area of pitch and frequency effects. A very important reference for general use.
3. Wever, E. G., *Theory of Hearing* (New York: Wiley, 1949). The serious student should be familiar with this book. It is somewhat old, and more recent data pertaining to auditory theory does exist. It is still just about the most complete treatment of auditory theory under one cover that I know of. The early chapters are of particular interest to the reader interested in historical perspective.
4. Licklider, J. C. R., "Three Auditory Theories," in S. Koch (ed.), *Psychology: A Study of Science*, Volume I, *Sensory, Perceptual, and Physiological Formu-*

lations (New York: McGraw-Hill, 1959). This entire chapter by Professor Licklider is well worth reading. The three theories which he describes are those of signal detection, which we touched upon in Chapter 4; speech intelligibility, which will be concidered in the next chapter; and pitch perception, considered in the present chapter. The roughly 35 pages devoted to theory of pitch perception is quite appropriate for this chapter and certainly worth reading. It is a rather technical presentation and requires concentration. For the student interested in getting at the bottom of current thinking on the matter, the chapter is required reading.

5. From M. Lawrence, "Hearing," in M. Alpern, M. Lawrence, and D. Wolsk, *Sensory Processes* (Belmont, Calif.: Brooks/Cole, 1967). I have recommended this publication before, both for vision, and for the last chapter on sound intensity. Pages 91–98 are especially pertinent to the theoretical explanation of pitch perception. I highly recommend this short excerpt from Lawrence's chapter.

16

COMPLEX AUDITORY PROCESSES

In this chapter we examine several auditory functions which do not quite fit into the previous topics of intensity and frequency, or loudness and pitch. Perhaps some of these topics might be considered more akin to perception than to sensory processes. Because of their apparently fundamental and basic nature, however, and their simple dependence upon the auditory sense, we shall consider them at this time.

AUDITORY SPACE PERCEPTION

Introductory Comments

Man has two ears, one on either side of his head. As a result of this rather fortunate circumstance, sounds at the two ears are not quite the same. One ear is often farther away from the source of the sound, and the head blocks off (partially, at least) some of the sound from one side. Obviously, the two ears do not "hear" exactly the same thing. It is this difference in the stimuli to the two ears that makes localization of sound sources possible.

We shall in the next few pages make reference to "cues" for direction. Do not conclude that we sense these interaural differences and then interpret them as direction. The direction of an auditory source is probably sensed as directly as is visual space. We did not conclude that a person learns to interpret his disparate visual images as three-dimensional. Neither is it likely that we learn to interpret our auditory cues as spatial localization. The word "cue" is used not to indicate an experience which the listener interprets as auditory space but simply as a convenient term to indicate possible physical characteristics that lead automatically and unconsciously to the sensation of directionality.

Learning does play some part in auditory space perception. We probably learn that a human voice of low amplitude is coming from a speaker at a distance, while a loud voice indicates a speaker somewhat closer.

Judging the direction of a sound source, however, is not based on such a simple comparison. What are the cues for sound direction? How do we know, for example, that a sound is coming from the left?

Cues for Direction. There are perhaps four differences in the signals to the two ears that can be experienced in terms of direction of the source of a sound. First, sounds, unless they lie directly in the sagittal plane, reach one ear before the other. Particularly in the case of clicks or similar transients, simple time of arrival may be a clue to direction. Secondly, due to these time differences, pure tones or near-pure-tone frequencies will be in different phase at the two ears, which may serve as a cue for direction; thirdly, a sound will appear louder to the closer ear; and finally, sounds made up of complex combinations of high and low frequencies (such as speech) will arrive at the two ears with differing amounts of

FIG. 16-1.   Sound cage. Used for studying auditory cues for localization. (Courtesy Marietta Apparatus Company.)

distortion due to the differences in absorption/reflection and bending patterns of the high and low frequencies.

Methods for Studying Cues. Before examining cues for distance and direction in more detail, let us consider briefly the manner in which they are studied. An equipment often used for studying the perception of direction of auditory signals is a sound cage. As shown in Fig. 16-1, a sound cage is a device that permits the precise positioning of a loudspeaker in various orientations with respect to the listener's ears. One can study the ability of an individual to localize a single sound as a function of amplitude, frequency, tonal complexity, and other variables.

Another, more analytical approach is to use a pair of headphones, manipulating the dichotic sounds to the two ears. One can thus simulate three-dimensional or stereophonic hearing. By varying differences in loudness, phase, etc. these individual cues can be analyzed individually or in combination with each other.

A simpler technique, in vogue before the use of electronic headphones became commonplace, involved tubes to the two ears, with the sound source being placed at varying locations within the tube. One could thus change the time relations to the two ears by changing the relative lengths of the left and right segments of the tube.

Let us now examine the manner in which differences in the signals to the two ears are sensed as direction of the source.

Temporal Differences

Klemm, in 1920, and other experimenters who followed him, were able to show that two clicks, presented dichotically to the ears with a time differential as small as .03 millisecond, were heard as a single click, localized to one side of the median or sagittal plane. It was further demonstrated, that, as the time between clicks is increased, the apparent source moves away from the medial plane, until with a temporal difference of about .65 millisecond, the click appears at a 90° angle, or directly to the side of the head; that is, opposite the ear which has the leading click. If the time difference is increased, the click remains at the leading ear until a difference of about 2.5 milliseconds results in the hearing of two separate clicks, one in each ear.

That the important cue in the early, rather crude experiments was time and not loudness was demonstrated by von Hornbostel and Wertheimer (1920). They showed that even with differences in loudness favoring the ear getting the delayed click, the sound was still perceived as coming from the side receiving the leading click. Only when the loudness of the delayed click was very much greater than that of the leading click could the perceived direction be reversed. Thus it was demonstrated that a small time difference would prevail over an appreciable, opposing intensity difference.

It is rewarding to notice how closely the phenomenal data of Klemm and his followers agree with the physical times based on distance the sound must travel for various binaural aspects. Figure 16-2 shows the physical time differences required for sound transmission for various angles from the sagittal plane to a point opposite one ear.

According to the curve in this figure, it requires about .65 additional millisecond for a sound to reach the distant ear when it originates from the side of the head (90° point). This was precisely the experimental delay required for a sound to be localized directly opposite the ear. At the other end of the curve, it may be seen that a time differential of .027 millisecond should result from a source 3° from the sagittal plane. Early workers, as we mentioned, found the smallest temporal difference that could be interpreted as directionally to be about .03 millisecond, and remarkably, the minimum angle of a source from the median plane that can be reliably discriminated is something on the order of 3°. The experi-

FIG. 16-2. Temporal differences to the two ears as a function of direction of sound. This figure indicates that a sound from an angle 50° from the sagittal plane arrives at the distant ear about 0.45 milliseconds later than at the nearer ear.

mental data do indeed agree astonishingly well with the physics of the situation.

Phase Differences

Temporal differences, as described in the preceding paragraphs, relate to the onset of a sound, and are particularly effective for complex waves such as clicks and those with relatively sudden or steep onsets. In the case of pure-tone stimulation, localization is possible without the sudden onset and the transients of clicks. Time differences for the two ears may arise as a result of differences in phase of the sounds reaching the two ears. In practice, for research purposes, pure tones of the same frequency and amplitude are delivered to the two ears, but with a slight delay for one ear, thus resulting in the corresponding sinusoids being out of phase. When this is done it appears that the necessary and sufficient condition for the sensation of direction is the temporal relationships of corresponding points on the tone's compression waves. In other words, the ear does not recognize phase directly; rather, the points of maximum pressure of the two waves, for example, arrive at the two ears with the delays corresponding to the phase differences. It is the delay that is important, not the phase differences.

Nevertheless, the question of whether one detects phase differences directly or simply utilizes the temporal differences of the waves has bothered numerous investigators and the question is not entirely settled at the present writing. Shaxby and Gage (1932), for example, showed that in order to counteract a localization cue for intensity, the critical factor was *not* the degree of phase shift, but rather the actual temporal delay. They found that for different frequencies the amount of delay was constant, not in terms of degrees phase shift but rather in terms of delay time or time of arrival to the separate ears.

Whether there is indeed a sensitivity to phase differences or simply a sensitivity to time differences is perhaps of mere academic importance. Within limits the ears *can* utilize such cues to localize the source of sounds. One limit to localization ·as a function of temporal or phase differences is that of the frequency of the signal. The auditory response, like all other physiological functions, occurs in time. Just as we indicated a lower limit for the discrimination of temporal differences for clicks (about .03 millisecond) there is a temporal limit for continuous tones. Translated in terms of the frequencies of the signals, this appears to be something of the order of 1,500 Hz. Frequencies higher than this figure cannot be localized with the same precision as lower frequencies, at least not by temporal or phase differences. It would appear that dichotic differences other than phase or time must be important for the localization of higher-frequency tones.

Intensity Difference

The fact that sounds are louder in the nearer ear than in the other appears to be the basis for considerable localization ability. Since a sound has farther to travel (as much as 10 inches) to get to the opposite ear, it will be less loud at that ear. Note, however, that intensity or power decreases only 6 db for each doubling of distance. A sound arising 100 feet away will not be much weaker as a result of traveling an additional 10 inches—probably not enough differential to even be noticed. How then can intensity be a cue for direction if distance per se is so insignificant?

The answer lies in the nature of sound-wave transmission. Long sound waves, like waves of the ocean, bend around obstacles in their path. A 100-Hz tone, with a wavelength on the order of 11 feet, is not blocked off by the head. It reaches the opposite ear with, to all intents and purposes, the same amplitude as the closer ear. Higher-frequency tones, however, do not bend around the head in the same manner. They tend to be blocked off, reflected, or absorbed by the head. Sivian and White (1933) calculated the loss in intensity at the distant ear for an angle of incidence of 15°. Their calculations show, for a 300-Hz tone, a loss of less than 1 db, for a 4,000-Hz tone a loss of 5 db, and a difference of 10 db for a 15,000-Hz tone. Such data explain why intensity difference serve as cues, primarily for the tones of relatively high frequency.

Probably the most nearly complete recent research on the relation between temporal and intensity cues for direction is that of Mills (1958). Mills showed that from 250 to 1,400 Hz, localization depends primarily on temporal differences; on the other hand, for frequencies with wavelengths greater than the distance between the two ears, intensity differences are of importance. According to Mills, interaural intensity differences as small as 0.5 db can serve as cues for direction.

When cues are in conflict—that is, temporal factors indicate one direction and loudness the opposite direction—the former seems to have priority. Perhaps if most of our listening involved only high-frequency tones this would not be true.

Timbre as a Cue for Direction

Complex sounds should sound differently to the two ears. They should differ in timbre, or as we described it earlier, the complexity of the wave pattern. Timbre, to be sure, is the composite result of the three variables just described, so that it is perhaps not an independent cue. On the other hand, there may be a characteristic of timbre which is unique and goes beyond the three cues listed above. Perhaps, in the case of timbre we have a learning factor at work, just as with such secondary cues for visual depth as shadows and aerial perspective. The sound of an orchestra will be different in the right ear as contrasted with the left ear, unless it originates directly in the sagittal plane of the auditor. The near ear will tend to hear more of the higher frequency overtones which will be somewhat more attenuated in the opposite ear. Similarly, the complex sounds of speech will be differentially attenuated, such that the result-ants to the two ears will be different. Our excellent ability to locate a speaker may be partially due to learning, to interpreting the differing timbres to the two ears as spatial localization. In the case of quite com-plex sounds, perhaps we do indeed learn to interpret cues.

Practical Applications

In addition to the rather obvious stereo recording of music with two spatially separated microphones and subsequent reproduction with separate speakers or headphones, numerous, less prosaic applications of auditory space perception data might be described.

Direction Cues for Passive Detection. Your author once assisted in the devlopment of a passive detection device to be used by Civil Defense personnel (1956). The proposed apparatus consisted of a hard hat, carry-ing two radio receivers on the top, with their individual antennae pointed in divergent directions. (See Fig. 16-3). The receivers were tuned for air-

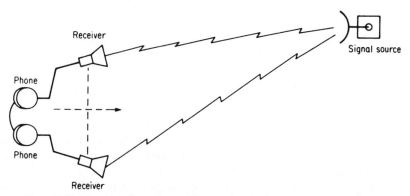

FIG. 16-3. Passive detection radio receivers. Receiver antenna horns are worn on head, thus picking up radar signals from approaching air-craft. Pulse repetition frequency of airborne radar is heard by listener.

borne search radar, the idea being that the listener could hear the pulse repetition frequency (prf) of an approaching aircraft's radar before visible contact could be made. With the left-divergent antenna horn feeding a radio receiver for the left ear and the right horn feeding the right ear, the hope was that the wearer could "hear" the direction of an approaching aircraft and could, by unconsciously matching the signals to the two ears, search in the correct direction. He might say "I cannot see it yet, but it sounds like it's in *that* direction."

Recognizing that temporal differences are probably of more importance than loudness differences, we performed a series of experiments utilizing signals to simulate the airborne radar's prf and general auditory characteristics. In addition, we manipulated both temporal delays and loudness differences to the two ears. Figure 16-4 shows the results of

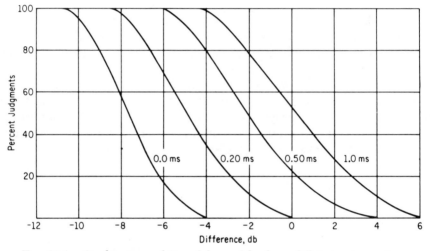

Fig. 16-4. Combinations of time delay and loudness differences to produce auditory localization. Stimulus material was trains of pulses with a prf of 400 rather than the conventional sinusoidal frequencies.

some of these data. In this figure four delays, from 0 to 1.0 millisecond were employed. The abscissa of the figure shows the intensity differences necessary to produce the percent correct directional judgments shown on the ordinate. The figure shows, for example, that with a zero delay, a difference in loudness of about 8 db is required to produce 80 percent correct judgments as to direction. But with a delay of 1.0 millisecond, the leading tone would need to be only slightly over 2 db more intense for 80 percent correct direction identification. The figures on the ordinate to the right of the zero are cases where the leading tone is lower in amplitude than the delayed tone. For instance, a tone with a delay of 1.0 millisecond can be localized accurately 40 percent of the time, even though the delayed tone is 1 db louder than the leading tone.

There were problems in the application of the technique. Judgments were not as good as might be hoped for. For one thing, signals were not optimum, being trains of pulses rather than sine waves, and of higher-than-ideal frequency. Secondly, time delays would have had to have been produced artificially, since to all intents and purposes radio waves reach the two ears at the same time. While the perfected article never reached the production stage, it was an interesting exercise in the application of psychophysical data.

Person-to-Person Communication in an Atmosphere-free Environment. Figure 16-5 is a schematic drawing of a portion of a highly

Fig. 16-5. Pictorial version of person-to-person communications for an atmosphere-free environment. The three hornlike devices are microwave guides for transmitting and receiving antennae.

sophisticated communication system I once recommended for our space program (1960).* As everyone is aware, the normal conversation we take for granted in our everyday life is unattainable on, say, the moon or some other planet, or for deep-sea divers walking on the bottom of the sea. Direct aural contact is simply not attainable in an atmosphere-free environment. Except when they are in sealed, pressurized cabins, such persons must wear helmets with conventional walkie-talkie radios. There

---

* While no criticism of the system was ever made, it was never employed. In light of other, more pressing and critical considerations, the capability of recognizing just where a speaker's voice is coming from, was not thought to be of sufficient importance to warrant development of the actual hardware.

is no provision for "Hey, Joe look here, see what I found," with Joe recognizing instantly where the speaker is. To be sure, our astronauts on the moon were able to converse together, but the direct recognition of the source of the speaker was not attainable, either with respect to direction or distance. The device illustrated in Fig. 16-5 was meant to bring back "normal" conversation to persons working in an environment restricted to radio or similar electronic communications.

The hornlike affair at the man's mouth is indeed a horn, but a microwave horn that provides directionality to the microwave transmission. The horns at the ears are directional receiving antennae which feed signals to separate receivers for the two ears. With a properly designed horn configuration and judicial selection of frequencies, appropriate amplitude differences at the ears could result from directional differences, and could be made to truly simulate amplitude differences for airborne sound and God-given ears. Furthermore, temporal differences, to reinforce the amplitude differences, could be produced electronically by means of variable delay circuits. It was further suggested that the loudness of the auditory signal be made consonant with distance, so that conversational-level signals could be heard for distances no greater than those encountered in airborne vocal communication. For long-distance communications conventional radio equipment would be retained, but for general person-to-person conversation everything possible should be done to reproduce the acoustic and auditory milieu of terrestrial man.

While our first astronauts on the moon did not utilize such a sophisticated simulation of natural speech, something like this will probably be done when the man on the moon becomes hundreds of men (and women too) on the moon.

SPEECH INTELLIGIBILITY AND NOISE CRITERIA

A problem long of interest to psychologists and of particular importance to those associated with the military and military communications is that of speech intelligibility. Under conditions of noise and signal loss speech clearly becomes less intelligible. Can we understand the effects of noise on speech and do something to mitigate its deleterious effects? The basic problem is to determine just how intelligible speech might be when subjected to various noise backgrounds, and under various conditions of filtering, clipping, or time-sharing.

Use of Test Material

Early work in the study of speech intelligibility involved the use of actual speech material, either recorded by a trained speaker and played back to a listener, or delivered live over the system to be tested. In some cases face-to-face presentations of test material were employed. The writer once tested Air Force single-side-band communications equipment by providing aircraft and ground stations with prerecorded test tapes which could be transmitted over the air/ground and ground/air link, recorded at the receiving end, and later analyzed for intelligibility.

Test material to be used might be phonetic sounds, nonsense syllables, short monosyllabic words, or meaningful sentences. The percentage of the material heard correctly would differ widely depending upon the nature of the test material; phonetic sounds or nonsense syllables would be much more difficult to identify correctly than meaningful words, or at the easiest extreme, connected discourse. Figure 16-6 shows some approx-

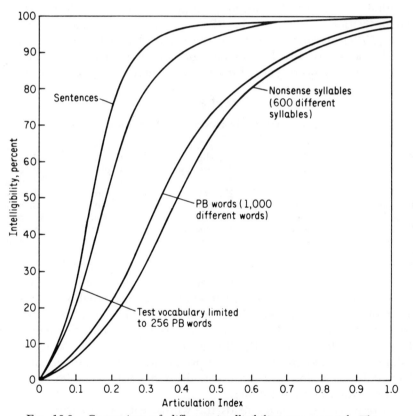

Fig. 16-6. Comparison of different intelligibility test material. The values given must be considered as approximations, since such factors as the skill of the speakers and listeners, the methods used, etc. all tend to influence the results. (Adapted from *Human Engineering Guide to Equipment Design* by Morgan, Cook, Chapanis, and Lund, copyright 1963, with permission of McGraw-Hill Book Company. Data from Kryter, 1955, French and Steinberg, 1949, and Pickett and Kryter, 1954.)

imations of speech intelligibility in percent as a function of several different test materials. The abscissa for this figure is the Articulation Index (AI), a construct to be discussed in the next section. For purposes of understanding this figure, AI is simply a measure of the "goodness" of the speech, with 1.0 representing the ideal, broad-band no-noise condition, and 0.0 being the hopeless extreme.

Note from this figure that syllables at an AI of 0.5 are 70 percent intelligible, PB (phonetically balanced) words are about 84 percent intelligible, while sentences are almost 100 percent intelligible. An individual using any of these test materials would have to generalize carefully in order to predict for the operational situation.

PB Word Lists. The test material which probably received the most attention and therefore achieved the highest degree of sophistication and standardization was that of the PB or phonetically balanced word lists. Egan (1949) and his associates at the Harvard Psycho-Acoustic Laboratory developed twenty lists of 50 words each which were said to be phonetically balanced. (See, for example, Table 16-1.) That is, each of

TABLE 16-1

PHONETICALLY BALANCED (PB) WORD LIST 1

1. smile	11. there	21. rub	31. hive	41. folk
2. strife	12. then	22. slip	32. bask	42. bar
3. pest	13. fern	23. use (yews)	33. plush	43. dike
4. end	14. box	24. is	34. rag	44. such
5. toe	15. deed	25. not	35. ford	45. wheat
6. heap	16. feast	26. pile	36. rise	46. nook
7. hid	17. bunt	27. are	37. dish	47. pan
8. rat	18. grove	28. cleanse	38. fraud	48. death
9. creed	19. bad	29. clove	39. ride	49. pants
10. no	20. mange	30. crash	40. fuss	50. cane

the lists contained the same number of phonetic sounds, and the frequencies of occurrence of different sounds was presumably the same as the frequency of occurrence in general speech. The lists were therefore representative of speech in general and quite comparable, one to the other. A sample of one of the lists is shown in the table. In use it was customary to randomize the order of presentation of the individual words. Thus, unless learning was too great, the same list might be used more than once for the same listener.

In practice the speaker reads the words, each in a carrier sentence, and the listener writes down what he hears. It should go without saying that careful attention to the speaker's output level, enunciation, and pronunciation must be maintained at all times. Curiously enough, the carrier sentence is rather important. One might say quite naturally, "You will write *smile*." If you try this you will notice the position of your tongue at the end of the word "write" is not in a natural position to form the first consonant of the test word. The last sound preceding the test word should ideally be a neutral vowel, one not requiring tongue or lip movement. The carrier sentence we used was "You will tra *smile*" with a vowel sound like the "a" in "art," enabling the speaker to move effortlessly from the carrier sentence to the test word. And too, a vowel sound preceding the test word made it possible for the speaker, by means of a decibel meter, to monitor his speech level somewhat more precisely.

The results of the actual intelligibility test, of course, are simply stated in terms of percent of words reproduced correctly. Naturally, since this is a test of intelligibility only, any spelling of the word is accepted. "Their" for "there," for example, is a perfectly legitimate spelling, or "kat" for "cat" is also perfectly acceptable.

Either with the use of monosyllabic words or syllables, one can also arrive at individual percentages for different speech sounds if one so desires. In analytical research such a capability is highly desirable.

Articulation Index

An experimentally developed construct, known as the *Articulation Index*, is particularly useful for predicting the effect of various noises and bandwidth restrictions on the intelligibility of speech. Such a technique is particularly useful in the case of electronic transmission, where bandwidths and background noise levels can be ascertained in advance.

TABLE 16-2

FREQUENCY BANDS THAT CONTRIBUTE EQUALLY TO INTELLIGIBILITY

Band No.	Lower Frequency	Middle Frequency	Upper Frequency	Band Width
1	200	270	330	130
2	330	380	430	100
3	430	490	560	130
4	560	630	700	140
5	700	770	840	140
6	840	920	1,000	160
7	1,000	1,070	1,150	150
8	1,150	1,230	1,310	160
9	1,310	1,400	1,480	170
10	1,480	1,570	1,660	180
11	1,660	1,740	1,830	170
12	1,830	1,920	2,020	190
13	2,020	2,130	2,240	220
14	2,240	2,370	2,500	260
15	2,500	2,660	2,820	320
16	2,820	2,900	3,200	380
17	3,200	3,400	3,650	450
18	3,650	3,950	4,250	600
19	4,250	4,650	5,050	800
20	5,050	5,600	6,100	1,050

It has been determined, largely by French and Steinberg (1947) and by Beranek (1947) and his co-workers, that the auditory spectrum from 200 to 6,100 Hz can be divided into 20 bands, each of which contributes equally to the intelligibility of speech. The upper and lower limits and the widths of these 20 bands are shown in Table 16-2 (Beranek, 1947).

In utilizing the Articulation Index technique a chart such as shown in Fig. 16-7 is employed. The bottom curve of this figure shows the

FIG. 16-7. Figure for computing articulation index. The 20 bands contributing equally to intelligibility are shown on the abscissa (not in scale), the ordinate is the sound-pressure level in db re .0002 dyne/cm². Since unit bandwidths are employed, levels below −20 db *per cycle* are possible for threshold. Also shown are levels of speech minima, peaks, and average level of speech for the condition shown (raised voice, 69 db at one meter distance). (With permission of Beranek, 1947.)

threshold of audibility for continuous-spectrum sounds, at least those within the frequency range of importance for the perception of speech. The useful range of speech sounds, then, lies above this threshold curve and within the general limits set by the other curves: speech minima, average levels, and levels of speech peaks. These curves refer to a man talking in a raised voice, measured one meter directly in front of him. According to the originators of the technique, if the spectrum levels of the speech lie above the threshold curve and above any ambient noise, and also below some maximum (overload) level not shown on the curve, speech intelligibility will be nearly perfect. On the other hand, loss of any frequencies by masking or attenuation will result in some loss of intelligibility, which can be stated in terms of the Articulation Index.

This latter is determined by adding up the individual contributions of each of the 20 bands, each based on the amount of signal above the threshold and not masked by noise in that particular band.

In order to predict the efficiency of a transmission system, it is necessary to determine (1) the energy shape of the output, and (2) the amount of noise in each of the 20 bands. When these are known it is a relatively simple matter to calculate an Articulation Index by summating the contribution of each of the 20 bands.

It is also possible to "shape" the transmitted speech in such a manner that all (or a maximum) of the components will lie above the noise, and yet below the overload limit. Frequency-modulated radio uses a "shaping" system at the transmitter end, greatly amplifying high-frequency components before transmission. Your receiver, then, reshapes the received audio signal to provide a realistic reproduction of the original sounds. The purpose of this procedure is to insure that all signal components will be well above the level of the noise in the system.

Figure 16-6 has the Articulation Index as its abscissa. With this, and similar curves one can go from Articulation Index to prediction of speech intelligibility, and it matters not whether the departure from perfect intelligibility is due to the addition of noise in the system or to the removal of important speech frequencies. There are some problems when the interfering noise is not continuous but made up essentially of pure-tone components or, even worse, such complex elements as impact noises or clicks. However, progress is being made in the prediction of the amount of interference produced by such special conditions.

Speech-Interference Level

The computation of the Articulation Index is rather time-consuming and, due to inaccuracies and uncontrollable variables in its measurement, often not warranted for practical applications. In this case a simplified procedure, resulting in a measure known as the *Speech-*

Interference Level (SIL), is often resorted to. The SIL is simply the arithmetic average of the sound-pressure levels in the three bands: 600 to 1,200, 1,200 to 2,400, and 2,400 to 4,800 Hz. If the level in the 300–600-Hz band is 10 db or more greater than the level in the 600–1,200-Hz band, then all four bands are employed in the calculation of the SIL.

In some modern applications three octave bands with centers at 500, 1,000, and 2,000 Hz are used. The SIL is especially useful in predicting intelligibility in noisy environments, such as offices and schoolrooms. Furthermore, since most measuring equipment provides octave-band levels rather than the 20-band units, the SIL is more easily obtained than the Articulation Index.

Figure 16-8 shows the relation betwee Speech-Interference Level and distance between speaker and listener for several arbitrary levels of speech. These curves indicate the various combinations of distance and Speech-Interference Level permitting reliable conversation, that is, 75 percent PB word intelligibility.

FIG. 16-8. Speech-interference level for reliable (75 percent PB words) conversation at four-voice levels. Data should be considered as approximations, since many variables, such as nature of speaker, listener, etc. would work to determine precise values. (Based on data from Beranek, 1954, adapted from *Human Engineering Guide to Equipment Design* by Morgan, Cook, Chapanis, and Lund, copyright 1963, used with permission of McGraw-Hill Book Company.)

Noise Criteria

A final measure of noise effects to be mentioned briefly is that the NCA curves, which consider the entire gamut of effects of noise, such as damage and annoyance as well as interference with speech. These curves are basically maximum-tolerance levels for various conditions and are of interest primarily to acousticians involved in reducing or minimizing

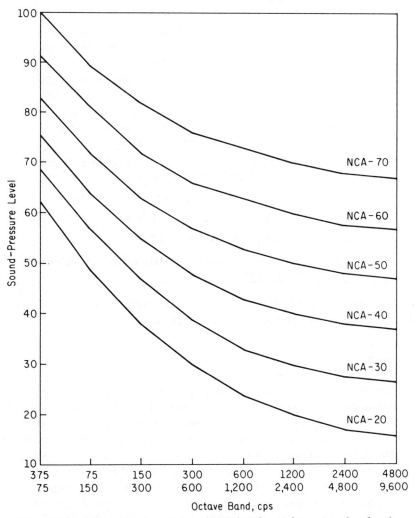

Fig. 16-9. Noise criterion curves (NCA). The eight octave bands of interest are shown on the abscissa with the levels in db per band shown on the ordinate. (From Beranek, 1957, with permission.)

the effects of noisy equipments, workplaces, and similar industrial and domestic situations. Figure 16-9 illustrates the NCA curves.

Some of the criteria (limits) for specific applications are shown in Table 16-3 (Beranek, 1957). This table applies primarily to person-to-

TABLE 16-3

NOISE CRITERIA FOR VARIOUS APPLICATIONS (BERANEK, 1957)

NCA	Application
20–30	Very quiet office, telephone use satisfactory.
30–35	Quiet office, satisfactory for conferences at 15-foot table, normal voice range 10–30 feet, telephone use satisfactory.
35–40	Conferences at 6–8 foot tables, normal voice range 6–12 feet, telephone use satisfactory.
40–50	Conferences at 4–5 foot tables, normal voice range 3–6 feet, raised voice, 6–12 feet, telephone use slightly difficult.
50–55	Unsatisfactory for conferences of more than 2 or 3 people, normal voice range 1–2 feet.
55–60	Very noisy office, telephone use difficult.
60–70	Raised voice range 1–2 feet.
70–80	Telephone use very difficult.
above 80	Communication extremely difficult, telephone use unsatisfactory.

person voice communications and telephone communication. Additional tables are available for various other applications.

SUMMARY

Two major topics were considered in this chapter: (1) the ability to localize sounds in space, and (2) the prediction of speech intelligibility in noise. With respect to the former, we considered four possible "cues" for direction: loudness differences, temporal differences, phase difference, and differences in timbre of the sounds of the two ears. We recognized the possibility that these cues might not be mutually exclusive, since timbre is really the result of all the other cues. We also suggested that phase differences might better be considered as temporal differences, at least so far as the ear is concerned. We recognized the complex interaction among the cues and presented two specific applications wherein a knowledge of auditory cues for localization might be applied.

In the last half of the chapter we examined four approaches to the specification of speech intelligibility and the influence of noise. We considered first the direct assessment approach, utilizing syllables, nonsense words, and meaningful material; secondly, we considered prediction by means of the Articulation Index; the third aproach involved the Speech-Interference Level; and finally we presented the noise-criterion approach, including the annoyance factor of noise as well as intelligibility of speech.

SUGGESTED READINGS

1. From R. S. Woodworth and H. Schlosberg, *Experimental Psychology*, rev. ed. (New York: Holt, 1954). Pages 349–361 present a very good description of how one senses space by means of the auditory mechanism. Both direction and distance are considered and numerous tables and figures make the presentation both interesting and informative.
2. Miller, G. A., *Language and Communication* (New York: McGraw-Hill, 1951). This entire book is recommended for the student who is especially interested in the subject matter. It is a rather advanced book, ideal for the graduate student, who can make more use of it than the casual undergraduate. Pages 47–49 are particularly appropriate for an understanding of speech perception. One should at least be aware of the existence of this book, if for no other reason than possible later reference.
3. Egan, J. P., "Articulation Testing Methods," *Laryngoscope* 58, (1948), 955–91. Probably the best of the early descriptions of articulation testing methods. While it may be more difficult to obtain than most of the suggested readings, for the really interested reader, the effort may indeed be worthwhile. This article has good historical perspective and detailed descriptions of "why" and "how." Much of the material in this article may also be found in several technical reports: OSRD Report 3802, 1944, from the Psycho-Acoustical Lab., Harvard Univ. and PNR-36 of the Office of Naval Research, 1947, also from the Psycho-Acoustical Lab.
4. From L. L. Beranek, *Acoustics* (New York: McGraw-Hill, 1954). An excellent book in its entirety. For a generally readable and informative book on acoustics I feel it has no peers. Of particular interest to this chapter, however, is the 26-page material of Parts XXXI and XXXII, Speech Intelligibility and Psychoacoustic Criteria. Incidentally, Part XXX of this book also presents a very readable and relatively complete description of much of the material we have included in the preceding two chapters.
5. From C. T. Morgan, J. S. Cook, III, A. Chapanis, and M. W. Lund (eds.), *Human Engineering Guide to Equipment Design* (New York: McGraw-Hill, 1963). Chapter 4 of this rather unlikely sounding reference presents an excellent description of speech communications. Section 4.1 (8 pages) is

an excellent short summary concerning the nature of speech which we did not cover in this chapter; Section 4.2 considers speech intelligibility in excellent detail with examples of test material and methodology. These 13 pages are especially recommended. The balance of the chapter is concerned with noise criteria, component selection, and systems requirements.

17

THE CHEMICAL SENSES—GUSTATION

It may seem strange to the reader that we have waited until this late point in the book to consider the most primitive, elemental senses of all, the chemical senses. They are perhaps the bases for all the other senses and might very well have been considered first. Yet despite their evolutionary primacy (or perhaps because of it) they are the least understood of all our sensory capabilities. There is even a question as to just what the physical stimuli are in some cases! Had we disclosed our lack of knowledge concerning such significant organism/environment relations in Chapter 5, many readers would perhaps have turned away, appalled by our apparent ignorance.

From a historical point of view, we need make no apologies for our chemical senses. Attempts at satisfying their unique whims has literally shaped the destiny of mankind. Early ocean navigators blazed trails to find new sources of spices and scents. The exploits of Christopher Columbus might never have occurred had there not been a demand for a safer route to the spice-rich Orient. Note also the Biblical tale of the gifts presented by the Magi in Bethlehem. In the days before daily bathing and modern cooking, people had practical reasons for using perfumes and incense, and needed strong spices to mask the unpalatable odors and to preserve food that otherwise would have spoiled without refrigeration.

Today, Madison Avenue never lets us forget the need for deodorants, perfumes, and good-tasting food. Foods and drinks are not often advertised for their nutritional value, but because they taste or smell good. Our chemical senses may no longer be as important to individual survival as they once were, but for the survival of our modern economic system, they are probably critical.

CHEMICAL SENSITIVITY

Chemical sensitivity is apparently basic to all living matter. The basic animate functions such as growth, reproduction, or assimilation are all mediated by chemical means and organisms which lack sensitivity to such environmental influences as light and sound, still respond to chemical influences. In the processes of evolution the simple (?) chemical sensitivity of protoplasm has apparently developed profoundly, culminating in the establishment of receptors whose sole function appear to be the response to chemical stimulation.

Some of the most promising of current research on chemical sensitivity involves the study of *chemotaxis* of quite low forms of life. For example, it has been demonstrated in the case of *Escherichia coli,* a common bacterium found in the human digestive tract, that the organism has at least five different *chemoreceptors* (Adler, 1969). That is, it behaves differentially to at least five different chemical substances.

The chemical senses we refer to as *gustation* (taste) and *olfaction* (smell) are merely extensions to and elaborations of the basic, primary chemical reactions of elemental protoplasm. In higher-order animals, much of the chemical function has been taken over by highly specialized receptors in the mucuous linings of the oral and nasal cavities; many lower-order animals, on the other hand, retain a chemical sensitivity over much of their body surface. In addition to the usually considered chemical sensitivities, as we shall see in the next paragraphs, some remnants of a quite primitive, reflexive chemical sense still remain, even in the highly developed vertebrates.

COMMON CHEMICAL SENSE

Among the so-called chemoreceptors three categories or classes might be disclosed (Pfaffman, 1951). There is first a common chemical sense such as found on mucuous membranes like the eyeball, nasal and oral cavities, and presumably on the skin surface of many organisms, especially those inhabiting the water. The free nerve endings mediating such a sense are less sensitive, provide far less discriminability, and are among the most general in their response of all the senses. While their response may be to stimuli similar to those eliciting conventional gustation, olfaction, and tactual experiences, common chemical sensitivity is said to be distinct from the other, more specific senses (Crozier, 1916).

As an example, two classes of receptors have long been recognized in the nasal passages. In addition to the true olfactory nerve endings which are able in some way to discriminate different odors, there is a common chemical sense, mediated by simple endings of the trigeminal nerve. Being sensitive to irritating vapors, for example, stimulation of these receptors may cause discomfort or pain, often leading to reflexive sneezing, crying, or coughing. Parker and Stabler, in 1913, determined sensitivities of the common chemical sense, contrasted with the gustation and olfactory senses. Using alcohol, which is an adequate stimulus for all three, they showed that a concentration of from 5 to 10 mol* was required to evoke the common chemical sense, while the taste response could be evoked at a concentration of 3 mol and an odor response could result from a concentration of only 0.000125 mol.

Although common chemical sensitivity is quite fascinating, it will be left to the researchers and not considered further in this book. Rather, let us turn to the remaining two classes of chemoreceptors. The second and third categories of chemoreceptors can be identified as those mediating taste and those responsible for conventional odor sensitivity.

GUSTATION AND OLFACTION

Most of the experience we refer to as flavor is mediated by these two receptor types, along with some tactual cues (texture, for example), temperature, and perhaps pain in some cases, as with very hot Mexican food. But the distinction between the two chemical modalities is not always clear. Does an onion taste hot? We are told that if the olfactory sense is eliminated one cannot tell the difference in taste between an apple and an onion. The onion, however, normally evokes responses from the olfactory system and perhaps the common chemical receptors, as evidenced by the irritation-associated tears and red eyes.

Manufacturers claim in their ads that some cigarettes "taste" better. Do they really taste better, or do they simply smell better? Nearly everyone has experienced the condition of a clogged nose and the subsequent loss of olfactory sensitivity. Food when you have a cold does not taste the same. Professional wine tasters probably spend as much time studying the bouquet of a wine as they do tasting it. Indeed, the interdependency of pure tatse and pure olfaction is much too obvious to belabor.

For practical applications, such as developing better-tasting food or more pleasing soft drinks, it generally does not matter whether taste or smell is involved. One simply creates a product that is preferred by the public, one that has the preferred flavor, and whether taste or smell is of greater importance is an academic question.

Since academic questions are just the sort of questions of interest to us in this book, we will do well to study the chemical senses as *individual entities*—not just something to be manipulated in order to sell

* Mol is the abbreviation for molar concentration. The number of grams of a solute, divided by its molecular weight equals the gram-molecular weight. A molar concentration of 1.0 is a solution containing one gram-molecular weight in one liter of solution.

more beer, or to manufacture a perfume women will buy. Under controlled laboratory conditions it is feasible to study the chemical senses
individually and know which one is involved. We will examine the gustatory sense first, reserving an examination of the olfactory sense for the
following chapter.

GUSTATION

Gross Anatomy of the Gustatory Organ

Complicated end-organs for taste are found on the tongue and soft
palate of man, the adult *homo sapiens* having about 9,000 of these *taste
buds,* although younger members of the species frequently have more.
First appearing in the human fetus at about three months, taste buds in
the young child are found over the entire upper surface of the tongue
and the inside of the cheeks. Ontogenetic development (mirroring phylogenetic development?) results in a pronounced decrease in the total
number of taste buds as well as concentrating them in limited loci in the
oral cavities.

In the adult, taste buds are largely limited to the areas shown in
Fig. 17-1. Interestingly enough, different areas of the tongue tend to be
sensitive to different tastes. The rear portion of the dorsal surface tends to
have taste buds sensitive to "bitter." Near the lateral edges of the dorsal
surface, areas sensitive to "sour" are found, with experiences of "salty"
and "sweet" being localized nearer the tip of the tongue. The area near
the central midline of the dorsal surface has no taste buds and is insensitive to any taste. There are also some taste buds, in limited numbers,
on the palate, pharynx, larynx, and other areas of the oral cavity.

Taste Buds

Taste buds are generally located on *papillae,* small elevations such
as illustrated in the middle drawing of Fig. 17-1. Each taste bud is made
up of a number of receptor cells containing fine fingerlike extensions,
known as *microvilli,* which appear to increase the functional surface of
the cell. Chemical materials in solution, reaching the microvilli by way
of tiny pores in the papillae, and in some manner not yet fully understood, produce a neural response in the sensitive taste receptors.

A remarkable bit of information is the life span of these taste cells.
In the cat and rabbit, their life span is on the order of three to five days,
and is probably similar for humans (Beidler, 1963). Investigators who
once thought they had identified different types of sensory cells (corresponding to different taste sensitivities) were probably observing the

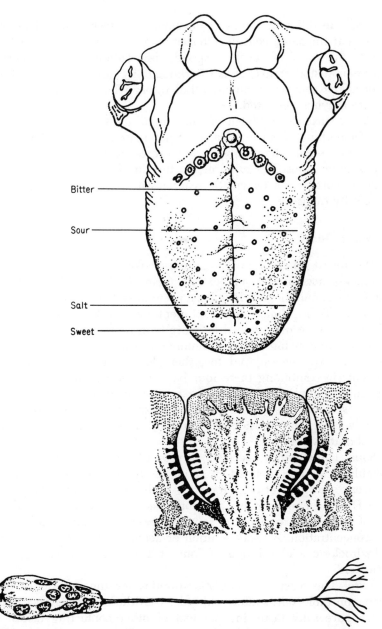

Fig. 17-1. The gustatory sense. Taste receptors are located on the surface of tongue, as shown in the top drawing. The middle drawing illustrates one papilla containing many individual taste buds. The many taste buds are shown on the figure as the white fingerlike processes. The bottom drawing shows an individual taste bud with its nerve fiber. (From "Taste and Smell," A. J. Haagen-Smit, copyright 1952, by Scientific American, Inc. All rights reserved.)

same cells in different stages of development. Recent investigators have shown that the same cell, in different stages of development within the three to five days' life cycle, responds differentially in accordance with its developmental status. Thus discriminability appears to be a function not of *which* cells are stimulated, but rather what stage of development they are in when activated.

To be sure, the problem of differential areas of the tongue still remains something of an enigma. It is not reasonable to believe that the base of the tongue should always have receptor cells in a state of development unlike those, for example, on the tip of the tongue. Recent work on the importance of enzymatic reactions in the mediation of taste may help clarify the issue.

Primary Tastes

We found, in color vision, primary colors that can in combination presumably account for all possible nuances of hue. The existence of primary taste qualities has long been posited, and even today we generally accept the four primary qualities mentioned earlier: salt, sour, bitter, and sweet. There may indeed be more than four primary taste qualities, but for the time being this small number appears adequate to account for most taste experiences. And too, there have been some successful experiments in combining these four basic tastes experimentally to match other more complex compounds for taste equivalency.

The stimuli necessary to produce these four primary tastes are not perfectly clear, but considerable progress is being made through current laboratory research.

Sour. The stimulus necessary to produce the experience of sour, has probably been best defined. It most surely results from the presence of a weak acid in solution, interacting with the oral saliva. The existence of an H^+ ion in solution is apparently necessary for the normal experience of sour. The experience of sour, however, is not simply related to the acid concentration. A weak solution of acetic acid tastes just as sour as an hydrocloric acid solution of four or five times the strength of the acetic acid.

Salty. The most characteristic stimulus for the experience of salty is common table salt, sodium chloride. It is the only substance that will elicit a pure salty taste, independent of other conflicting tastes. Other salts such as potassium chloride or sodium bromide produce additional tastes of bitter or sweet. It is rather apparent that the cation (negative ion) plays an important role in the experience of salty. While the process is not fully understood, there is a high degree of relationship between anions (H^+) and the experience of sour, and cations (e.g., Cl^-) and the experience of salty. Note that a bit of salt on a sour grapefruit reduces the sourness quite effectively—the cations of the salt presumably combine with the anions of the fruit's acid, changing the overall result to a more nearly neutral (less sour) taste.

Sweet and Bitter. The situation with respect to the experiences of sweet and bitter is not nearly so clear. As a matter of fact, some complex substances may be changed from sweet to bitter, or conversely, by changing only a small portion of their complex molecule. Some persons even feel that a single receptor mechanism may be involved in bitter-sweet sensitivity. Many persons feel there should be two taste classifications: sour-salty, mediated by ionic activity, and sweet-bitter, mediated perhaps by enzymatic reactions. Only a few generalizations might be made: most, but not all, compounds of sugars, saccharins, and the like produce a sweet taste, while the alkaloids such as quinine, strichnine and other toxic agents frequently have a bitter taste. While the inorganic salts provide the salty taste, heavier salts based on organic compounds frequently taste bitter. A proper understanding of just how the primary tastes (assuming there are any) are mediated will have to await the results of current efforts by our chemist friends and by those individuals studying primitive chemotaxes as mentioned earlier.

Gustatory Sensitivity

Measurements of sensitivity aimed at determining thresholds for various sapid substances vary tremendously. Techniques for introducing the agents vary widely, and there are numerous variables such as locus and area of application of the substance, its concentration, its temperature, and the adaptation level and overall condition of the organism. With respect to this latter, pregnant women show a marked threshold elevation for both sodium chloride and acid (Hansen and Langer, 1935). Anyone who has tasted an orange immediately after eating a piece of candy knows how sour the normally sweet fruit may taste. The level of sugar in the blood has a noticeable effect on the taste threshold for sweet. Also, there are inherited characteristics, such as the sensitivity or lack thereof, to phenylthiocarbamide, the PTC so often used in genetic studies.

We may, however, attempt some broad generalizations. One study, for example, showed threshold molar concentrations for sucrose, sodium chloride, hydrochloric acid, and quinine sulfate to be respectively .02, .035, .002, and .0000004 (Pfaffman, 1951). At least it would appear that the bitter taste for quinine can be experienced at a much lower level of concentration than can the other tastes. Note too, as we indicated previously, acetic acid is more effective in eliciting the experience of sour than is hydrochloric acid.

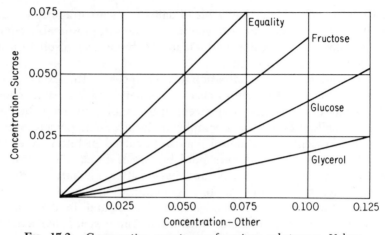

Fɪɢ. 17-2. Comparative sweetness of various substances. Values
on the abscissa are the concentrations of the listed agents necessary
to produce subjective equality of sweetness with concentrations of
sucrose shown on the ordinate. All concentrations are in gram-mol
percent, i.e., 1/10 the value of the molar concentration. (Adapted
from Pfaffman, 1951, with permission.)

Figure 17-2 shows the results of an experiment in equating sweetness. These curves show the concentrations required for various sweet
substances in order for them to taste as sweet as sucrose. The curves
show that in order for fructose to taste as sweet as a .050 gram-mol percent solution of sucrose, it must have a concentration of about .080 gram-
mol percent.

For purposes of neurological examination, an interesting graded
series of stimuli has been found to be of practical use (Börnstein, 1940).
To the normal subject the following concentrations in Table 17-1, in

TABLE 17-1

Cᴏɴᴄᴇɴᴛʀᴀᴛɪᴏɴs ᴏꜰ Sᴛɪᴍᴜʟɪ

	Easily Recognizable	Moderately Strong	Very Strong
Sucrose	4.0	10.0	40.0
Sodium chloride	2.5	7.5	15.0
Citric acid	1.0	5.0	10.0
Quinine monohydrochloride	0.075	0.5	1.0

grams per 100 cc of water, were found to produce the indicated experiences when drops of the solution were applied to different parts of the
tongue.

The utilization of such a technique makes it possible to detect or at least suggest the presence of lesions or other damage in the gustatory portions of the central nervous system. To be sure, such thresholds are crude, and perhaps only radical departures from normal taste sensitivity can be detected.

Let us look in slightly more detail at a few of the factors already referred to that make precise determinations of taste thresholds so difficult.

Area and Duration. In general there is an inverse relation between the area stimulated and the concentration of a substance necessary to elicit a taste response. A weaker solution, spread over a wider area will apparently encounter more taste receptors and, as a general rule, produce an experience more quickly than if a more limited area is stimulated. Presumably the apparent specificity of individual papillae results in less likelihood of a response if the area stimulated is sufficiently restricted. The factor of duration also influences thresholds, but apparently not in such a simple, straightforward manner as in the retinal elements discussed in a previous chapter.

Temperature. The temperature of the solution influences taste thresholds but this relation in not at all simple. Even substances that evoke the same experience do not behave in the same way. Some sweet-eliciting substances increase in their evocation potential with an increase in temperature; others remain relatively constant. While most chemical reactions are enhanced by a rise in temperature, only the tasting of some sweet-producing substances seems to follow this principle. At the other extreme, the experience of salt seems to follow a reverse curve, with higher temperatures resulting in higher thresholds while the bitter taste

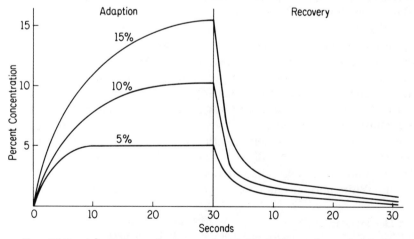

Fig. 17-3.   Adaptation and recovery for NaCl. Ordinate shows threshold for adaptation with indicated concentrations, for times shown on abscissa. (Adapted from Hahn, 1934.)

produced by quinine seems to show an exponential function in the same direction.

Adaption. It has long been known that adaptation plays an important part in taste sensitivity. In some ways it resembles the adaptation effects of vision, but in other ways it is much more complex, and certainly less well understood. Taste does decrease as the sapid material in held in the mouth; in some cases adaptation may be complete, with the taste actually disappearing. Here again, despite some confusion, adaptation and recovery curves *have* been plotted for many substances. Figure 17-3 is an example of the results of one such study. These curves show the threshold concentrations of NaCl required for various adaptation times, up to 30 seconds, and for recovery times up to the same limit. Note the rapid recovery when the adapting substance is removed. Somewhat similar curves have also been demonstrated for cane sugar and glycol (sweet) (Hahn, Kuckulies, and Taeger, 1938). With the exception of such short durations for adapting and recovering to the same substance, surprisingly few generalizations with respect to gustatory adaptation can be made.*

For example, adaptation to sour substances generally lowers sensitivity to all sour-producing agents, but adaptation to salty materials appears quite specific. It has been shown, for example, that with 24 different salts, adaptation to any one does not affect the threshold for the others (Pfaffman, 1951). There is some evidence that adaptation to sucrose (sweet) or to sodium chloride tends to enhance sensitivities for other qualities, while quinine increases the sensitivity to salt and sour, but not to sweet.

It has been suggested that gustatory adaptation is due to changes in the permeability of the taste-cell membrane for a specific agent. Thus the cell is still able to respond to other, noninhibited substances. Cross-adaptation and cross-enhancement among various substances still remain something of a puzzle to the student of taste. About all that can be said is that adaptation phenomena occur, but general principles to predict taste experience cannot be established with any degree of reliability.

Internal Factors. There is no question that the internal condition of the organism influences its gustatory sense. In 1942 C. P. Richter reported his now classic studies on self-selection of foodstuffs by rats. This study demonstrated the ability of the animals to compensate for various nutritive, endocrine, and vitamin deficiencies by altering their feeding patterns. While normal rats tend to prefer a weak solution of salt to pure

---

* The long-lasting "taste in your mouth" and apparently long-lasting changes mentioned earlier are probably due not so much to changes in the sensitivity of individual receptors as to the presence in the saliva of the adapting agent. Researchers are very careful to remove all traces of the material being tested before continuing with precise laboratory studies.

water, it was shown that adrenalectomized rats show such an increased preference for salt as to voluntarily ingest enough of the mineral as to successfully counteract the normally fatal adrenal insufficiency.

It was once believed that the animals deficient in salt had a lowered threshold, so that they could detect the presence of salt in much weaker solutions than could be detected with no deficiency. Pfaffman and Bare (1949) showed that the threshold for detecting salt is the same whether the animal is deprived or not. The change is apparently not one of sensitivity of the taste buds, but rather a higher-order, inexplicable hunger for the needed substance.

It has also been shown that insulin injection, which results in increased sugar consumption, does not change absolute thresholds for sweet, at least when electrical recordings of taste-bud response are employed as the dependent variable. Mayer-Gross and Walker (1946), however, found a reduced supraliminal sensitivity for sugar following insulin injection. Reduction of blood-sugar level below 50 milligrams per 100 cc resulted in an animal's preferring a 30 percent sucrose solution, which would, under normal blood-sugar levels, have been rejected as too sweet.

In summary, it would appear that internal factors do not increase absolute sensitivities to weak concentrations of a needed substance. Internal changes, however, seem to produce "hungers," causing the animal to eat more of the needed substance "because it tastes good." An animal deprived for some time of salt may literally spend hours licking from a salt block with, anthropomorphically speaking, great relish. And animals in need of sugar can be fed quantities of food with artifical sweeteners such as saccharine, which supply none of the needed nutrient. Apparently, in some manner we do not understand, the need for a specific substance simply heightens the pleasure experienced from eating it.

SUMMARY

In this chapter we addressed ourselves to the more primitive, chemical senses. We examined first the basic phenomenon of chemical sensitivity, and the manner in which it is commonly evidenced: as a common chemical sense, as the gustatory sense, and as olfaction. Leaving olfaction for the following chapter, we examined briefly the anatomy of the taste organ and the receptors, known as taste buds. We considered primary tastes and gustatory sensitivity. With respect to the latter, we indicated the amazing complexity of taste sensitivity relationships. We considered as important factors: the area of application of the sapid substance, its temperature, and the nature of adaptation and internal factors as determinants of taste experience.

SUGGESTED READINGS

1. Crocker, E. C., *Flavor* (New York: McGraw-Hill, 1945).
2. Moncrief, R. W., *The Chemical Senses* (New York: Wiley, 1946). These two books have been listed together because they represent the two standard references in the area of taste and smell. They are relatively old books, and recent chemical research has tended to clarify some of the problems and controversies they originally presented. I am not suggesting that the interested reader read these two volumes in their entirety. They are, however, useful reference books and do much to set the stage historically for more recent research. The interested student should at least be familiar with these two important volumes.
3. From C. G. Mueller, *Sensory Psychology* (Englewood Cliffs, N.J.: Prentice-Hall, 1965). Chapter 5, consisting of 10 easy-to-read pages, is devoted entirely to taste. It examines primary taste qualities, adaptation and contrast, taste thresholds, and possible physiological mechanisms. One cannot present a complete description of taste in 10 pages, but these 10 pages come about as close to presenting the full story as any short reference available.
4. Wolsk, D., "Chemical Sensitivity" in M. Alpern, M. Lawrence and D. Wolsk, *Sensory Processes* (Belmont, Calif.: Brooks/Cole, 1967). Another fairly elementary treatment of the subject, in keeping with the coverage of this book. The 21 pages of this selection are perhaps a little more advanced than the Mueller reference above, but less technical than the following reference by Pfaffman. The latter 10 pages of this reference are devoted to taste, while the first eleven pages are concerned primarily with olfaction.
5. Pfaffman, C., "Taste and Smell," in S. S. Stevens (ed.), *Handbook of Experimental Psychology* (New York: Wiley, 1951). These 26 pages are particularly recommended for the serious student. The first 16 pages are devoted to taste, the last 10 to olfaction. Particularly valuable for an extensive bibliography of original reports. A must for the really serious student.
6. Adler, J., "Chemoreceptors in Bacteria," *Science* 166 (1969), 1588–97. This is by far the most difficult reading included for this chapter. For the student interested in the basics of taste sensitivity and the identification of primary chemical substances, this reading is worthwhile. Some knowledge of chemistry is a practical necessity for the complete understanding of this article, hence it is recommended only for the serious student.

18

THE CHEMICAL SENSES—OLFACTION

The sense of olfaction retains a primitive nature, similar to that for the sense of taste. It lacks most of the discriminative capabilities, spatial characteristics, and high level of development of the visual and auditory senses. In the case of man, it might even be considered somewhat of a degenerated or at least degenerating sense. The proportion of the brain, for example, devoted to the chemical senses in lower animals is much greater than that for man. The highly developed olfactory lobes found in fishes are not even detectable in man, at least not with an olfactory function.

The olfactory sense is rather obviously of extreme importance for many lower species. In the animal world both predators and prey require a keen sense of smell in order to survive. Mating behavior is much influenced by the olfactory sense. It has been recently shown that destruction of the olfactory bulb in male hamsters totally destroys their mating behavior (Murphy and Schneider, 1970).

While the olfactory sense may have lost much of its survival value for man, it is still of considerable importance. Miners must use canaries to detect the presence of minute amounts of poisonous gases to which the human nostril is inadequately sensitive, and hunters must resort to the employment of dogs to trail game. Nevertheless, the perception of odors does have some survival value. Note that noxious substances frequently have rather unpleasant odors, just as they frequently have bitter tastes. The formation of harmful bacteria in decaying foodstuffs and body wastes is often accompanied by very unpleasant, putrid odors, thus serving as a warning to the potential eater. Many lower animals disdain eating food with a putrid or rotten smell.

To modern man the matter of esthetics, cleanliness, and so on, as discussed in the last chapter, probably pay a much more important role in his interest in olfaction. As previously indicated, flavor is made up of both taste and smell, and the latter is probably of no less importance

329

than the former. I suspect, in fact, that olfaction plays a more important role in flavor, than does taste.

A critical problem in olfaction, as indeed in all the senses, is the specification of the stimulus. While we will discuss this matter in some detail in the pages to follow, some general statements may be made at this time. As with taste, odorous materials must be in chemical form, and must be soluble in water, at least to some extent. In addition, it would appear that in order to be detected by the olfactory mechanism, a substance must be volatile, it must be in the form of airborne particles. Finally, it would appear that odorous materials must be soluble in lipids (fatty substances) in order to penetrate through the lipid layer that forms the surface membrane of the sensory cells.

Before examining the nature of substances that can produce the experience of odor, or smell, it will help to examine the physiological and anatomical mechanism involved.

OLFACTORY ANATOMY

In the human, olfactory receptors are found exclusively in a pair of small patches located in the two nasal cavities; the area of each of these patches being about 2.5 cm^2, or somewhat less than one-half square inch. The patches are found on the medial wall of the *superior concha* and the adjacent lateral wall of the *nasal septum*, and can be identified by the presence of a yellowish brown mucous membrane. (See Fig. 18-1.)

Unlike most sensory cells, the sense cells for olfaction perform both the primary reception and conduction functions. Their fine unmyelinated axonal fibers, as small as 0.2 mμ in diameter, leave the nasal cavity by way of fine perforations in the bony *cribriform plate*. This combining of both sensory and conduction in the same cell is similar to that found in the primary senses of insects, and in the case of higher-order animals is unique to the olfactory sense. Such an arrangement probably contributes to the enhanced sensitivity of the olfactory mechanism through the elimination of one synapse. The axon of the bipolar olfactory cell simply synapses with a second-order neuron which transmits the olfactory impulse directly to higher-order olfactory centers.

In spite of the rather restricted anatomical area of the sensitive surface, the functional area for olfactory reception is incredibly large. The densely packed sensory cells number some 100,000 per square millimeter, for a total in the hundreds of millions, perhaps a number even greater than the number of visual rods and cones as described in an earlier chapter. But that is not all that contributes to olfactory sensitivity.

Note from Fig. 18-2 that each individual cell terminates in numerous

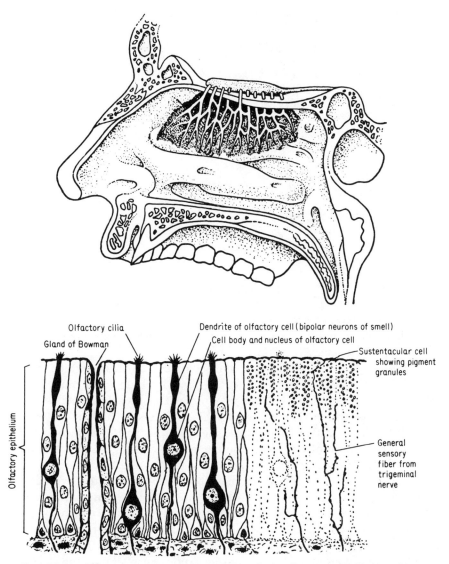

Olfactory cilia

Gland of Bowman

Dendrite of olfactory cell (bipolar neurons of smell)

Cell body and nucleus of olfactory cell

Sustentacular cell showing pigment granules

General sensory fiber from trigeminal nerve

Olfactory epithelium

FIG. 18-1. Olfactory sensory system. (Top figure from A. J. Haagan-Smit, "Smell and Taste," copyright 1952, by Scientific American, Inc. All rights reserved. Bottom figure modified from Rasmussen.)

fingerlike processes or *cilia*. It has been estimated that a single sensory cell may have as many as 1,000 of these processes. These numerous tendrils, ranging in length from 1 to 100 mμ, greatly increase the receptive area of the dendritic end of the receptor cell, so that the 2.5-cm^2 surface

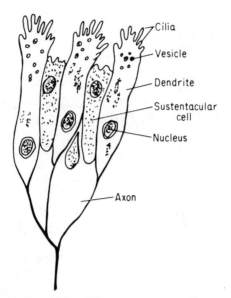

FIG. 18-2.   Olfactory receptor cells.

becomes, in effect, as great as an area of 600 cm² or more. Such an areal magnification probably plays an important role in the extreme sensitivity of the olfactory sense.

There is yet an additional morphological situation which might contribute to extreme sensitivity. In the olfactory bulb (first brain level), thousands of receptor cell axons synapse with only about 100 second-order neurons, which then transmit their impulses to higher centers. In the rabbit about 26,000 axonal processes synapse with 100 second-order neurons, for a ratio of 260 to 1. Another reference suggests that the ratio should be 1,000 to 1. Whichever figure we take as the truth, such a summative process should greatly increase the sensitivity of the overall system. The entire olfactory system seems to utilize a summation effect which, in the case of vision, is largely restricted to the relatively peripheral rods. If there are olfactory fibers that maintain the relative one-to-one direct pathways of foveal cones, they have not been disclosed. But then, olfaction does indeed play a rather crude, survival role and does not provide the perceptual experiences analogous to form perception in vision, or the speech analysis function of audition.

SENSITIVITY

While we might expect, on the basis of the preceding anatomical description, that the olfactory sense would show a high degree of sensitivity, the observed facts are almost beyond belief. The amount of an odorant necessary to produce an olfactory experience is almost infinitesimal. The amount of odorous material deposited by a rabbit as it leaves its trail for the pursuing beagle must be exceedingly slight; detection of a cow in heat, perhaps a mile away, must be the result of an unbelievably small amount of the chemical substance reaching sensitive areas of the bull's nasal cavity. With respect to the small amount of substance necessary to elicit an olfactory response, Wolsk (1967) suggests, for example, that if the active ingredient of musk, originally obtained from the anal scent gland of the musk deer, were to be spread on a surface exposed to a continuous breeze, in one million years it would lose only about one percent of its potency as an odorant. The rapid disappearance of perfume from the opened bottle, on the other hand, is due to the rapid evaporation of the volatile vehicle, not to the direct loss of any great amount of odorant per se.

DeVries and Stuiver (1961) have considered the extreme sensitivity of olfaction. They calculated that in mercaptans, such as those involved in skunk smell, thresholds can be achieved with as few as one molecule for every two receptor cells. They further suggested that the threshold for stimulating a single olfactory cell is at most 8 molecules of the odorant substance.

Methods for Studying Olfaction

While some progress has been made, equipment used to study olfactory sensitivity does not differ greatly today from that designed some years ago by Zwaardemaker and Elsberg and illustrated in Fig. 18-3. The top drawing shows schematically the Olfactometer of Zwaardemaker (1895), while the bottom drawing is the more recent blast-injection device of Elsberg (1935). Some modern devices meter the odorant with greater precision, and many devices are capable of mixing various odorants in relatively known quantities, but the basic principles of these two devices remain the tools of today's researcher.

In Zwaardemaker's Olfactometer, the odorant lines the outside tube. As the inner tube is moved back and forth, the amount of odorant exposed to air, and hence subject to being sniffed by the subject, is varied. A standard unit of odorant sometimes employed is the length, in centimeters, of the odorant which need be exposed in order to achieve threshold. The amount of odorant exposure needed for threshold detection is called an *olfactie*. One olfacti of india rubber equals 0.7 centimeter, at least for a tube with the dimensions employed by Zwaardemaker. Less odorous substances might require more than 0.7 centimeter of exposure in order to be detected, while a highlly odorous substance such

Fɪɢ. 18-3.   Olfactometer of Zwaardemaker and blast-injection device of Elsberg. See text for explanation.

as the mercaptans might be detected with an exposed area of appreciably
less than 0.7 centimeter.

It should be obvious to the reader that such a measure is not very
precise, since such uncontrollable variables as the strength of the subject's
sniffing or inhalation would markedly affect the amount of air passing
over the exposed odorant, and therefore the threshold.

The second device pictured, Elsberg's blast-injection device, does
remove the variable of sniffing, but at the same time provides a less
realistic perceptual or sensory task. In this case a measured amount of
air is forced under pressure into a bottle by means of a small syringe
or pump. When the exhaust valve is opened, a known amount of the odor-

ant laden air is forced into the nostril or nostrils of the subject.* By using more than one bottle at the same time, it is possible to mix odorants in relatively known amounts, or to deliver one odorant to one nostril and a different odorant to the other.

Thresholds

Determination of olfactory thresholds, both absolute and difference, is indeed a complex, difficult task. There are so many variables involved that even if the concentration of the odorant could be specified with precision, results would still be highly imprecise. The complex physical nature of the nasal cavities makes an understanding of the aerodynamic character of the space surrounding the sensory patches almost impossible to understand. Probably no two people have olfactory cavities of precisely the same size and shape. Thus the amount of odorant actually reaching the sensitive receptor surface must be largely a matter of conjecture. Also, such factors as temperature and humidity influence thresholds for odors, largely because they influence the volatility of the odorant.

Absolute Thresholds. When monorhinic stimulation is used, thresholds for detection are higher than when dirhinic stimulation is employed. Perhaps this difference can be explained in the same way as the differences between monaural and binaural auditory thresholds—in terms of probability rather than any hypothesized neural summation. The still primitive, crude nature of olfactory research, and the general dearth of knowledge, however, militate against any firm conclusion on the matter.

Acquired *hyposmia* (impaired olfactory sensitivity) and/or *parosmia* (distortion or changes in perceived quality of an odor) may result from nasal infections and some diseases. Thus the problem of determining "normal" thresholds if further complicated. Normal variations in sensitivity may also occur from day to day. Women may experience *hyperosmia*, or increased olfactory sensitivity, during their menstrual period (Elsberg, Brewer, and Levy, 1935). The entire matter is exceedingly complex.

We can make some crude comparisons among various odorant materials and at least get a vague sort of feel for the relative sensitivity of the olfactory mechanism to different substances. While many different measures of the concentration of an odorant might be used, such as mols or molecules per unit volume, perhaps the commonest measure is that of milligrams per liter of air.

---

* While the drawings picture a single output for one nostril, more often than not, both nostrils are stimulated simultaneously. In the former case, *monorhinic* stimulation is said to be employed; *dirhinic* stimulation refers to simultaneous stimulation of both nostrils, and hence both olfactory areas, by means of a simple bifurcation of the exhaust tube.

Table 18-1 shows some thresholds which have been published, all based on milligrams of odorant per liter of air, and are mostly from the work of Allison and Katz (1919).

TABLE 18-1

THRESHOLDS FOR NINE COMMON ODORANTS

Odorant	Concentration
Ethyl ether	5.83
Carbon tetrachloride	4.53
Chloroform	3.30
Ethyl acetate	0.69
Amyl alcohol	0.225
Ethyl mercaptan	0.046
Isobutyl mercaptan	0.008
Amyl thioether	0.001
Artificial musk	0.00004

That such figures can at best be accepted only as relative and perhaps only suggestive of true thresholds, can be demonstrated by an imaginative technique described by Moncrief (1946). If a known amount of odorant is evaporated in a room with a known volume of air, the concentration of the odorant is relatively simple to determine. To be sure, a subject in the room has continuous opportunity to sniff the odorant-laden air and draw it over his olfactory receptors, but the results are still astonishing. Using this method, the threshold for ethyl mercaptan was found to be something like .00000004 milligram per liter of air, or about one millionth the threshold concentration determined in laboratory olfactometry tests.

The method described by Moncrief illustrates still additional problems in determining olfactory sensitivity. In all methods, odors are sensed in a background of air. But how often is air perfectly odorless? It is almost like trying to determine visual brightness thresholds against a background of starlight. In the blast-injection technique it might be possible to fill the bottle with pure, odorless air, but once the odorant reaches the nasal cavity it is mixed with the residual air which must occupy this oddly shaped space. Except perhaps for highly artificial laboratory preparations, we may never be able to determine true absolute thresholds for olfaction.

Difference Thresholds. The determination of differences in strengths of odorants necessary for recognition of a difference presents an even more formidable methodological problem. We are probably safe in concluding that relatively large changes in concentration are needed in order for quantitative differences to be detected. Gamble in 1898 calculated Weber fractions from about ⅙ to ½—rather large values, compared with those for most other senses. Zigler and Holway (1935) calculated DL's more recently; they too found that rather large differences are required in order for two odors to differ in strength. They found values of $\Delta I/I$ on the order of $\frac{1}{5}$ to $\frac{9}{10}$ for different concentrations of india rubber, a relatively strong odorant material frequently used in laboratory research.

Adaptation

Another serious problem besetting the researcher in olfaction is that of adaptation. The speed and extent (even completeness) of olfactory adaptation is very great. Recollect how quickly one can adapt to odors in a room, or, over time, to the odors of his own home or place of business. Other persons may notice the odors, but not the person regularly inhabiting the area.

Figure 18-4 is an example of results from a laboratory experiment on adaptation to two substances, benzoin and rubber. The abscissa of this curve shows the adaptation time, in seconds, to two different concentrations of each of the two substances. The ordinate shows the threshold for the substances, in olfacties. Note how rapidly the adaptation takes place.

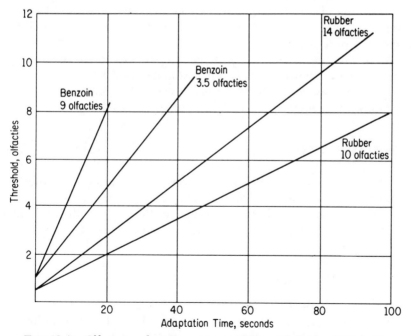

FIG. 18-4.   Olfactory adaptation curves. (From Pfaffman, 1951, with permission, based on data from Zwaardemaker, 1925.)

While the time for complete adaptation to any substance may be directly proportional to the molecular concentration of the odorant in the air (Woodrow and Karpman, 1917), the matter of cross-adaptation is indeed complex. Adaptation to one substance may or may not effect the sensitivity to another stimulus. Exposure to camphor elevates thresholds for eucalyptal and eugenol. Indeed, there is a mutual effect among all three. On the other hand, benzaldehyde has little effect on the thresholds for these three substances. Pfaffman (1951) proposes that such findings suggest a receptor mosaic made up of groups of sensitive units, each of which is sensitive to a different family of chemical stimuli.

Odorant Mixtures

The results of mixing or blending different odors cannot always be predicted. In some cases a phenomenon of masking can be demonstrated. Substances that show mutual adaptation effects, as described above, may tend to mask each other when presented together.

Some times the odorous materials may remain distinct, each retaining its own character; or blending may occur, in which the resultant odor still resembles both of the original components. When many components are blended together, analysis and identification of the individual odors may be quite difficult. Interestingly enough, training, such as obtained by professional perfume chemists, may markedly improve the ability to analyze complex odors.

When different odors are presented separately to the two nostrils, the technique is known as *dichorhinic* stimulation. The writer has been unable to find any generalizable results utilizing this technique that shed any light on the enigmatic functioning of the olfactory system.

ODOR CLASSIFICATION

Olfactory theory has progressed over the centuries from the early attempts at classifying and defining odors, all the way to current theory involving the "how" of olfactory sensitivity. But even with our modern "how" theories, a truly parsimonious classification system is still an elusive target.

Linnaeus' Odor Classification

Probably the first attempt at classifying odors which remains of importance today, was that of Carl Linné (latinized as Carolus Linnaeus), the eminent botanist and father of taxonomy. In his cataloguing of plants he attempted to establish a meaningful system for the description of their odors. In 1752 he presented a system made up of seven classes of odors:

1. Aromatic
2. Fragrant
3. Ambrosia
4. Alliaceous
5. Hircine
6. Foul
7. Nauseous

In addition to Linnaeus' classification, the eighteenth century saw several additional classifications. Albrecht von Haller, the physiologist, described a three-component theory, consisting of (1) sweet-smelling or ambrosiac odors; (2) intermediate odors; and (3) stenches. There were also two theories developed in the nineteenth century by D. Lorry, in 1784, and A. F. de Fourcroy, in 1798, both based on chemical characteristics of odorants. After five or six additional, less popularized attempts at classification in the nineteenth century, Hendrik Zwaardemaker, the Dutch physiologist, came onto the scene.

Zwaardemaker's Classification

In 1895 Zwaardemaker presented his nine-class system of olfactory taxonomy which was to have such a profound effect on olfactory thinking. Even today this system is sometimes used, since the nine odors described by Zwaardemaker do indeed appear to be unique, and since most complex odors can be fitted into one or more of his categories without undue straining of the imagination. On the basis of more recent research with such techniques as cross-adaptation, it is clear that Zwaardemaker's nine classes are not mutually exclusive, and some changes in the system are called for. Nevertheless, it was and still is a useful classification and worth noting for practical as well as historic interest.

Zwaardemaker's classification utilized the seven odors of Linnaeus, with the addition of one from each of Haller's and Lorry's systems. His classification, with examples to help define the basic odor names follows:

1. Aromatic—camphor, cloves, citron, almonds, anise
2. Fragrant—flowers, vanilla, balsam, violet
3. Ambrosiac—amber, musk
4. Alliaceous—onion, acetylene, iodine, chlorine
5. Hircine (also called caprylic)—goaty, cheese, rancid fat, sweaty
6. Foul—narcotics, some bugs, nightshade
7. Nauseous—carrion, feces
8. Ethereal (from Lorry)—ether, beeswax, fruits

9. Empyreumatic (from Haller)—roasted coffee, tobacco smoke, benzene

With numerous subclasses within the nine major classes, Zwaardemaker's classification met with universal acceptance, at least until the advent in 1915 of Henning's smell prism.

Henning's Prism

The result of an elaborate investigation of qualitative similarities in odors, Hans Henning (1924) constructed a prism with six primary groups of odors and many intermediate odors lying on the edges and surfaces of the prism. In Henning's system all odors lie on one of the five

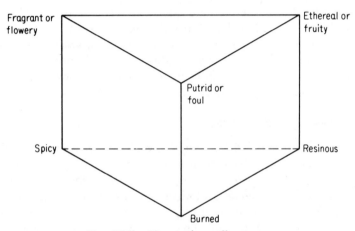

FIG. 18-5. Henning's smell prism.

surfaces or edges of the prism; no odors are found inside the prism. The six primary classes of odors as shown in Fig. 18-5 were related to Zwaardemaker's nine classes and were identified thus:

1. Ethereal (E)—Corresponds to Zwaardemaker's ethereal
2. Fragrant (F)—Corresponds to Zwaardemaker's fragrant
3. Spicy (S)—Corresponds to part of Zwaardemaker's aromatic
4. Resinous (R)—Corresponds to the remainder of Zwaardemaker's aromatic
5. Burned (B)—Corresponds to Zwaardemaker's empyreumatic
6. Putrid (P)—Corresponds to Zwaardemaker's foul and nauseous

Henning considered some odors to be duplex—that is, lying on a line between two primary classes. Geranium, for instance, lies on the line between fragrant and ethereal, while cinnamon occupies a point on the line between spicy and putrid. Other odors were quadruplex—that is, lying on the surface of the prism, hence defined by four primary classes. Cedar is located on the FESR plane, while garlic occupies a point on the FPSB plane.

The alliaceous odors of Zwaardemaker fall in the middle of the FPSB surface, while the hircine (caprylic) odors really do not have a specific locus. Myrtle, for example, would be hircine in Zwaardemaker's system but falls on the line between spicy and resinous for Henning; balsam is resinous for Henning, fragrant for Zwaardemaker.

Most recent investigations have shown that, at least by gross approximation, the classification of Henning seems to work, but in details of the system, there are pronounced difficulties. As in all systems up to this time, Henning's classification was based purely on phenomenology, the way the substances "smell" to human subjects. Any classification based on more fundamental chemical or physical parameters of the stimulus was to wait until relatively recent times.

Crocker and Henderson (1927)

A more pragmatic system, utilized "because it works" was developed by Ernest P. Crocker and Lloyd F. Henderson of the Arthur D. Little Laboratories. While it may indeed be an oversimplification to try to describe all odors in terms of just four basic types, for practical applications the system seems to work, and a trained observer can, according to the authors, recognize the degree to which a substance contains the four basic odors. The primary odors proposed by Crocker and Henderson are:

1. Fragrant or sweet
2. Acid or sour
3. Burnt or empyreumatic
4. Caprylic or goaty

Trained observers, evaluating foodstuffs, perfumes, and deodorants, are able to assign numbers from 1 to 8 to each of the four components making up any complex odor. For example, ethyl alcohol has an odor defined as 5414, vanillin as 7122 (considerable fragrant or sweet), and a rose as 6423. The Crocker-Henderson system is not based on any elegant analytical chemical or physical basis. It is purely pragmatic, the result of years of research in the applied-flavor field. For describing commercial foodstuffs and the like, the system appears quite adequate.

OLFACTORY THEORY

Theories to explain the sense of smell have been with us for many years, perhaps millennia would be more precise. Yet even today the matter is far from settled.

Historical

Two thousand years ago the Roman poet Lucretius (1951) suggested that the "palate" contained minute pores of various shapes and sizes. Every odorous substance, he speculated, gave off tiny "molecules" of a particular shape which fitted into these pores. The identification of the odor depended, then, on which pores were occupied by appropriate molecules. While we may have once laughed at his naiveté, modern olfactory theory has made a wide circle and has now come back to an explanation that would surely have warmed the heart of Lucretius.

In the interim between Lucretius and modern theorists such as Moncrief, Amoore, Rubin, and Johnston, numerous attempts at explaining olfactory phenomena have been described. Faraday noted that many odorous substances strongly absorb radiation in the infrared region of the spectrum. Thus a theory of olfaction based on possible infrared sensitivity was engendered. Even today, numerous investigators emphasize the importance of infrared radiation (Beck, 1950; Beck and Miles, 1947). However, even though infrared absorption can be shown to be correlated with odorant strength, it is obvious to the scientific mind that it cannot therefore of necessity be used as an explanation. The explanation for odorant efficacy may be simply the same explanation as for the existence of the marked infrared absorption, some characteristic of the atomic or molecular nature of the odorous substance.

Modern Theory

In 1949 R. W. Moncrief proposed an hypothesis not greatly unlike that offered some 2,000 years earlier by Lucretius. He suggested that there are a limited number of types of receptor cells, each representing a different "primary" odor, and that molecules of odorant material produce their effects by fitting into the correct "slots." Actually, Moncrief's explanation is similar to the "lock and key" concept currently employed in explaining the action of enzymes with their substrates, antibodies with antigens, and a host of similar relationships so popular with modern theorists.

Recently a classification based largely on the shape of complex molecules, and hence the nature of the olfactory receptor sites, has resulted in a very promising theory of odors. John E. Amoore at the University of Oxford succeeded in identifying seven primary odor classes and their characteristic molecular natures, five being identified by their shape (and hence the shape of the receptor "slot") and two by their electrical charges. The seven primary odor classes of Amoore and their identifying substances are shown in Table 18-2.

TABLE 18-2

PRIMARY ODOR CLASSES OF AMOORE

Odor Class	Substance
Camphoraceous	Camphor, moth repellent
Musky	Angelica root
Floral	Roses
Pepperminty	Mint candy
Ethereal	Dry-cleaning fluid
Pungent	Vinegar
Putrid	Rotten eggs

Of more significance than the remarkable agreement with both Linnaeus' and Zwaardemaker's odor classifications, is the relation between Amoore's primary odors and the molecular shape of the odorant substances. It was found that substances with the camphoraceous odor had molecules of a generally spherical nature, and were all of about the same size, on the order of seven angstrom units (0.7 mμ) in diameter. Thus it was hypothesized that the "slot" for the camphoraceous odor must be shaped like a hollowed-out bowl, and must have a diameter on the order of seven angstrom units.

When the characteristic molecules of the other odorants were examined it was found that they fell into four additional shape groups, and that their odors could be largely predicted on the basis of the shape of their molecules. Musk, floral, pepperminty, and ethereal seemed to result from additional molecular shapes for which appropriate receptor "slots" could be hypothesized. Figure 18-6 is a schematic drawing of the approximate shapes hypothesized for the first five primary odorant classes in both vertical and cross sectional view.

For pungent and putrid odors, no characteristic shapes were evident.

| Camphoraceous | Musky | Floral | Pepperminty | Ethereal |

FIG. 18-6. Approximate shapes of hypothetical "slots" into which odorant molecules fit. The top row of figures show the approximate shapes of the hypothesized sites, while the bottom row shows the same "slots" in cross section. (Data from Amoore, et al., 1964.)

Fortunately it was found that a characteristic electrical charge identified these two remaining odor classes—that pungent substances carried a positive electrical charge, and putrid substances could be identified by a negative charge.

That is about where we are today in the circuitous history of olfactory theory. We certainly do not understand olfaction with the perceptive insights we hold for vision and audition. But there are many unanswered questions with respect to these senses, and experts differ widely in their explanations for many visual and auditory phenomena. The stereochemical theory of odor answers many questions, but it also leaves many questions unanswered. The necessity of appending the two odor classes resulting from molecular charges, raises more than a grain of doubt. However, until a better, more complete theory is advanced, we will have to admit to the likelihood that this one is correct.

SUMMARY

In this chapter we tried to examine what is known about the olfactory sense, the sense of smell. After considering the anatomy of the olfactory organ briefly, we looked into the problem of sensitivity, including the determination of absolute and difference thresholds, adaptation, and the results of complex odor mixtures. Emphasizing throughout the colossal difficulties in conducting highly controlled research in the olfactory domain, we stressed the imprecision of psychophysical techniques applied to olfaction. Finally we examined odor classification from an historical perspective, concluding with what appears to be the best, most logical classification, that based on the so-called stereochemical theory of odors.

SUGGESTED READINGS

1. Crocker, E. C., *Flavor* (New York: McGraw-Hill, 1945).
2. Moncrief, R. W., *The Chemical Senses* (New York: Wiley, 1946). These are the same two books recommended for the preceding chapter. They are of equal significance to the material considered in Chapter 18.
3. From C. G. Mueller, *Sensory Psychology* (Englewood Cliffs, N.J.: Prentice-Hall, 1965). Chapter 6 is devoted entirely to olfaction. Its 10 pages are written much in the manner of Chapter 5 on taste, referred to as a reading for the preceding chapter. Chapter 6 is recommended as highly pertinent to the material covered in this chapter, as well as interesting and fairly easy reading.
4. Wolsk, D., "Chemical Sensitivity," in M. Alpern, M. Lawrence and D. Wolsk, *Sensory Processes* (Belmont, Calif.: Brooks/Cole, 1967). This is the same reference included in the last chapter. The half of the chapter devoted

to olfaction is the portion recommended as a reading at this point. It is good reading, somewhat more technical than the Mueller reference, but less technical than the following reference.

5. Pfaffman, C., "Taste and Smell," in S. S. Stevens (ed.), *Handbook of Experimental Psychology* (New York: Wiley, 1951). The same reference recommended for the last chapter. As in the case of gustation, it is a valuable reference for olfaction. Its bibliography is particularly recommended.

6. Haagen-Smit, A. J., "Smell and Taste," *Scientific American*, March 1952. A short article of six pages which presents the available knowledge on the chemical senses in a highly readable manner. A brief history is included and an introduction to chemical theory is presented. This is a good starting point for someone interested in the chemical senses. The article is perhaps more directly applicable to the sense of olfaction than taste, hence its inclusion here rather than in the preceding chapter.

7. Amoore, J. E., J. W. Johnston, Jr., and M. Rubin, "The Stereochemical Theory of Odor," *Scientific American*, February 1964. One of the more recent, and better descriptions of modern thinking with respect to olfactory theory. It is somewhat technical, to be sure, presenting the theory involving shapes and charges of molecules and their fitting into "slots" on the olfactory endings. This is good reading for the student interested in modern olfactory theory.

19

THE SKIN SENSES

The remaining two sensory provinces are first, those relating to sensing the position of the body and to awareness of internal, e.g., visceral, events, and second, those relating to physical events acting directly on the living tissue of the organism from the outside. For the sake of expository simplicity we shall treat the experiences of such events in separate chapters, divided somewhat in an arbitrary manner. In this chapter we deal primarily with events originating from the outside which stimulate the organism by way of its skin, or outer integumental covering. The matter of internally generated stimulation is considered in the final chapter.

The mammalian integument is indeed a complex organ. In addition of its purpose of keeping the animal from falling apart and flowing about like a mass of jelly, the skin serves many organic purposes. It aids in temperature regulation, it is an excretory organ, it serves a respiratory function, and it has numerous important protective functions. Of particular significance to us in this book is the functioning of the skin as a sensory organ, the specialization of protoplasm's irritability function. Perhaps more accurately we should recognize that the skin serves as a locus for many different sensory organs.

That the skin is a very complex organ can be seen from Fig. 19-1. Indeed, it is a much more complicated organ than Fig. 19-1 would appear to indicate. This figure shows nerve endings in the form of tactile corpuscles as well as dendritic fibers entwined about a hair follicle. Actually, there are perhaps dozens of additional primary forms and secondary modifications of nerve endings in the skin. There are sensory nerve endings in the walls of the blood vessels and there are free nerve endings in the skin, as well as several additional specialized receptors to which various sensory experiences such as cold or warm have been attributed.

CUTANEOUS RECEPTORS

Traditionally, the student of cutaneous sensitivity has spent considerable time identifying receptors in the skin and attempting to determine their roles in the experience of cutaneous sensations. Since the latter part of the nineteenth century it has been recognized that the skin is not uniformly sensitive throughout its area. If a small area is mapped by means of different types of stimuli, such as those producing warmth, cold, touch, and pain, particular loci for sensitivity to the various stimuli may be found. Most companies supplying equipment for use in psychological laboratories still include in their inventories rubber stamps to be used for transferring an inked grid to a portion of skin, thus enabling an experimenter to "map" the skin for areas sensitive to the various cutaneous stimuli. When stimuli such as a warm object, a cool or cold object, a needle (for pain), and a hair (for touch) are applied within the inked grid, punctiform loci sensitive to the various stimuli can be plotted with relative precision. Many of these spots will remain stable over long periods of testing (Gilmer, 1942).

A common-sense assumption, and one that served as a primary motivating force for such pioneers as Max von Frey, would be that there must be some sort of specialized organs in the skin with differential sensitivities to the various stimuli. With this in mind, several exceptionally well-motivated, gung-ho researchers have been known to strip off pieces of their previously mapped skin, stain them appropriately, and subject them to microscopic analysis. As a result of some of this early work, there were many accounts of just what end organs were sensitive to just what stimuli. Unfortunately, the data were highly contradictory and did not serve to prove that *any* end organs served *any* cutaneous modalities exclusively. For example, according to some experimenters, a healthy cornea is sensitive to most if not all of the cutaneous modalities such as cold, warm, touch, and pain; yet there are no specialized end organs to be found there, only free nerve endings.

While the assigning of a specific function to a particular form of nerve ending has not met with a great deal of success, there are some relationships that do appear meaningful. Consequently, it might still be helpful to consider the nature of the relationship between cutaneous experience and the existence of various end organs before proceeding with the psychophysical relations of cutaneous sensitivity.

As can be seen from Fig. 19-1, the skin can be divided into two primary layers, the outer *epidermis* and the inner *dermis*. The former can in turn be divided into an outer, dead layer, containing neither nerves nor blood vessels, and an inner, living layer (*Malpighian layer*) containing free nerve endings but no vascular supply. The dermis, on the other hand, is richly endowed with numerous nerve endings, specialized receptors, blood vessels, cutaneous glands, and so on. The dermis tends to merge, without clear lines of demarcation, into the subcutaneous tissue.

Cutaneous Pain

Probably the most widely distributed neural receptors in the skin—indeed in the entire body—are the free nerve endings. It would be reason-

Fig. 19-1. Schematic cross section of skin. (From W. Montagna, "The Skin," copyright 1965, by Scientific American, Inc. All rights reserved.)

able to guess that they represent more primitive stages of development than do the more specialized receptors.

It is generally agreed that free nerve endings mediate cutaneous pain. W. L. Jenkins (1951) suggests that throughout the body only free nerve endings exist in sufficient abundance to account for the almost universal presence of pain spots. Furthermore, the cornea, particularly susceptible to pain, has only free nerve endings. Some pain, as Nafe has suggested, may also arise from spastic activity of the blood vessels, but even then it is probably the free nerve endings associated with the blood vessels which, in the final analysis, actually mediate the sensation of pain.

In spite of the above observations, a universally accepted explanation for pain is not possible at this time. Some research, for example, has pointed to the existence of specific pain spots, so that the prick of a pin may miss a spot and no pain will ensue. At the other extreme, under some conditions of *hyperalgesia,* even a light touch may result in excruciating pain. While pain is often associated with tissue damage, it is obvious that not all tissue damage results in pain, and some pain can be produced in the absence of tissue damage. On the other hand, it is clear that increasing the intensity of an otherwise nonpainful stimulus may very well result in the experience of pain. Perhaps it is the number of sensory fibers evoked, or the rate of their discharge, that is significant for pain. More often than not pain is the result of strong or intense stimulation.

Some experts believe there are more than one "pains," that they arise from different classes of stimuli and behave differently (Lewis, 1942). According to Lewis, the two "pains" are mediated by two types of fibers, one myelinated and rapid in conduction, the other unmyelinated and relatively slow. The nature of pain is far from being a closed subject, even though the consensus places heavy reliance on the activity of free nerve endings as a physiological basis.

Touch or Pressure

Deep Pressure. There are two types of sensitivity to touch or pressure. The basis for one of these, the relatively deep-lying sense of pressure or movement, is almost assuredly attributable to deformations in the *Pacinian corpuscle.* This organ is a multilayered spherical body, about 0.02 to 0.06 inch in length, much like an onion, with alternate cellular and liquid layers and containing an unmyelinated nerve ending in its core. It lies generally beneath the dermis in subcutaneous tissue and is found throughout the body, around muscles, in mesenteries, etc. It is a very sensitive organ, research having shown that a movement of about .0001 inch is all that is necessary to evoke a response from it.

Were it not for the fact that they do appear to mediate deep pressure, as when one presses firmly against the skin, we would not have mentioned Pacinian corpuscles until the next chapter, where they really seem to be more applicable.

In the second broad category of touch sensitivity, those experiences apparently mediated by nerve endings nearer the surface of the skin (generally in the Malpighian layer), at least three types of endings appear to be of importance.

Encapsulated Nerve Endings. There are a number of corpusclelike bodies found in the skin which have been credited with mediating tactual sensitivity; two in particular being *Meissner* corpuscles and *Merkel's* cells. (See Fig. 19-2.) While each of these organs, as well as such other specialized endings such as *Ruffini* cylinders, *Krause* end bulbs, and *Glomus* bodies was once thought to be structurally distinct and truly unique, some

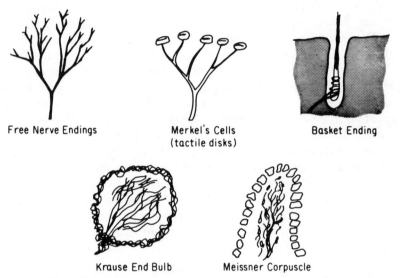

Free Nerve Endings   Merkel's Cells   Basket Ending
                            (tactile disks)

Krause End Bulb   Meissner Corpuscle

FIG. 19-2.   Some representative cutaneous nerve endings.

modern workers hold that they are all stages of development lying on a continuum. A group at Oxford University denies there are separate capsules for different stimulus modalities (Wolsk, 1967). Jenkins (1951) further points out, that there are so many intermediate forms of encapsulated endings that "any strict division into types is of dubious merit."

On the other hand, it has been found that Meissner corpuscles are abundant in those parts of the body which are relatively hairless, such as the palms of the hands and soles of the feet. Conversely, on parts of the body which are richly endowed with hair, the next type of nerve endings to be discussed, *basket endings,* are found, and Meissner corpuscles are nonexistent. Certainly, circumstantial evidence points to the importance of Meissner corpuscles as mediators of tactual sensitivity.

Basket Endings. The existence of basketlike entwining of nerve endings around the hair bulbs (see Fig. 19-1) help lend additional credence to the idea that Meissner corpuscles are responsible for tactual sensitivity. There can be little doubt that these fibers, entwined about the roots of the hair, signal any slight movement of the hair itself. Where hairs do not exist, tactual sensitivity is often still quite acute, and there, and only there, one finds Meissner corpuscles. Where hair exists, tactual sensitivity can be aroused by simply moving the hair, without actually touching the skin. But too, destroying hair root endings does not completely remove such sensitivity; apparently moving the hair also results in distorting the skin so that other touch receptors are activated.

Free Nerve Endings. Sensitivity to touch is apparently the result, also, of a deformation gradient in the skin, particularly where hair follicles do not exist. If a finger is immersed in mercury, there is contact all over the finger, but the touch experience is only elicited at the surface of the liquid, where the pressure gradient must exist. Or, if a small object is glued to the skin and alternately depressed and pulled gently, most persons cannot distinguish between the two activities. Deformation of the skin surface is clearly a necessary concomitant of touch sensitivity where hair does not exist. Probably both free nerve endings and Meissner corpuscles are involved in the sense of touch. In the cornea, for example, as indicated earlier, free nerve endings must perforce be responsible; in other parts of the body, who can say for sure?

Temperature

Separate Receptors. Jenkins suggests that, with respect to receptors for warm and cold, our ignorance is profound. The early suggestion of von Frey, that Ruffini cylinders are the receptors for warmth and Krause end bulbs serve the same function for cold, has never been verified. The case for assigning cold sensitivity to Krause end bulbs has some plausibility. There is often found a topological relationship between sensory cold spots and the existence of Krause end bulbs in the skin. Areas of the body that are particularly sensitive to cold, such as the nipple, are found to be richly supplied with Krause end bulbs. Negative evidence, on the other hand, is equally abundant. Many areas of the body with excellent sensitivity to cold do not evidence Krause end bulbs. Perhaps the best that can be said is that the endings may be cold receptors in some parts of the body, but in other portions of the body some other mediational unit must be responsible for the sensation of cold.

There has never been any evidence in support of the Ruffini cylinders as receptors for warmth. To his credit, von Frey did not assign the sensation of warmth to these organs. He simply said that "perhaps" they might be responsible. Some weak evidence for the importance of Ruffini cylinders as mediators of warmth evolved about comparative depths of the various receptors and consequent time delays in sensing the nature of the stimuli. Early research had placed receptors for warmth at a greater depth than cold receptors. Hence the deeper Ruffini cylinders were indicated as receptors for warmth. But the evidence for shallow and deep temperature sensitivity is not good, both warm and cold can be sensed with a wide range of temporal delays and presumably with receptors at varying depths.

Evidence for the existence of some sort of specific receptors for warm and cold is also found as a result of stimulation with nonadequate stimuli. The jab of a fine needle or an electric shock can produce either an experience of warmth or cold, depending apparently on just what receptor is stimulated. As early as 1883 one experimenter succeeded in producing either cold or warm experiences by means of electric shock. Various chemicals can produce either the experience of cold or warmth, further leading one to believe in the existence of separate receptors for the two temperature conditions.

The existence of *paradoxical cold,* and perhaps *paradoxical warmth,* has long been recognized and often employed as evidence for separate receptors for warm and cold. Paradoxical cold can be produced by stimulating an area (or point) on the skin with a temperature on the order of 45° centigrade (113° Fahrenheit), and on occasion paradoxical warmth has been achieved as a result of stimulation with temperatures lower than the normal skin temperature. The assumption might be made that there must be separate receptors for the two temperature extremes.

"Warm" and "Cold" Fibers. Another important approach considers the thickness of the afferent fibers as being significant. While there does seem to be some relation between the primary modality (including pain, touch, and temperature) and the size of nerve fibers, the relationship is not at all clear, and there is considerable overlapping in size of fibers serving the different modalities. Evidence from higher levels, such as the spinal cord, does point to different fibers for pain or touch, as contrasted with temperature. But for distinguishing between warm and cold, such evidence is far from convincing.

Some fibers have been found that increase their rate of firing when temperature is increased, while other fibers show an increase in firing rate with a decrease in temperature. Under conditions of high temperature, both types of fibers increase their rate of firing, and the experience is one of heat or "hot." An interesting demonstration can be made that tends to support the conclusion that "hot" results when both warm and cold receptors fire simultaneously. If one stimulates the forearm with an arrangement of parallel thin strips, alternately warm and cool, the experience is that of heat. Presumably some fibers increase their rate of firing as a result of the warm stimuli, while others increase their rate because of the cool stimuli. The result is the same as if all the fibers were stimulated by a hot stimulus.

Perhaps some of the difficulty in identifying temperature receptors may be due to the fact that warm and cold are not unitary experiences. Some writers hold that there are two forms of temperature stimulation, and hence appropriate receptor mechanisms: radiant and contact application (Hardy and Oppel, 1937). There are puzzling differences between the effects of radiant and contact stimulation, and perhaps the attempt to lump the temperature sense into only two so-called "modalities" may be an impossible task.

Vascular Theory. An interesting theory, for which there is insufficient evidence to either completely support or completely refute, is the vascular theory advanced by John Paul Nafe (1938). According to this theory, free nerve endings in the walls of the fine blood vessels indicate changes in the diameter of the vessels as they either dilate or constrict as a function of impinging temperature changes. This theory capitalizes on one particular fact: that the temperature sense is basically a sense of *change* in temperature. As we shall see in a later section, adaptation to temperature is quite profound, and by and large, only changes in temperature are sensed. It is an interesting theory, but not entirely defensible. If the cornea is indeed sensitive to cold, there must be some basis other than changes in capillary size in this admittedly nonvascular tissue. And too, such phenomena as nonadequate stimulation seem to point rather clearly to the existence of specific receptors (Jenkins, 1939).

CUTANEOUS EXPERIENCE—ADAPTATION

Some of the various phenomena associated with cutaneous experience are discussed below, the experience being related to the physical event wherever possible, and viewed in the context of the various explanations for cutaneous sensitivity we have considered. Most of the psychophysical methods referred to earlier have been employed in studying the skin

FIG. 19-3.   Tactile adaptation times for different body areas. (Data taken from Zigler, 1932.)

senses, and we shall consider such things as absolute thresholds, difference thresholds, and subjective scaling.

Before proceeding with psychophysical relations, however, let us examine the subject of adaptation, which plays such an important role in cutaneous experience.

Touch

As with many other senses, adaptation plays a very significant role in cutaneous experience. In touch, adaptation is very pronounced, even complete, within a relatively short period. Note how you quickly become oblivious to your clothing in contact with your skin.

Time required for such complete adaptation is a function of the particular individual, as well as pressure of the stimulus, the area of skin involved, and the particular location on the body. Figure 19-3 shows mean times for eight subjects required for complete adaptation to different pressures on several body locations. In this experiment a weight, shown on the abscissa, was lowered gently to the skin and allowed to rest there until the subject reported that it could no longer be felt. This time, then, is the time for total adaptation (Zigler, 1932).

Another approach to tactile adaptation involves a matching procedure, and in a sense, evaluates the pressure sensation. In one experiment, a stimulus of known weight was applied for four seconds to a point on the forearm. A nearby area was simultaneously stimulated periodically with weights of varying size to determine subjective equality. As can be seen from Fig. 19-4, after three seconds a weight of only 20 percent as

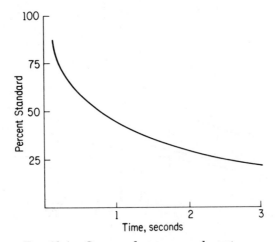

FIG. 19-4.   Course of pressure adaptation.
(After von Frey and Goldman, 1915.)

great was judged equal to the standard. In other words, the pressure experience had declined to only 20 percent of its original sensory magnitude in a mere 3 seconds.

It is unlikely that any explanation for tactile adaptation in the manner of that suggested for the chemical senses and for vision is either warranted or needed. The sense of touch is a sense of movement or change; it is produced by externally induced movements—compression, bending, shearing, in sensitive receptor endings. When the movement ceases, the stimulation ceases. The short adaptation times that do exist may reflect mechanical adaptation of the skin and underlying tissues as they readjust to the original deformation. Such a description accounts for the advantage of "active" touch over "passive" touch. If you wish to feel the texture of something you slide your fingers over it, producing a series of changes, of tactual experience. Sandpaper feels like sandpaper only if the fingers "scan" it. Note too, that the reader of Braille must move his finger tips over the raised characters if he is to perceive them properly.

Pain

The reader might question whether there is true adaptation to pain. Evidence indicates that adaptation to pain does indeed exist, and can be, like adaptation to touch, complete. But it seems to take longer. In one study, involving pain produced by inserting needles in the forearm, as long as five minutes were required for complete disappearance of the pain. For shallower insertions of the needle (2.5–25-gram pressure) adaptation times on the order of one and one-half minutes or less were found.

The longer adaptation times commonly reported in the case of pain provide additional evidence for the theory that pain is in some way associated with damage-producing stimuli and is possibly mediated by receptors other than those mediating pressure or touch. Pain appears to be more than just rapid, intense firing of conventional tactile fibers.

Temperature

No one need be apprised of the existence of temperature adaptation. Stepping into a tub of water can result in a rude awakening if one has been adapted to a noticeably different air temperature. At the other extreme, with gradual adaptation, one can actually hold his hand in water so hot as to damage the tissue. Probably some cases of severe sunburn may be due to an unawareness of the temperature adaptation taking place.

A very great number of studies on temperature adaptation have been published in the scientific literature. Some of these bear on the extent to which complete adaptation can take place—that is, the extent to which a cold or hot stimulus may, with time, achieve a neutral apparent tempera-

ture. The human cannot adapt completely to as wide a range of temperatures as can the frog in the hot water we referred to earlier (if the whole
matter is not simply an old wive's tale). At extreme temperatures, adaptation to a point of neutrality simply does not occur. If you place your
hand in boiling water it will not reach an experience of neutral temperature, at least not before it is severely damaged. Yet for a rather wide
but restricted range of temperatures on either side of the normal skin
temperature, complete adaptation can occur.

The time required to adapt completely to various temperatures depends on how far away the adapting temperature is from the normal skin
temperature. Figure 19-5, based on studies of Hensel (1950), show times
required for adaptation to various temperatures indicated on the abscissa.
These data are based on a single resting skin temperature, represent only
one form and size of stimulating device, and are for only one body location. They are however fairly representative and serve to show the general
trend. Note that an increase of 5° requires about 10 minutes for complete
adaptation, while a decrease of the same amount adapts out in only 5
minutes.

Another approach to temperature adaptation is to study the course
of the adaptation and involves the stimulation of different skin areas. We
might adapt both hands to the same level by immersing them in water of
a known temperature, for example 38° centigrade (100°F). At the end
of the preadaptation we immerse the left hand in water of a different

FIG. 19-5. Adaptation to different temperatures. See text for explanation. (Smoothed curve drawn from data published by Hensel, 1950.)

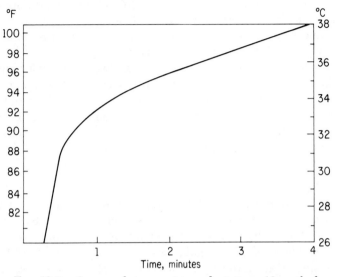

FIG. 19-6. Course of temperature adaptation. (Smoothed
curve, based on data from Hahn, 1930.)

temperature, such as 26°C (79°F). At regular intervals following this
new adaptation of the left hand, we present test stimuli to the right hand
and ask the subject to report whether the test temperatures are warmer,
colder, or equal to the temperature of the left hand, still being adapted
to the new level. As can be seen from Fig. 19-6, at time 0, the right hand
requires a 26° stimulus to achieve equality with the left hand's 26° adaptation stimulus. (Both had been adapted to the same temperature immediately before). After about one minute a temperature of 34°C (93°F)
applied to the right hand feels equal to the 26° of stimulation of the left
hand. By 4 minutes, adaptation is complete, and a 38° stimulus feels the
same temperature to both hands. What has apparently happened is that
both hands have, in four minutes, achieved a physiological zero, such that
the 26° stimulus to one hand feels the same as a 38° stimulus to the other.

Experiments like these show the possible range of temperature adaptation, and time for adaptation, and disclose many critical variables such
as the size of the stimulated area and its location. What apparently is hap-
pening in all these instances of temperature adaptation is a distortion,
either moderate or profound, of the underlying sensory scale.

CUTANEOUS EXPERIENCE—SENSITIVITY

In spite of the universal problems inherent in determining absolute
and difference thresholds for the cutaneous senses, many researchers have

attacked the problem, and with some degree of success. In spite of the numerous difficult problems involving adaptation, bodily location, and even identification of the adequate stimulus, the results achieved are surprisingly consistent, and well worth noting.

Before examining the data in more detail, we might point out that in general the cutaneous senses are much less sensitive than vision or audition. The almost infinitesimal amounts of energy required for these senses is far inadequate to evoke most of the cutaneous receptors. It has been suggested that some of the skin receptors are more than a billion times less sensitive than the auditory or visual receptors.*

Touch

Several different experimental approaches to the study of the touch or pressure sense suggest themselves. These include the determination of absolute thresholds, the two-point threshold, and thresholds for vibration.

Absolute Threshold. Thresholds for touch are generally obtained by gently pressing against the skin with an object of known weight, and hence pressure or force. Frequently a fine bristle or hair is used to minimize areal effects and assure punctiform stimulation. By pressing with a hair of known stiffness just to the point where it begins to bend, a known force may be applied. One set of hairs, graded in stiffness and thereby permitting differing forces, is known as von Frey hairs, named after the early cutaneous experimenter we mentioned earlier. A similar set may still be obtained today from manufacturers of psychological laboratory equipment. Modern techniques, of course, permit much better control of pressure and rate of application of the stimuli.

Sensitivity to tactile stimuli varies with the region of the body stimulated. Table 19-1, based on the early work of von Frey, shows some typical absolute thresholds for different areas of the body. Although these values were obtained many years ago and might not agree in absolute value with data obtained by more recent, better-controlled methods, the relative differences for the various regions of the body would probably hold.

The area of surface being stimulated is an important factor. As the areal size of the stimulus is increased, the force exerted must be increased to maintain threshold. It would appear that the critical measure is the force per unit area, rather than the total force exerted. Above some maximum area, the relationship no longer holds, causing some theorists to suggest that the important factor in determining thresholds is not the

---

* If the reported experiments by the Russians, in which persons are able to "read" with their finger tips are verified, then some change in thinking about the cutaneous receptors might be called for.

TABLE 19-1

ABSOLUTE THRESHOLDS FOR TOUCH

Skin Region	AL, grams/mm^2
Tip of tongue	2
Tip of finger	3
Back of finger	5
Front of forearm	8
Back of hand	12
Calf of leg	16
Back of forearm	33
Loin	48
Sole of foot	250

vertical force applied, but rather the lateral tension in the cutaneous membranes which result from the vertical distortion.

Two-point Threshold. A well-known measure of tactile acuity is the two-point threshold which is analogous to resolving power in the case of the visual system. The two-point threshold is defined as the minimum distance between two tactile stimuli that can be reliably detected as two. A device known as an *esthesiometer* is used to measure the two-point threshold. This is an instrument not unlike a pair of draftsman's dividers, except perhaps with somewhat blunted points. The experimenter touches the two points to the subject's skin simultaneously, and the subject reports whether he feels one point or two. The experimenter repeats the procedure many times, with many different separations of the points, such that, at one extreme, consistent reports of "two points," and at the opposite extreme, consistent reports of "one point" are obtained. By psychophysical methods, not unlike the procedures we described for calculating difference thresholds, the experimenter can determine two-point thresholds for various regions of the body.

One might expect that sensitive areas of the body, such as the fingertips, would show small two-point thresholds as contrasted with relatively unsensitive areas such as the back or the feet. Generally speaking, this is precisely what is found. Typical two-point thresholds are given in Table 19-2.

TABLE 19-2

TWO-POINT TACTILE THRESHOLDS

Region of Skin	Two-Point Threshold, mm
Leg	68
Forearm	40
Forehead	22
Lips	4.5

One might suppose that the two-point threshold is determined solely by the richness of nerve endings in the skin, or the number of pressure receptors available, as did von Frey. The matter does not appear to be quite that simple. Many years ago A. W. Volkman showed that changes in the two-point threshold could be obtained with practice, and that improvements obtained on one forearm might be transferred to the bilateral arm. Apparently learning plays an important role, and the two-point threshold is not simply an indication of the richness of the neural supply. Perhaps touch receptors are no more plentiful in the fingertips than in the back; one simply has more practice feeling things with the fingertips.

Vibration. If not a separate cutaneous "sense," sensitivity to tactile vibration is certainly a highly specialized capability of the skin. Vibratory sensitivity is similar in many ways to auditory pitch sensitivity, a fact recognized by many contemporary researchers. The curve for vibratory thresholds (frequency on the abscissa and amplitude on the ordinate) looks surprisingly like the curve for auditory sensitivity (Fig. 14-1) but with several differences. First, considerably more power is required to obtain vibratory thresholds—perhaps a difference of 100,000 to one. Secondly, the frequency spectrum for the vibratory sense is quite different from that for the auditory sense, being displaced in a downward direction by a factor of about ten. The 50–20,000-Hz auditory range corresponds roughly to a 10–2,000-Hz cutaneous vibration-sensitivity range, although it is said that this range can be considerably expanded if sufficiently intense signals are employed. Furthermore, the point of maximum sensitivity for the auditory sense, of about 2,000 Hz, corresponds to a point of maximum sensitivity for the vibratory sense of about 200 Hz. At this point of maximum sensitivity a movement of the skin on the order of .001 millimeter can be sensed. Contrast this with minimum detectable movements of the ear drum of .00000001 millimeter, and movements of $\frac{1}{100}$ this value at the basilar membrane!

There appear to be other parallels between the skin's sensitivity to vibration and the basilar membrane's response to acoustic stimuli. The matter of sharpening or funneling, which we referred to in a previous chapter, seems to play a role in the cutaneous vibratory sense, too. Might not the skin, perhaps, be used as an auditory organ? Actually, attempts have been made to do just that. By reducing frequencies by a factor of ten, and activating a tactual vibrator against the skin of the forearm, some experimenters have succeeded in "teaching" subjects to recognize quite a few of the many vocal sounds or phonemes.

In a somewhat different approach, aimed at providing the deaf with a communication code of their own, Geldard (1957) attached vibrators to the fingers, employing a code made up of three intensity levels and three durations of vibration. At the time of the report, one subject had already reached a "reading rate" of 38 words per minute.

Perhaps some day we may have a truly efficient technique for transferring auditory signals into vibratory stimuli that will enable the deaf to hear with their skin.*

Pain

Thresholds for cutaneous pain can be determined in much the same manner as was done for the determination of touch or pressure thresholds, except that in this case a pain-producing stimulus must be used, and if we are to believe the earlier workers in the field, specific pain "spots" must be located.

Absolute Thresholds. To produce the table that follows, von Frey used a very sharp needle to locate and measure the sensitivity to pain "spots." Note the extreme variability in sensitivity to pain shown in Table 19-3, a range of 1,500 to one, as contrasted with a range of 125 to one in

TABLE 19-3

THRESHOLD FOR PAIN

Skin Region	AL for pain, grams/mm^2
Cornea	0.2
Conjunctiva	2.
Abdomen	15.
Front of forearm	20.
Back of forearm	30.
Back of hand	100.
Sole of foot	200.
Fingertip	300.

the case of pressure or touch thresholds, determined by the same man, and described in Table 19-2.

One might note the rather marked differences between this table and that presented earlier for touch sensitivity. Notice in particular the difference in sensitivity for touch and pain in the case of the fingertips. The fingertips seem to be quite sensitive to touch but relatively insensitive to pain. The soles of the feet, on the other hand, are relatively insensitive to both types of stimuli. Does a comparison of these two tables tell you anything about the possible physiological mechanisms involved?

---

* Conventional lip reading, accomplished by touching the listener's finger tips to the speaker's lips, is largely a matter of recognizing unique, characteristic consonants such as p's and b's which are associated with lip movement. Recognition of vowels by virtue of their primary frequency components (*formants*) is not generally achieved.

Difference Thresholds. In spite of the difficulty in even specifying the stimulis, numerous attempts have been made to determine difference thresholds for pain. Possibly the most successful of these attempts was first reported by Hardy, Wolff, and Goodell (1948), who used radiant heat as the pain-producing stimulus. They were able to employ nine values of heat intensity, ranging from one which just barely evoked threshold pain, to the most intense stimulus, just below a level that would blister the skin. These investigators proposed a scale of pain, based on the *dol*,* where one dol is a unit of painfulness equal in size to two jnd's in pain intensity. By subjecting 73 subjects to a stimulus of 8 dols (16 jnd's above threshold) and utilizing a fractionation method of scaling, the authors felt that they had developed a truly subjective scale of pain intensity, linearly related to sensed painfulness.

Temperature

An absolute threshold for sensing temperature is probably a meaningless concept, since it is changes in temperature that are sensed, not absolute values. All temperature experiences are experiences of differences, rather than absolute values. As contrasted with absolute judgments of pitch, sweetness, or weight, absolute judgments of temperature are virtually impossible. Due to the efficiency of visual adaptation, one cannot make absolute judgments of light intensity; possibly for similar reasons, one cannot make absolute judgments of temperature. For light, however, there is a true zero; with temperature, the concept of no temperature is completely alien to our experience. All temperatures exist only to the extent that they differ from our basic, underlying, physiological reference point. Hence temperature experience is essentially a function of difference, rather than absolute thresholds.

The ability to detect changes in temperature is apparently the result of several factors, and varies widely according to the method used to investigate it. Wolsk, for example, suggests that we are able to detect changes in temperature as slight as $\frac{1}{100}$ degree per second. This speed, incidentally, is one piece of evidence militating against Nafe's vascular theory. It is unlikely that the smooth muscle-mediated changes in capillary size could be rapid enough to account for such prompt recognition of temperature changes.

At the opposite extreme, adaptation effects, over broad areas of skin, are such that changes at a relatively rapid rate often cannot be detected. Gertz found that changes of about 0.2°C per minute were threshold, quite a difference from the previously cited $\frac{1}{100}$ degree per second. With changes at the rate of roughly 10° over a period of 35 to 45 minutes, no

---

* The word "dol" is derived from the latin word *dolor*, meaning pain or grief.

change in experienced temperature could be detected by Gertz's subjects. The matter is quite complex, and we still have much to learn about temperature sensitivity.

SUMMARY

In this chapter we tried to cast light on a subject of which surprisingly little is known with certainty. We first examined the nature of the cutaneous receptors, describing several possible receptors for pain, touch, and temperature experiences. We referred to such possible receptors as free nerve endings, basket endings, and the encapsulated endings such as Krause end bulbs, Ruffini cylinders, Meissner corpuscles, Pacinian corpuscles, and Merkel's cells. Evidence available to attribute particular cutaneous experience was considered and evaluated. We examined in some detail the phenomenon of cutaneous adaptation, describing it for touch, pain, and temperature sensitivity. Finally, we examined the available knowledge on the psychophysics of cutaneous experience, absolute and difference thresholds, including the ubiquitous two-point threshold for tactile experience. We concluded the chapter on a note of uncertainty, recognizing that our ignorance with respect to the skin senses is profound.

SUGGESTED READINGS

1. Montagna, W., "The Skin," *Scientific American* 212 (1965), 56–66. These 10 pages are relatively easy reading, covering such topics as a little anatomy, the nature and function of hair, finger prints, and sweat glands. The article is not particularly germane to the subject of sensory processes of the skin, but does provide considerable background on the skin from a general point of view. Not *must* reading, but certainly an interesting addition to the information provided in the preceding chapter.
2. Donaldson, H. H., "On the Temperature-Sense," in W. Dennis (ed.), *Readings in the History of Psychology* (New York: Appleton, 1948). This selection is not *must* reading either. It does, however, present an interesting bit of historical perspective. The nine pages are not especially difficult to read, considering the publication date of 1885, and the serious student may find the endeavor rewarding.
3. Jenkins, W. L., "Somesthesis," in S. S. Stevens (ed.), *Handbook of Experimental Psychology* (New York: Wiley, 1951). Pages 1172–1185 are of particular value to the student interested in cutaneous sensitivity. This reference should be familiar to the serious student.
4. From R. S. Woodworth, and H. Schlosberg, *Experimental Psychology*, rev. ed. (New York: Holt, 1954). Chapter 10, "The Cutaneous Senses," provides in 30 pages just about the best short account of the cutaneous senses

that I know of. It is very well referenced and covers in greater detail just about all the topics referred to in the preceding chapter. Its bibliography is excellent, though somewhat old. A very important reference for the interested student.

5. From C. G. Mueller, *Sensory Psychology* (Englewood Cliffs, N.J.: Prentice-Hall, 1965). Chapter 7 of this previously suggested book is a good, short (16-page) summary of current information on touch and temperature sensitivity. It is recommended as rather easy reading, interesting, and informative.

6. From S. H. Bartley, *Principles of Perception*, 2d ed. (New York: Harper, 1969). Chapter 12, "The Senses of the Skin," provides a detailed description of much of the material covered in this chapter. Its 35 pages are well worth reading, and provide a wealth of detailed information beyond that which we have just covered. This reference is highly recommended for the interested student.

20

ORGANIC AND INTERNAL SENSES

For this, the last chapter of our description of the senses, we have reserved discussion, I dare say, of more actual sensory receptors than were considered in all of the previous chapters combined. There are probably more individual receptors and sensory nerve endings under the heading of this chapter than the entire total of receptors involved in all of the preceding chapters.

Sensory nerve endings and/or specialized receptors are to be found in virtually every organ of the body—from tiny blood vessels to the heart, from large muscles to deep centers of the brain. Indeed, many sense organs have other sense organs in them. The muscles inside the eye have sensory nerve endings which presumably indicate the state of the muscles for accommodation and pupillary adjustment. Many of the responses from such sensory entities do not even reach a level of consciousness, but they are still part and parcel of our vast sensory system.

But we are not devoting a corresponding amount of space to the receptors for such a vast range of stimuli and of such importance. There are several reasons for this: for one thing, many of them are "silent" systems —they do not provide an output that involves our conscious experience, except in some cases where the absence of some "normal" experience is observable. For the most part they are probably conspicuous only by their absence. We walk about, sit, stand, and perform countless skeletal muscular actions without ever realizing the importance of the steady flow of impulses from sensory cells in our joints or muscles, and from our *vestibular* (inner-ear) apparatus. Outputs from delicate sensory endings in the brain maintain a continuous equilibrium in animate processes. The level of oxygen in the blood, sugar level, respiration, and pulse rate are all conditions which are self-adjusting, and by virtue of internal receptors cooperate to maintain the condition known as *homeostasis*. Only when the departure from normal is extreme do we even become aware of such things as low blood sugar or oxygen deficiency. And then it is probably secondary results of such imbalances that produce the awareness, rather than activity of the primary, organic sense organs.

A second reason for not devoting more space to the internal senses is that we actually know much too little about them. Much of what we do "know" is based on supposition and secondary or circumstantial evidence. Direct experimentation with such inaccessible and difficult to identify organs is indeed difficult.

To simplify our discussion and to bring a little order to a confusing situation, it might be well to divide the internal senses into perhaps four rather arbitrary categories. We will discuss in order first the deep pressure or subcutaneous sense alluded to in the previous chapter; second, the visceral/organic senses; third, the proprioceptive sense, involving movement and positioning of the body and limbs, and last, the highly specialized vestibular sense, located in the inner ear.

SUBCUTANEOUS SENSES

The two principal experiences provided by receptors lying in tissue beneath the skin would appear to be those of pressure and pain. The latter is probably mediated by free nerve endings, but as with cutaneous pain, our lack of knowledge is vast.

Large end organs known as Pacinian corpuscles are believed to mediate deep pressure (See Fig. 20-1). This receptor organ has been studied quite thoroughly. As mentioned in the preceding chapter, its rather large, laminated, onionlike body has been excised and shown to respond to pressure, movements as small as .0001 inch being sufficient to produce a discharge in its axial nerve fiber (Lowenstein, 1960). Located in mesenteries and in tissue around muscles, as well as in subcutaneous tissue, this organ is most surely involved in pressure sensitivity. It is one of the few receptors concerning whose function we can be reasonably certain.

Paciniun Corpuscle   Muscle Spindle   Golgi Tendon Organ

FIG. 20-1.   Some subcutaneous nerve endings involved in proprioception.

VISCERAL SENSES

Because of difficulties in experimentation, not too much is known concerning the sensitivity of the internal parts of the body. Conventional touch sensitivity, as one might guess, appears to be lacking throughout most of the internal organs. It is also unlikely that many internal organs contain receptors for temperature, at least very few that effect conscious experience. Both the esophagus and stomach, however, are said to have temperature sensitivity, but no sensitivity to light touch (Boring 1915a and b). On the other hand, both must have something like deep pressure or strain sensitivity, since moderate distention produces an experience different from simple touch or conventional pain. With extreme distention, of course, an unquestionable experience of pain may result.

The general existence, or lack thereof, of visceral pain presents additional problems. Most solid organs such as the kidneys and liver are insensitive to painful stimuli. They can be cut, burned, and crushed without producing pain. The brain itself is presumably devoid of pain receptors, as is the heart muscle. Pain receptors are plentiful, however, in the mesenteries, connective tissues, and body walls. The peritoneum is quite sensitive to pain from stretching. "Gas on the stomach" produces pain, but undoubtedly not so much from the intestines themselves as from the mesenteries and abdominal walls which take the brunt of the spasmodic stretching and "thrashing about." It is these structures, not the visceral organs themselves, which appear to contain the free nerve endings which mediate pain.

An interesting aspect of visceral pain is that of *referred pain* (Jenkins, 1952). Pain arising from specific internal disturbances is often referred (localized) to other, more external and hence accessible portions of the body. Attacks of *angina pectoris* often leave a tenderness in the skin on the left side of the chest (Lewis, 1942). Frequently following the segmented arrangement of the spinal nerves, such localizations can often be used to pinpoint an internal problem and facilitate diagnosis.

There are numerous additional complex experiences arising from within our bodies that might be called "senses." Is hunger a sense? Is nausea a sense? What about such difficult to describe experiences as those associated with suffocation, sexual arousal, fear, and the like? The best that can be said is that such experiences are simply recognition, at a conscious level, of patterns of basic underlying sensory responses of the type we have been describing. Perhaps they are more than this; no one really knows for sure.

Most of our internal receptors never produce a response that evokes a conscious experience. Receptors that maintain our internal homeostasis and regulate such variables as body temperature, calcium metabolism, water intake, or excretion rarely fall within the domain of sensory psychology.

Most of these internal receptors are either mechanoreceptors (stretch, pressure) or chemoreceptors and are deeply involved with low-level, organismic processes of the central nervous system. For example, cells have been found in the hypothalamus highly sensitive to temperature change (Nakayama et al., 1961), and most certainly the presence or absence in the blood of such substances as calcium, oxygen, and carbon dioxide must excite to action specific receptors. Many internal receptors must be considered as part of the endocrine system, contributing to the constant give-and-take that is life, and whose absence would mean the ultimate in homeostasis, death.

Such sensory processes as these are certainly critical for our survival. But they are not a part of our sensory experience, hence not a suitable subject for inclusion in this book. With that one statement we can write off as inappropriate a sensory system, far more extensive than the total of all those previously considered.

PROPRIOCEPTION

Two of the three examples of subcutaneous nerve endings shown in Fig. 20-1 are most certainly involved in *proprioception*, the sense of movement and bodily position. While much of our awareness of bodily position is mediated by the semicircular canals of the vestibular body, which are often included in the proprioceptor domain, we reserve consideration of that organ until the next section. In the meantime, we will survey the other possible receptors or nerve endings which help us to remain aware of the position of our body and limbs.

Role of Vision

In adidtion to the proprioceptive senses and their associated neural structures to be considered in this section, vision plays a very important role in maintaining bodily position. The association, at a neurological level, between vision and the vestibular mechanism must be quite intimate, as evidenced by nystagmic movements of the eyes, possible nausea, and other symptoms that may be produced when conflict exists between the visual experience and those of the vestibular and proprioceptive systems.

Tactile Receptors

Although they are not too often emphasized, the tactile and stretch receptors of our skin play an important role in proprioception. Bending an arm results in tightening of the skin on one side and relaxation or compression on the other side. Surely such sensations arising from the skin must aid us in knowing which joints are being flexed and which are being extended.

Kinesthesis

Notice that most proprioceptive experiences are also *kinesthetic* experiences. They are the result of movement, of change. Without continuous movement of some sort we would be unable to know for long just how our bodies are oriented. It is actually possible, as when flying an airplane or a trainer, to be upside-down for some time and not know it. Even the sensed internal strains and altered blood-pressure relationships may be adapted to, and unless there are suprathreshold changes in position one may in effect not know which end is up.

Several different receptors for kinesthesis, or the sense of movement, have been identified. Endings associated with muscles are most certainly of significance. As can be seen from Fig. 20-1, free nerve endings (*muscle spindles*) are found wrapped around small bundles of muscle fibers. These sensory endings appear to be stretch fibers, ostensibly firing when the muscle is extended, not when it contracts. Thus the response from a given muscle arises only when the antagonistic muscle contracts, thereby stretching the former.

The *Golgi tendon ending*, on the other hand, appears to respond when the muscle contracts. In the form of spirals around the end of a tendon where it attaches to a muscle, the Golgi endings seem to complement the muscle spindles. Thus afferent impulses from a single muscle can disclose whether the muscle is contracting, stretching, or, in the absence of any clear signal, remaining at rest.

While the existence of receptors at the joints is still a matter of conjecture, a mounting consensus holds that spray-type endings in the capsules of the joints play an important role. According to Boyd and Roberts (1953), each spray-type receptor covers a 15–30° range of movement and provides a beautifully simple coding of body posture. While it is not entirely clear how they do it, there is evidence that *spray-type* endings in the joint are able to indicate static position of the joints, rather than simply movement, as appears to hold for the muscle and tendon receptors.

Pacinian corpuscles, previously referred to as receptors for deep pressure, probably play a role in kinesthesis. Located often in the *fascia* (sheaths) of muscles, these receptors must be activated as a result of pressure variations set up by movements of limbs and other muscular activity.

Locomotor Ataxia

A classic example of what may happen when proprioceptive functioning is impaired can be seen in the disorder *locomotor ataxia*. As described in Chapter 1, this disease was so named because it appears that the shuffling or foot-slapping gait of the victim is the result of problems in the motory or musculature system. The patient does not appear to have adequate control of his legs and feet. In truth, the trouble is sensory rather than motory. Usually it is the result of a syphilitic infection of the *dorsal horn* of the spinal cord, that part of the cord containing afferent fibers leading from the sense organs of the limbs to the central nervous system. When the ascending tracts are destroyed (*tabes dorsalis*), impulses from proprioceptors in the joints and muscles of the extremities can no longer reach the brain. Hence the victim must look at his feet to see exactly where they are, and with the uncertainty he has, he either shuffles carefully or slaps his feet firmly against the ground to maximize any feedback cues that may be produced.

Proprioceptive Experience

The bellwether of the senses for psychophysical study was that of proprioception. Some of the earliest studies were done, for example, with lifted weights; experiments wherein judgments of weight were made on the basis of conscious experiences arising from proprioceptive sensitivities. Even today, practically all psychological supply houses list sets of calibrated weights so that any student can replicate the psychophysical

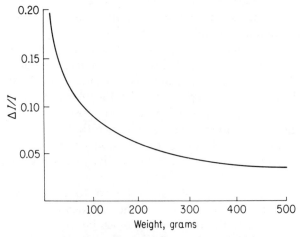

FIG. 20-2.   Hypothetical difference threshold function for lifted weights.

studies of Weber and his followers and come up with difference threshold curves such as shown in Fig. 20-2.

Current interest in the proprioceptive and kinesthetic senses often concerns the ability of people to make specific movements with known time durations and levels of accuracy. For example, "blind positioning" movements, so necessary for the operation of many complex equipments, may be studied. The science of human engineering studies the variables that determine how well a person can set a control or track a moving target, all as a function of his proprioceptive feedback. Repetitive movements, also based on adequacy of proprioceptive feedback, are a further subject of study.

VESTIBULAR SENSE

The "sense of balance" is mediated largely by a remarkable organ, located deep in the bone of the skull, and identified as a part of the inner ear. The entire inner ear, as indicated in Chapter 13, is known as the *labyrinth* and consists of two major divisions, the *cochlear* apparatus, responsible for audition, and the *vestibular* apparatus of importance for balance and equilibrium. (See Fig. 20-3.) We will briefly examine the

FIG. 20-3. Vestibular and cochlear organs. (From Hardy.)

anatomy of this vestibular apparatus before considering some of the ramifications of its functioning.

Anatomy of Vestibular Apparatus

The vestibular apparatus consists of three *semicircular canals* and the
so-called *otolith organs,* the *utricle* or *utriculus,* and the *saccule* or *sac-
culus,* along with assorted blood vessels and a generous nerve supply. The
three semicircular canals lie roughly one in each of the three possible
physical planes. As a result, turning the head in any direction will, by
centrifugal force, set the fluid in motion in at least one of the three canals.
Thus an awareness of which canal is involved in the movement, and in
which direction the fluid is moving, will serve to indicate changes in the
position of the head.

The semicircular canals are continuous at their bases with the utricle
(sometimes called the *vestibular organ*), from which they arise, and the
saccule which is joined to the utricle by a short duct. All three canals and
the two chambers are filled with endolymph, the same primitive and
nutritive fluid referred to earlier as occupying the cochlear or endotic
duct of the cochlear canal.

Receptors for the semicircular canals are found in the three *ampullae,*
thickened bulges at the base of each canal. Each ampulla contains many
ciliated receptor cells (hair cells) which respond in a manner, as yet not
clear, to movement of the fluid therein. It is generally presumed that a
gelatinous mass, the *cupula,* has enough inertia to act like a swinging door
in the ampulla, thereby stimulating the sensitive hair cells.

The utricle and saccule seem to have a function somewhat different
from that of the semicircular canals. They appear to be more responsive
to movement and vibration than do the positional/directional sensitive
ampullae of the semicircular canals. The utricle appears to be sensitive
to linear rather than rotational movement, and also to gravity. The function of the saccule is not entirely clear, and in fish it is believed by some
to still be a vibratory (sound?) receptor.

The vestibular organs contain an *otolithic membrane* lying over the
hair cells which is free to move about somewhat as a function of gravity.
Such movement stimulates the hair cells, especially as a result of linear
movement of the head. Both the utricle and saccule also contain tiny
calcareous crystals, up to 14 microns in diameter in mammals, called
otoliths. Associated with the otolithic membrane, these little stones are
perhaps able to move about in the viscous endolymph and presumably
elicit responses from delicate hair cells attached to the walls of the chambers. Thus the semicircular canals provide a primary response to rotation,
while the utricle and saccule indicate linear movement.

Nerve fibers from the delicate hair cells combine and leave the labyrinth by way of the vestibular portion of the VIIIth cranial nerve. One major branch arises from each of the three ampullae, one branch comes from the utricle, two from the saccule, and a seventh (Oort's nerve) from the cochlea. The vestibular fibers number about 19,000 and make up roughly half of the VIIIth nerve, the other half being auditory fibers from the basilar membrane of the cochlea.

Balance and Equilibrium

The vestibular apparatus is of extreme importance in maintaining balance and equilibrium. The ability of a cat to right itself in midair upon being dropped is a function of the reflexive vestibular reaction alone. Even in complete darkness a cat will succeed in righting itself unless the vestibular organs have been destroyed, in which case it will land in a heap, with no attention to top or bottom.

Over 130 years ago Flourens showed that a bird with damage to just one of the three canals will not fly voluntarily, and if forced to fly his behavior is crude and uncoordinated, and he quickly descends. The removal of all three canals on one side leaves an animal unable to even maintain a standing position.

In the normal adult human, much of the balance/equilibrium function is also a result of vision and the numerous proprioceptive and kinesthetic impulses constantly bombarding the brain. With a poorly performing vestibular apparatus, one can survive, but closing the eyes can result in loss of balance and general disorientation. For immediate, automatic, reflexive awareness of bodily position, the inner-ear mechanism is essential. In addition, damage to the inner ear, or disorders resulting from serious infections, can produce nausea, extreme dizziness, and even changes in heart beat and blood pressure.

Eye Movements

Reflexive relationships between the vestibular apparatus and the positioning of the eyes have been well established, although not worked out in complete detail. As a result of feedback from the vestibular apparatus, as well as proprioceptive and visual stimuli, eye movements to maintain fixation tend to be quite automatic and comparatively effortless. Such involuntary movements often result in a phenomenon called *nystagmus*, reflexive eye movements, generally in the horizontal plane.

One method of studying nystagmus is to rotate a blindfolded subject in a chair at a constant speed. When the rotation is stopped, horizontal eye movements may be observed. A primary nystagmus may be observed, followed by a long-lasting secondary nystagmus in the opposite direction.

There are usually slow sweeping movements followed by rapid, saccadiclike movements, the cycle repeating itself perhaps many times, depending on the original angular velocity and duration. Nystagmus apparently results from the involuntary, reflexive adjustments arising from the interaction of the various "senses" of motion and position. The eyes make an adjustment; having overadjusted they return, but then overadjust in the opposite direction until finally a point of neutral or balanced enervation is reached.

The association between nystagmus and such organismic symptoms as dizziness and nausea is certainly recognized, although the cause-and-effect relations are not always evident. It is said that performers who must spin rapidly on their vertical axes, such as ice skaters and dancers, thus causing the visual scene to rotate raipdly about them, have a unique way of preventing the ill effects of nystagmus. They allegedly fixate, for an instant, a stationary object as they spin past it, allowing one fixation per revolution, thus avoiding the rotary pursuit movements of the eye which, if not eliminated, apparently contribute to nystagmus and, in many cases subsequent dizziness.

Many persons have studied nystagmus in considerable detail and the matter is much too complex and controversial to be treated in depth here. The interested reader is encouraged to read the Wendt reference and the pertinent bibliographical entries at the end of it.

Motion Sickness

Motion sickness is an interesting, albeit unpleasant phenomenon arising largely from activity of the vestibular apparatus. Producing nausea, headache, sweating, and feelings of muscular weakness, the disorder may persist after termination of the motion and last in some cases for several days. In general, slow, vertical movements and movements in several planes at once are most effective in producing motion sickness. There also is a psychological factor, both of expectation which may enhance the effect and habituation which may ultimately result in its nonexistence. Visual activity, too, also plays a role in motion sickness, as might be expected, since the relation between the vestibular apparatus and reflexive eye movements is so intimate. That motion sickness is largely a result of vestibular activity is evidenced by the fact that some deaf individuals who lack vestibular sensitivity do not become motion-sick.

Results of Vestibular Damage

Surgical removal of the entire labyrinth or cutting of the VIIIth nerve may or may not produce profound effects. In lower animals the effects seem to be much more serious than in man. Bilateral destruction in the case of the pigeon results in violent movements and an inability to maintain an upright posture. After several days some recovery occurs, probably through use of proprioceptors and visual senses. Although it can still stand and walk, albeit unsteadily, the animal does not fly or even feed itself.

The effects in mammals are much less striking. Unsteadiness in standing, head tremors, and impaired movements may result, but nothing as severe as found in the case of the lower animals.

Deaf people are often lacking in their vestibular response. According to Wendt, about 20 percent of deaf people lack all vestibular response. Such people have somewhat impaired equilibrium, but not severe enough to handicap them noticeably. In Ménière's disease, the vestibular nerve is sometimes sectioned, thus eliminating the vestibular function entirely. Patients, especially if the disease was severe, appear to get along much better with no vestibular function than with a diseased one.

SUMMARY

In this final chapter we examined the remaining sense organs, those of an organic, reflexive nature, frequently lying deep within the body. We considered them under four, general, arbitrary classes: the subcutaneous senses, such as the deep pressure sense mediated by the Pacinian corpuscle; the visceral senses, evoked by mechanical and chemical means; proprioception and its dependency on movement and pressure, and the vestibular sense, mediated by the semicircular canals and the otolith organs of the inner ear. With respect to these various organs we considered briefly their structure, functioning, and their significance for human behavior.

SUGGESTED READINGS

1. Wendt, G. R., "Vestibular Functions," in S. S. Stevens (ed.), *Handbook of Experimental Psychology* (New York: Wiley, 1951). This chapter from the Stevens handbook is probably the best moderate length description of vestibular functions of which I am aware. Its 33 pages include a particularly excellent bibliography of over 200 entries. It is a relatively difficult reading, including a considerable amount of detail. For the serious student it should prove to be a valuable source of information.
2. From C. G. Mueller, *Sensory Psychology* (Englewood Cliffs, N.J.: Prentice-Hall, 1965). Chapter 8 of this previously cited reference covers the vestibular and kinesthetic senses. The 12 pages are quite easy to read and provide a treatment somewhat different from what we have presented. It is recommended for the general reader as a source of additional information.

3. From W. L. Jenkins, "Somesthesis," in S. S. Stevens (ed.), *Handbook of Experimental Psychology* (New York: Wiley, 1951). There are four pages in this reference which do justice to the topic of this chapter. Pages 1184–1188 include excellent, short descriptions of deep sensitivity, kinesthesis, and internal or organic sensitivities. A reference as short as this, and at the same time so well presented, is a must reading for the serious student.
4. Neff, W. D., "Studying Proprioception," in T. G. Andrews (ed.), *Methods of Psychology* (New York: Wiley, 1948). This 30-page chapter is more than just methodology. While methodology is indeed covered adequately, the reference includes valuable information on structure, physiology, and general functioning of the proprioceptive senses which are defined so as to include kinesthesis and the vestibular function. This is very worthwhile reading. Its age should not seriously detract from its value for the interested student.
5. From S. H. Bartley, *Principles of Perception,* 2d ed. (New York: Harper, 1969). Chapter 13 includes 24 well-written pages which elaborate on the material we have just covered. For additional general material, of a somewhat more technical nature, this reference is highly recommended.

BIBLIOGRAPHY

Alder, J., "Chemoreceptors in Bacteria," *Science* 166 (1969): 1588–97.
Adrian, E. D., *The Physical Background of Perception.* London: Oxford University Press, 1947.
Allison, V. C., and S. H. Katz, "An Investigation of Stenches and Odors for Industrial Purposes," *J. Industr. Eng. Chem.* 11 (1919): 336–38.
Alpern, M., M. Lawrence, and D. Wolsk, *Sensory Processes.* Belmont, Calif.: Brooks/Cole Publishing Company, 1967.
Amoore, J. E., J. W. Johnston, Jr., and M. Rubin, "The Stereo-Chemical Theory of Odor," *Scientific American,* February, 1964.
Andreas, B. G., *Experimental Psychology.* New York: John Wiley & Sons, Inc., 1960.
Andrews, T. G. (ed.), *Methods of Psychology.* New York: John Wiley & Sons, Inc., 1948.
Arbib, M., *Brains, Machines and Mathematics.* New York: McGraw-Hill Book Company, 1964.
Arey, L. B., *Developmental Anatomy,* 7th ed. Philadelphia: W. B. Saunders Company, 1965.
Attneave, F., *Application of Information Theory to Psychology.* New York: Holt, Rinehart and Winston, Inc., 1959.
Barlow, H. B., and J. M. B. Sparrock, "The Role of After-images in Dark Adaptation, " *Science* 144 (1964): 1309–14.
Bartley, S. H., *Vision.* New York: D. Van Nostrand Company, Inc., 1941.
————, "The Psychophysiology of Vision," in S. S. Stevens (ed.), *Handbook of Experimental Psychology.* New York: John Wiley & Sons, Inc., 1951.
————, *Principles of Perception.* 2d ed. New York: Harper & Row, Publishers, 1969.
Beck, L. H., "Osmics: Theory and Problems Related to the Initial Effects in Olfaction," in O. Glasser (ed.), *Medical Physics.* Chicago: Year Book Publishers, 1950.
————, and W. R. Miles, "Some Theoretical and Experimental Relation-

ships between Infra-red Absorption and Olfaction," *Science* 106 (1947): 511.

Beidler, L. M., "Dynamics of Taste Cells," in Y. Zotterman (ed.), *Olfaction and Taste*. New York: The Macmillan Company, 1963.

Békésy, G. von, "Current Status of Theories of Hearing," *Science* 123 (1956): 779–83.

———, "The Ear," *Scientific American*, August 1957.

———, "Similarities Between Hearing and Skin Sensations," *Psychol. Rev.* 66 (1959): 1–22.

———, *Experiments in Hearing*. Trans. and edited by E. G. Wever. New York: McGraw-Hill Book Company, 1960.

———, and W. A. Rosenblith, "The Early History of Hearing—Observations and Theories," *J. Acoust. Soc. Amer.* 20 (1948): 727–48.

———, "The Mechanical Properties of the Ear," in S. S. Stevens (ed.), *Handbook of Experimental Psychology*. New York: John Wiley & Sons, Inc., 1951.

Bell, D. W., and G. Fairbanks, "TTS Produced by Low-Level Tones and the Effects of Testing on Recovery," *J. Acoust. Soc. Amer.* 35 (1963): 1725–31.

Beranek, L. L., "The Design of Speech Communication Systems," *Proc. Inst. Radio Engrs.* 35 (1947): 880–90.

———, *Acoustic Measurements*. New York: John Wiley & Sons, Inc., 1949.

———, *Acoustics*. New York: McGraw-Hill Book Company, 1954.

———, "Revised Criteria for Noise in Buildings," *Noise Control* 3 (1957): 186–88.

Bird, C., "Maturation and Practice: Their Effects upon the Feeding reaction of Chicks," *J. Comp. Psychol.* 16 (1933): 212–34.

Blackwell, H. B., and O. M. Blackwell, "Rod and Cone Mechanisms in Typical and Atypical Congenital Achromatopsia," *Vision Research* 1 (1961): 62–107.

Bolt, R. H., S. J. Lukasik, A. W. Nolle, and A. D. Frost, *Handbook of Acoustic Noise Control*, Volume I. *Physical Acoustics*. WADC-TR-52-40, Wright Air Development Center, Ohio, 1952.

Boring, E. G., "The Sensations of the Alimentary Canal," *Amer. J. Psychol.* 26 (1915): 1–57.

———, "The Thermal Sensitivity of the Stomach," *Amer. J. Psychol.* 26 (1915): 484–94.

———, *Sensation and Perception in the History of Experimental Psychology*. New York: Appleton-Century-Crofts, Inc., 1942.

———, *A History of Experimental Psychology*. 2d ed. New York: Appleton-Century-Crofts, Inc., 1950.

Börnstein, W. S., "Cortical Representation of Taste in Man and Monkey, Volume II. *Yale J. Biol. Med.* 13 (1940): 133–56.

Boyd, I. A., and T. D. M. Roberts, "Proprioceptive Discharges from the Stretch Receptors in the Knee Joint of the Cat," *J. Physiol.* 122 (1953): 38–58.

Brindley, G. S., *The Physiology of the Retina and Visual Pathway*. London: Edward Arnold, Publishers Ltd., 1960.

———, "Afterimages," *Scientific American*, October 1963.

Brink, F., Jr., "Excitation and Conduction in the Neuron," in S. S. Stevens (ed.), *Handbook of Experimental Psychology*. New York: John Wiley & Sons, Inc., 1951.

Brown, C. W., and E. E. Guiselli, *Scientific Method in Psychology*. New York: McGraw-Hill Book Company, 1965.

Buddenbrock, M. von, *The Senses*. Ann Arbor: University of Michigan Press, 1958.

Burtt, H. E., *The Psychology of Birds*. New York: The Macmillan Company, 1967.

Cameron, A. T., "The Taste Sense and the Relative Sweetness of Sugars and Other Sweet Substances," Scientific Report Series No. 9, Sugar Research Foundation, 1947.

Chapanis, A., "The Dark Adaptation of the Color Anomalous Measured with Lights of Different Hues," *J. Gen. Physiol.* 30 (1947): 423–37.

Cherry, C., *On Human Communications*. N. Y.: John Wiley & Sons, Inc., 1957.

Christman, R. J., "Figural After-effects Utilizing Apparent Movement as Inspection-Figure," *Amer. J. Psychol.* 66 (1953): 66–72.

———, "Shifts in Pitch as a Function of Prolonged Stimulation with Pure Tones," *Amer. J. Psychol.* 67 (1954): 484–91.

———, "The Perception of Direction as a Function of Binaural Temporal and Amplitude Disparity," in G. Finch and F. Cameron (eds.), *Air Force Human Engineering, Personnel, and Training Research*. Baltimore: Air Research and Development Command, 1956.

———, "Noise Reduction in Air Force Control Towers," *Noise Control* 5 (1959): 24–29.

———, "Person-to-Person Communication in an Atmosphere-Free Environment," in D. P. LeGalley (ed.), *Bioastronautics and Electronics, and Invited Addresses*. Proceedings of the Fifth Symposium on Ballistic Missiles and Space Technology. New York: Academic Press, Inc., 1960.

———, and W. E. Williams, "Influence of the Time Interval on Experimentally Induced Shifts in Pitch," *J. Acoust. Soc. Amer.* 35 (1963): 1030–33.

Cohen, J., and D. A. Gordon, "The Prevost-Fechner-Benham subjective colors," *Psychol. Bull.* 46 (1949): 97–136.

Committee on Colorimetry of the Optical Society of America, *The Science of Color*. New York: Thomas Y. Crowell Company, 1953.

Corning, W. C., and M. Balaban (eds.), *The Mind: Biological Approaches to its Functions.* New York: John Wiley & Sons, Inc., 1968.

Cornsweet, Tom N., *Visual Perception.* New York: Academic Press, 1970.

Corso, J. F., *The Experimental Psychology of Sensory Behavior.* New York: Holt, Rinehart and Winston, Inc., 1967.

Crafts, L. W., T. C. Schneirla, and R. W. Gilbert, *Recent Experiments in Psychology.* 2d ed. New York: McGraw-Hill Book Company, 1950.

Crocker, E. C., *Flavor.* New York: McGraw-Hill Book Company, 1945.

————, and L. F. Henderson, "Analysis and Classification of Odors," *Amer. Perfum.* 22 (1927): 325–356.

Crombie, A. C., "Early Concepts of the Senses and the Mind," *Scientific American,* May 1964.

Crozier, W. J., "Regarding the Existence of the Common Chemical Sense in Vertebrates," *J. Comp. Neurol.* 26 (1916): 1–8.

Cruze, W. W., "Maturation and Learning in Chicks," *J. Comp. Psychol.* 19 (1935): 371–409.

Dallenbach, K. M., "A Bibliography of the Attempts to Identify the Functional End-Organs of Cold and Warmth," *Amer. J. Psychol.* 41 (1929): 344–78.

Dartnall, H. J. A., *Visual Pigments.* New York: John Wiley & Sons, Inc., 1957.

Davis, H., "Psychophysiology of Hearing and Deafness," in S. S. Stevens (ed.), *Handbook of Experimental Psychology,* New York: John Wiley & Sons, Inc., 1951.

————, "The Excitation of Nerve Impulses in the Cochlea," *Ann. Otol. Rhinol. Laryngol.* 61 (1954): 469–81.

————, and S. R. Silverman (eds.), *Hearing and Deafness.* New York: Holt, Rinehart and Winston, 1970.

————, et al., "Final Report on Physiological Effects of Exposure to Certain Sounds," OSRD Report 889, Harvard University, 1944.

Davson, H. (ed.), *The Eye.* New York: Academic Press, Inc., 1962.

De Beer, Sir G., *Embryos and Ancestors,* 3d ed. Oxford: Clarendon Press, 1958.

De Lange, H., "Research into the Dynamic Nature of the Human Fovea-Cortex System with Intermittent and Modulated Light," *J. Opt. Soc. Am.* 48 (1958): 777–84.

De Lorenzo, A. J., "Studies on the Ultrastructure and Histophysiology of Cell Membranes, Nerve Fibers, and Synaptic Junctions in Chemoreceptors," in Y. Zotterman (ed.), *Olfaction and Taste.* New York: The Macmillan Company, 1963.

De Valois, R. L., "Analysis and Coding of Color Vision in the Primate Visual System," *Cold Spring Harbor Symposium on Quantitative Biology* 30 (1965): 567–79.

De Vries, H., and M. Stuiver, "The Absolute Sensitivity of the Human Sense of Smell," in W. A. Rosenblith (ed.), *Sensory Communications.* New York: John Wiley & Sons, Inc., 1961.

Dennis, W. (ed.), *Readings in the History of Psychology.* New York: Appleton-Century-Crofts, Inc., 1948.

Dethier, V. G., *The Physiology of Insect Senses.* New York: John Wiley & Sons, Inc., 1963.

Du Verney, J. G., *Traité de l'organe de l'ouie.* Paris, 1683.

Egan, J. P., "Articulation Testing Methods II," OSRD Rpt. 3802, Contract OEMsr-658, Psycho-Acoustic Lab., Harvard University, 1944.

———, "Articulation Testing Methods," PNR-36, Contract N5ori-76, ONR, Psycho-Acoustic Lab., Harvard University, 1947.

———, "Articulation Testing methods," *Laryngoscope* 58 (1948): 955–91.

———, A. I. Schulman, and G. Z. Greenberg, "Operating Characteristics Determined by Binary Decisions and by Ratings," *J. Acoust. Soc. Amer.* 31 (1959): 768–73.

———, and F. M. Wiener, "On the Articulation Efficiency of Bands of Speech in Noise," *J. Acoust. Soc. Amer.* 18 (1946): 435–41.

Eisner, T., R. E. Silberglied, D. Aneshansley, J. E. Carrel, and H. C. Howland, "Ultraviolet Video-Viewing: the Television Camera as an Insect Eye," *Science* 166 (1969): 1172–74.

Elsberg, C. A., E. D. Brewer, and I. Levy, "Concerning Conditions Which may Temporarily Alter Normal Olfactory Acuity," *Bull. Neurol. Inst. New York* 4 (1935): 31–34.

———, and I. Levy, "A New and Simple Method of Quantitative Olfactometry," *Bull. Neurol. Inst. New York* 4 (1935): 5–19.

Evans, R. M., *An Introduction to Color.* New York: John Wiley & Sons, Inc., 1948.

Fitzhugh, R., "The Statistical Detection of Threshold Signals in the Retina," *J. Gen. Physiol.* 40 (1957): 925–48.

Fletcher, H., *Speech and Hearing.* New York: D. Van Nostrand Company, Inc., 1929.

———, "Auditory Patterns," *Rev. Mod. Phys.* 12 (1940): 47–65.

———, *Speech and Hearing in Communications.* New York: D. Van Nostrand Company, Inc., 1953.

———, and W. A. Munson, "Loudness, its Definition, Measurement, and Calculation," *J. Acoust. Soc. Amer.* 5 (1933): 82–108.

Forgus, R. H., *Perception.* New York: McGraw-Hill Book Company, 1966.

French, J. D., "The Reticular Formation," in J. Field (ed.), *Handbook of Physiology,* Vol. II. Washington, D.C.: American *Physiological Society,* 1960.

French, N. R., and J. C. Steinberg, "Factors Governing the Intelligibility of Speech Sounds,"*J. Acoust. Soc. Amer.* 19 (1947): 90–120.

Frey, M. von, "Beitrage zur Sinnesphysiologie des· Haut," *Ber Sächs Ges Wiss Leipzig Math-Phys Cl.* 47 (1895): 166–84.

———, and A. Goldman, "Der zeitliche Verlauf der Einstellung bei den Druckempfindungen," *Z. Biol.* 65 (1915): 183–202.

Frisch, K. von, *The Dance Langage and Orientation of Bees.* Cambridge: Harvard University Press, 1967.

Fulton, J. F., *Howell's Textbook of Physiology.* Philadelphia: W. B. Saunders Company, 1947.

Galambos, R., "Neural Mechanisms of Audition," *Physiol. Rev.* 34 (1954): 497–528.

Gamble, E. M., "The Applicability of Weber's Law to Smell," *Amer. J. Psychol.* 10 (1898): 82–142.

Garner, W. R., and G. A. Miller, "The Masked Threshold of Pure Tones as a Function of Duration," *J. Exptl. Psychol.* 37 (1947): 293–303.

Geldard, F. A., *The Human Senses.* New York: John Wiley & Sons, Inc., 1953.

———, "Adventures in Tactile Literacy," *Amer. Physiol.* 12 (1957), 115–24.

Gibson, E. J., and R. D. Walk, "The Visual Cliff," *Scientific American,* April 1960.

Gibson, J. J., *The Perception of the Visual World.* Boston: Houghton Mifflin Company, 1950.

———, "Observations of Active Touch," *Psychol. Rev.* 69 (1962): 477–91.

———, "The Useful Dimensions of Sensitivity," *Amer. Psychol.* (1963): 1–15.

———, *The Senses Considered as Perceptual Systems.* Boston: Houghton Mifflin Company, 1966.

Gibson, K. S., *Spectrophotometry.* Washington, D.C.: National Bureau of Standards, Circular 484, 1949.

Gilmer, B. von Haller, "The Glomus Body as a Receptor of Cutaneous Pressure and Vibration," *Psychol. Bull.* 39 (1942): 73–79.

———, "The Relation of Cold Sensitivity to Sweat Duct Distribution and the Neurovascular Mechanism of the Skin," *J. Psychol.* 13 (1942): 307–25.

Glickstein, M., "Organization of the Visual Pathways," *Science* 164 (1969): 917–25.

Gorman, A. L. F., and J. S. McReynolds, "Hyperpolarizing and Depolarizing Receptor Potentials in the Scallop Eye," *Science* 165 (1969): 309–10.

Gottlieb, F. J., *Developmental Genetics.* New York: Reinhold Publishing Corporation, 1966.

Graham, C. H., "Visual Perception," in S. S. Stevens (ed.), *Handbook of Experimental Psychology.* New York: John Wiley & Sons, Inc., 1951.

———, "Color Theory," in S. Koch (ed.), *Psychology: a Study of a Science.* Volume I. New York: McGraw-Hill Book Company, 1959.

—— (ed.), *Vision and Visual Perception.* New York: John Wiley & Sons, Inc., 1965.

Granit, R., *Receptors and Sensory Perception.* New Haven: Yale University Press, 1955.

Green, B. F., *Digital Computers in Research.* New York: McGraw-Hill Book Company, 1954.

Green, D. M., "Psychoacoustics and Detection Theory," *J. Acoust. Soc. Amer.* 32 (1960): 1189–1203.

——, and J. A. Swets, *Signal Detection and Psychophysics.* New York: John Wiley & Sons, Inc., 1966.

Gregory, R. L., "Eye Movements and the Stability of the Visual World," *Nature* 182 (1958): 1214.

——, *Eye and Brain, The Psychology of Seeing.* New York: McGraw-Hill Book Company, 1966.

——, and O. L. Zangwill. "The Origin of the Autokinetic Effect," *Quart. J. Exptl. Psychol.* 15 (1963): 4.

Gross, C. G., and H. P. Zeigler (eds.), *Readings in Physiological Psychology: Neurophysiology/sensory Processes.* New York: Harper & Row, Publishers, 1969.

Grossman, S. P., *A Textbook of Physiological Psychology.* New York: John Wiley & Sons, Inc., 1967.

Guilford, J. P., *Psychometric Methods.* New York: McGraw-Hill Book Company, 1936.

——, *Psychometric Methods.* 2d ed. New York: McGraw-Hill Book Company, 1954.

Haagen-Smit, A. J., "Smell and Taste." *Scientific American,* March, 1952.

Haber, R. N. (ed.), *Contemporary Theory and Research in Visual Perception.* New York: Holt, Rinehart and Winston, Inc., 1968.

——, *Information-Processing Approaches to Visual Perception.* New York: Holt, Rinehart and Winston, Inc., 1969.

Hahn, H., "Die Psycho-physischen Konstanten und Variablen des Temperatursinnes," *Z. Sinnesphys.* 60 (1930): 198–232.

——, "Die Adaptation des Geschmacksinnes," *Z. Sinnesphysiol.* 65 (1934): 105–45.

——, G. Kuckulies, and H. Taeger, "Eine systematische Untersuchung der Geschmacksschwellen," *Z. Sinnesphysiol.* 67 (1938): 259–306.

Ham, A. W., *Histology,* Philadelphia: J. B. Lippincott Company, 1950.

Hansen, R., and W. Langer, "Über Geschmacksveränderungen in der Schwangerschaft," *Klin. Wschr.* 14 (1935): 1173–76.

Hardy, J. D., and T. W. Oppel, "Studies in Temperature Sensation III: The Sensitivity of the Body to Heat and the Spatial Summation of the End Organ Responses," *J. Clin. Invest.* 16 (1937): 533–40.

————, H. G. Wolff, and H. Goodell, "Studies on Pain: An Investigation of Some Quantitative Aspects of the Dol Scale of Pain Intensity," *J. Clin. Invest.* 27 (1948): 380–86.

Hardy, M., "Observations on the Innervation of the Macula Saculi in Man," *Anat. Rec.* 59 (1934): 403–18.

Hartline, H. K., "Visual Receptor and Retinal Interaction," *Science* 164 (1969): 270–78.

Hartline, H. K., and C. H. Graham, "Nerve Impulses from Single Receptors in the Eye," *J. Cellular Comp. Physiol.* 1 (1932): 277–95.

Hartline, H. K., and R. Ratliff, "Inhibitory Interaction of Receptor Units in the Eye of Limulus," *J. Gen. Physiol.* 40 (1957): 357–76.

Hawkins, J. E., Jr., and S. S. Stevens, "The Masking of Pure Tones and of Speech by White Noise," *J. Acoust. Soc. Amer.* 22 (1950): 6–13.

Hecht, S. "Rods, Cones and the Chemical Basis of Vision," *Physiol. Rev.* 17 (1937): 239–90.

————, C. Haig, and A. M. Chase, "Influence of Light Adaptation on Subsequent Dark Adaptation of the Eye," *J. Gen. Physiol.* 20 (1937): 831–50.

————, and S. Shlaer, "Intermittent Stimulation by Light. V: The Relation Between Intensity and Critical Frequency for Different Parts of the Spectrum," *J. Gen. Physiol.* 19 (1936): 965–77.

————, and M. H. Pirenne, "Energy Quanta and Vision," *J. Gen. Physiol.* 25 (1942): 819–40.

Helmholtz, H. L. von, *Sensations of Tone.* A. J. Ellis, (trans.) New York: Longmans, Green and Company, 1930.

Henning, H., *Der Geruch.* 2d ed. Leipzig: Barth, 1924.

Hinde, R. A., *Animal Behavior*, New York: McGraw-Hill Book Company, 1966.

Hirsh, I. J., *The Measurement of Hearing.* New York: McGraw-Hill Book Company, 1952.

————, E. G. Reynolds, and M. Joseph, "Intelligibility of Different Speech Materials," *J. Acoust. Soc. Amer.* 26 (1954): 530–39.

Holst, E. von, "Relation between the Central Nervous System and the Peripheral Organs," *Brit. J. Anim. Beh.* 2 (1954): 89.

Hornbostel, E. M. von, and M. Wertheimer, Über die Wahrnehmung der Schallrichtung," *Akad. Wiss.*, Berlin (1920): 288–96.

Huggins, W. H., and J. C. R. Licklider, "Place Mechanisms of Auditory Frequency Analysis," *J. Acoust. Soc. Amer.* 23 (1951): 290–99.

Jeffres, L. A., "A Place Theory of Sound Localization," *J. Comp. Physiol. Psychol.* 41 (1948): 35–39.

Jenkins, W. L., "Nafe's Vascular Theory and the Preponderance of Evidence," *Amer. J. Psychol.* 52 (1939): 462–65.

———, "Studies in Thermal Sensitivity: 17. The Topographical and Functional Relations of Warm and Cold," *J. Exptl. Psychol.* 29 (1941): 511–16.

———, "Somesthesis," in S. S. Stevens (ed.), *Handbook of Experimental Psychology.* New York: John Wiley & Sons, Inc., 1951.

Journal of the Acoustical Society of America, "Békésy Commemorative Issue," *J. Acoust. Soc. Amer.* 34 (1962): 1319–1533.

Judd, D. B., "Chromaticity Sensibility to Stimulus Differences," *J. Opt. Soc. Amer.* 22 (1932): 72–108.

———, *Colorimetry.* Washington, D.C.: National Bureau of Standards Circular No. 478 (1950).

———, "Basic Correlates of the Visual Stimulus," in S. S. Stevens (ed.), *Handbook of Experimental Psychology.* New York: John Wiley & Sons, Inc., 1951.

———, and G. Wyszecki, *Color in Business, Science and Industry.* 2d ed. New York: John Wiley & Sons, Inc., 1963.

Kellicott, W. E., *Outlines of Chordate Development.* New York: Henry Holt and Company, 1934.

Kelly, K. L., "Color Designations for Lights," *J. Research* (National Bureau of Standards) 31 (1943): 271.

Kennedy, D., "Inhibition in Visual Systems," *Scientific American,* July 1963.

Kistiakowsky, G. B., "On the Theory of Odors," *Science* 112 (1950): 154–55.

Klemm, ·O., "Untersuchungen über die Lokalisation von Schallreizen. Über den Einfluss des binauralen Zeitunterschiedes auf die Lokalisation," *Arch. Ges. Psychol.* 40 (1920): 117–46.

Koch, S. (ed.), *Psychology: a Study of a Science.* Volume I. New York: McGraw-Hill Book Company, 1959.

Köhler, W., and H. Wallach, "Figural After-Effects: An Investigation of Visual Processes," *Proc. Amer. Philos. Soc.* 88 (1944): 269–357.

Kryter, K. D., "Speech Communications in Noise," AFCRC-TR-54-52, Air Force Cambridge Research Center, USAF, Washington, D.C., 1955.

———, "On Predicting the Intelligibility of Speech from Acoustical Measurements," *J. Speech Hearing Disorders* 21 (1956): 208–17.

Lashley, K. S., and J. T. Russell, "The Mechanism of Vision: A Preliminary Test of Innate Organization," *J. Genetic Psychol.* 45 (1934): 136–44.

Lawrence, M., "Hearing," in M. Alpern, M. Lawrence, and D. Wolsk, *Sensory Processes.* Belmont, Calif.: Brooks/Cole Publishing Company, 1967.

Le Grand, Y., *Light, Color and Vision.* Trans. by R. W. G. Hunt. New York: John Wiley & Sons, Inc., 1957.

Lettvin, J. Y., H. R. Maturana, W. S. McCulloch, and W. H. Pitts, "What the Frog's Eye Tells the Frog's Brain," *Proc. Inst. of Radio Eng.* 47 (1959): 1940–50.

Lewis, T., *Pain*. New York: The Macmillan Company, 1942.

Lewison, L., *You and Your Eyes*. New York: Trinity Publishing Company, 1960.

Licklider, J. C. R., "Basic Correlates of the Auditory Stimulus," in S. S. Stevens (ed.), *Handbook of Experimental Psychology*. New York: John Wiley & Sons, Inc., 1951.

———, "Auditory Frequency Analysis," in E. C. Cherry (ed.), *Information Theory*. London: Butterworth Scientific Publications, 1956.

———, "Three Auditory Theories," in S. Koch (ed.), *Psychology: A Study of a Science*. Volume I. New York: McGraw-Hill Book Company, 1959.

———, and N. Guttman, "Masking of Speech by Line-Spectrum Interference," *J. Acoust. Soc. Amer.* 29 (1957): 287–96.

Loewenstein, W. R., "Biological Transducers," *Scientific American*, August 1960.

Lucretius, *The Nature of the Universe*. Trans. by R. E. Latham. New York: Penguin Books, 1951.

Lukasik, S. J., and W. W. Nolle (eds.), *Handbook of Acoustic Noise Control, Supplement 1 to Volume 1, Physical Acoustics*. WADC-TR-52-204. Dayton, Ohio: Wright Air Development Center, 1955.

Lüscher, E., and J. Zwislocki, "The Decay of Sensation and the Remainder of Adaptation after Short Pure-Tone Impulses on the Ear," *Acta otolaryng* (Stockholm) 35 (1947): 428–45.

MacLean, P. D., "Studies on the Limbic System ("Visceral Brain") and Their Bearing on Psychosomatic Problems," in E. D. Wittkover and R. A. Cleghorn (eds.), *Recent Developments in Psychosomatic Medicine*. Philadelphia: J. B. Lippincott Company, 1954.

MacNichol, E. F. Jr., "Three-Pigment Color Vision," *Scientific American*, December 1964.

Maier, N. R. F., and T. C. Schneirla, *Principles of Animal Psychology*. New York: McGraw-Hill Book Company, 1935.

Manner, H. W., *Elements of Anatomy and Physiology*. Philadelphia: W. B. Saunders Company, 1963.

———, *Elements of Comparative Vertebrate Embryology*, New York: The Macmillan Company, 1964.

Marks, W. B., W. H. Dobelle, and E. F. MacNichol, Jr., "Visual Pigments of Single Primate Cones," *Science* 143 (1964): 1181–83.

Masland, R. H., "Visual Motion Perception: Experimental Modification," *Science* 165 (1969): 819–21.

Mason, E., *Internal Perception and Bodily Functioning*. New York: International Universities Press, 1961.

Mavor, J. W., and H. W. Manner, *General Biology*. 6th ed. New York: The Macmillan Company, 1966.

Mayer, C. L., *Sensation: The Origin of Life*. Yellow Springs, Ohio: Antioch Press, 1961.

Mayer-Gross, W., and J. W. Walker, "Taste and Taste Selection of Food in Hypoglycemia," *Brit. J. Exp. Path.* 27 (1946): 297–305.

Mazokhin-Porshnyakov, G. A., *Insect Vision*. New York: Plenum Press, 1969.

Mellon, DeForest, Jr., *The Physiology of Sense Organs*. San Francisco: W. H. Freeman and Company, 1968.

Miller, G. A., *Language and Communication*. New York: McGraw-Hill Book Company, 1951.

———, "The Magical Number Seven, Plus or Minus Two: Some Limits on Our Capacity for Processing Information," *Psychol. Review* 63 (1956): 81–97.

Miller, W. H., R. Ratliff, and H. K. Hartline, "How Cells Receive Stimuli," *Scientific American*, September 1961.

Mills, A. W., "On the Minimum Audible Angle," *J. Acoust. Soc. Amer.* 30 (1958): 237–46.

Milne, L., and M. Milne, *The Senses of Animals and Man*. New York: Atheneum Press, 1962.

Moncrief, R. W., *The Chemical Senses*. New York: John Wiley & Sons, Inc., 1946.

Montagna, W., *The Structure and Function of Skin*. New York: Academic Press, Inc., 1962.

———, "The Skin," *Scientific American*, February 1965.

Morgan, C. T., *Physiological Psychology*. 3d ed. New York: McGraw-Hill Book Company, 1964.

———, J. S. Cook, III, A. Chapanis, and M. W. Lund (eds.), *Human Engineering Guide to Equipment Design*. New York: McGraw-Hill Book Company, 1963.

Mueller, C. G., *Sensory Psychology*. Englewood Cliffs, N.J.: Prentice-Hall, Inc., 1965.

Munn, N. L., *Psychological Development*. Boston: Houghton Mifflin Company, 1938.

Murphy, M. R., and G. E. Schneider, "Olfactory Bulb Removal Eliminates Mating Behavior in the Male Golden Hamster," *Science* 167 (1970): 302–3.

Nafe, J. P., and W. L. Jenkins, "On the Vascular Theory of Warmth and Cold," *Amer. J. Psychol.* 51 (1938): 763–69.

———, and D. R. Kenshalo, "Somesthetic Senses," *Annual Rev. Psychol.* 13 (1962): 201–24.

————, and K. S. Wagoner, "The Experiences of Warmth, Cold and Heat," *J. Psychol.* 2 (1936): 421–31.

————, and K. S. Wagoner, "The Nature of Pressure Adaptation," *J. Gen. Psychol.* 25 (1941): 323–51.

Nakayama, J., J. S. Eisenmann, and J. D. Hardy, "Single-Unit Activity of Anterior Hypothalamus during Local Heating," *Science* 134 (1961): 560–61.

Neff, W. D., "Studying Proprioception," in T. G. Andrews (ed.), *Methods of Psychology.* New York: John Wiley & Sons, Inc., 1948.

Nimeroff, I., *Colorimetry.* Washington, D.C.: National Bureau of Standards, Monograph 104, 1968.

Ochs, S., *Elements of Neurophysiology.* New York: John Wiley & Sons, Inc., 1964.

Olds, J., "Self-Stimulation of Hippocampus in Rats," *J. comp. Physiol. Psychol.* 61 (1966): 353–59.

Optical Society of America, Committee on Colorimetry, *The Science of Color.* New York: Thomas Y. Crowell Company, 1953.

Parker, G. H., and E. M. Stabler, "On Certain Distinctions between Taste and Smell," *Amer. J. Physiol.* 32 (1913): 230–40.

Patten, B. M., *Human Embryology.* Philadelphia: The Blakiston Company, 1946.

Peele, T. L., *The Neuroanatomical Basis for Clinical Neurology.* 2d ed. New York: McGraw-Hill Book Company, 1961.

Peterson, A. P. G., and L. L. Beranek, *Handbook of Noise Measurement.* 3d ed. Cambridge, Mass.: General Radio Company, 1956.

————, and E. E. Gross, Jr., *Handbook of Noise Measurement.* 6th ed. West Concord, Mass.: General Radio Company, 1969.

Peterson, W. W., T. G. Birdsall, and W. C. Fox, "The Theory of Signal Detectability," *IRE Trans.* PGIT-4 (1954): 171–212.

Pfaffman, C., "Taste and Smell," in S. S. Stevens (ed.), *Handbook of Experimental Psychology.* New York: John Wiley & Sons, Inc., 1951.

————, "The Pleasures of Sensation," *Psychol. Rev.* 67 (1960): 253–68.

————, and J. K. Bare, "Gustatory thresholds in normal and adrenalectomized rats," *J. Comp. Physiol. Psychol.* 43 (1950): 320–24.

Pfeiffer, J., and the editors of *Life, The Cell.* New York: Time, Inc., 1964.

Pickett, J. M., and K. D. Kryter, "Prediction of Speech Intelligibility in Noise," AFCRC-TR-55-4. Washington, D.C.: Air Force Cambridge Research Center, USAF, 1955.

Pierce, R. R., and E. E. David, Jr., *Man's World of Sound.* New York: Doubleday and Company, 1958.

Pirenne, M. H., *Vision and the Eye.* London: Chapman and Hall, Ltd., 1967.

————, and F. H. C. Marriott, "The Quantum Theory of Light and the Psycho-Physiology of Vision," in S. Koch (ed.), *Psychology: a Study of a Science.* Volume I. New York: McGraw-Hill Book Company, 1959.

Pollack, I., "Effects of High Pass and Low Pass Filtering upon Intelligibility of Bands of Speech in Noise," *J. Acoust. Soc. Amer.* 20 (1948): 259–66.

Polyak, S. L., *The Retina.* Chicago: University of Chicago Press, 1941.

Postman, L., and J. P. Egan, *Experimental Psychology: an Introduction.* New York: Harper & Row, Publishers, 1949.

Potter, R. K., G. A. Kopp, and H. C. Green, *Visible Speech.* New York: D. Van Nostrand Company, Inc., 1947.

Rasmussen, A. T., *Outlines of Neuro-anatomy.* 3d ed. Dubuque, Iowa: Wm. C. Brown Company, 1943.

Raven, C. P., *An Outline of Developmental Physiology.* Trans. by L. D. Ruiter, New York: McGraw-Hill Book Company, 1954.

Richter, C. P., "Self-Regulating Functions," *Harvey Lectures,* 38 (1942): 63–103.

Riesen, A. H., "Arrested Vision," *Scientific American,* July 1950.

Riesz, R. R., "Differential Intensity Sensitivity of the Ear for Pure Tones," *Phys. Rev.* 31 (1928): 867–75.

Rose, J. E., and V. B. Mountcastle, "Touch and Kinesthesis," in J. Fields (ed.), *Handbook of Physiology.* Vol. I. Washington, D.C.: American Physiological Society, 1959.

Rosenblith, W. A. (ed.), *Sensory Communication.* New York: John Wiley & Sons, Inc., 1962.

————, K. N. Stevens, and staff of Bolt, Beranek, and Newman, *Handbook of Acoustic Noise Control.* Volume II: *Noise and Man.* WADC-TR-52-204. Wright Air Development Center, Ohio, 1953.

Ruch, T. C., "Sensory Mechanisms," in S. S. Stevens (ed.), *Handbook of Experimental Psychology.* New York: John Wiley & Sons, Inc., 1951.

Rushton, W. A. H., "The Difference Spectrum and Photosensitivity of Rhodopsin in the Living Human Eye," *J. Physiol.* 134 (1956): 11–29.

————, "Rhodopsin Measurement and Dark-Adaptation in a Subject Deficient in Cone Vision," *J. Physiol.* 156 (1961): 193–205.

————, *Visual Pigments in Man.* Liverpool: Liverpool University Press, 1962.

————, "Color Blindness and Cone Pigments," *Amer. J. Optom.* 41 (1964): 265–82.

Sauer, E. G. F., "Celestial Navigation by Birds," *Scientific American,* August 1958.

Schneider, D., "Electrophysiological Investigation of Insect Olfaction," in Y. Zotterman (ed.), *Olfaction and Taste.* New York: The Macmillan Company, 1963.

Schouten, J. F., "The Perception of Pitch," *Philips Tech. Rev.* 5 (1940): 286–94.

Scott, W. A., and M. Wertheimer, *Introduction to Psychological Research.* New York: John Wiley & Sons, Inc., 1962.

Shaxby, J. H., and F. H. Gage, "The Localization of Sounds in the Median Plane," *Med. Res. Council Spec. Rept.*, Series No. 166. London: 1932.

Shepard, J. F., and F. S. Breed, "Maturation and Use in the Development of an Instinct," *J. Anim. Behav.* 3 (1913); 274–85.

Sherrington, C. S., *The Integrative Action of the Nervous System.* New Haven, Conn.: Yale University Press, 1947.

Shower, E. G., and R. Biddulph, "Differential Pitch Sensitivity of the Ear," *J. Acoust. Soc. Amer.* 3 (1931); 275–87.

Sidowski, J. B. (ed.), *Experimental Methods and Instrumentation in Psychology.* New York: McGraw-Hill Book Company, 1966.

Sivian, L. J., and S. D. White, "On Minimum Audible Sound Fields," *J. Acoust. Soc. Amer.* 4 (1933), 288–321.

Smelser, G. K. (ed.), *The Structure of the Eye.* New York: Academic Press, Inc., 1961.

Steinberg, J. C., H. C. Montgomery, and M. B. Gardner, "Results of the World's Fair Hearing Tests," *J. Acoust. Soc. Amer.* 12 (1940): 291–301.

Stevens, S. S., "The Volume and Intensity of Tones," *Amer. J. Psychol.* 46 (1934): 397–408.

―――, "The Attributes of Tones," *Proc. Nat. Acad. Sci.* 20 (1934): 457–59.

―――, "Tonal Density," *J. Exptl. Psychol.* 17 (1934): 585–92.

―――, "A Scale for the Measurement of a Psychological Magnitude: Loudness," *Psychol. Rev.* 43 (1936): 405–16.

――― (ed.), *Handbook of Experimental Psychology,* New York: John Wiley & Sons, Inc., 1951.

―――, "Measurement of Loudness," *J. Acoust. Soc. Amer.* 27 (1955): 815–29.

―――, "The Direct Estimate of Sensory Magnitudes: Loudness," *Amer. J. Psychol.* 69 (1956): 1–25.

―――, "Calculating Loudness," *Noise Control* 3 (1957): 11–22.

―――, "On the Psychophysical Laws," *Psychol. Rev.* 64 (1957): 153–81.

―――, "The Psychophysics of Sensory Function," in W. A. Rosenblith (ed.), *Sensory Communication.* New York: John Wiley & Sons, Inc., 1961.

―――, and H. Davis, *Hearing: Its Psychology and Physiology.* New York: John Wiley & Sons, Inc., 1938.

―――, and J. Volkmann, "The Relation of Pitch to Frequency," *Amer. J. Psychol.* 53 (1940): 329–53.

———, J. Volkmann, and E. B. Newman, "A Scale for the Measurement of the Psychological Magnitude Pitch," *J. Acoust. Soc. Amer.* 8 (1937): 185–90.

———, F. Warshofsky, and the editors of *Life, Sound and Hearing.* New York: Time, Inc., 1965.

Stiles, W. S., "The Directional Sensitivity of the Retina and the Spectral Sensitivity of the Rods and Cones," *Proc. Roy. Soc. Ser. B.* 127 (1939): 64–105.

———, and B. H. Crawford, "The Luminous Efficiency of Rays Entering the Eye Pupil at Different Points," *Proc. Roy. Soc. Ser. B.* 112 (1933): 428–50.

Subcommittee on Vision and its Disorders, National Advisory Neurological Diseases and Blindness Council, *Vision and its Disorders.* NINDB Monograph No. 4. Bethesda, Md.: U.S. Department of Health, Education and Welfare, 1967.

Swets, J. A., "Indices of Signal Dectability Obtained with Various Psychophysical Procedures," *J. Acoust. Soc. Amer.* 31 (1959): 511–13.

———, "Is There a Sensory Threshold?," *Science* 134 (1961): 168–77.

——— (ed.), *Signal Detection and Recognition by Human Observers.* New York: John Wiley & Sons, Inc., 1964.

———, W. P. Tanner, Jr., and T. G. Birdsall, "Decision Processes in Perception," *Psychol. Rev.* 68 (1961): 301–40.

Tanner, W. P., Jr., "Physiological Implications of Psychophysical Data," *Annals of the New York Academy of Sciences* 89 (1961): 752–65.

———, J. A. Swets, and D. M. Green, "Some General Properties of the Hearing Mechanism," Technical Report No. 30, Electronic Defense Group, University of Michigan, Ann Arbor, Mich., 1956.

Tansley, K., *Vision in Vertebrates.* London: Chapman & Hall, Ltd., 1965.

Tavolga, W. N., *Principles of Animal Behavior.* New York: Harper & Row, Publishers, 1969.

Teevan, R. C., and R. C. Birney (eds.), *Color Vision: Selected Readings.* Princeton, N.J.: D. Van Nostrand Company, Inc., 1961.

Thurlow, W. R., and A. M. Small, Jr., "Pitch Perception for Certain Periodic Auditory Stimuli," *J. Acoust. Soc. Amer.* 27 (1955): 132–37.

Thurstone, L. L., "Psychophysical Methods," in T. G. Andrews (ed.), *Methods of Psychology.* New York: John Wiley & Sons, Inc., 1948.

Torrey, T. W., *Morphogenesis of the Vertebrates.* New York: John Wiley & Sons, Inc., 1962.

Townsend, J. C., *Introduction to Experimental Methods.* New York: McGraw-Hill Book Company, 1953.

Underwood, B. J., *Experimental Psychology,* 2d ed. New York: Appleton-Century-Crofts, Inc., 1966.

Underwood, H., and M. Menaker, "Photoperiodically Significant Photo-reception in Sparrows: is the Retina Involved?," *Science* 167 (1970): 298–301.

Van Bergeijk, W. A., J. R. Pierce, and E. E. David, Jr., *Waves and the Ear*. New York: Doubleday Anchor Books, 1960.

Waddington, C. H., *Principles of Embryology*. New York: The Macmillan Company, 1960.

Wald, G., "Eye and Camera," *Scientific American,* August 1950.

———, "On the Mechanism of Visual Threshold and Visual Adaptation," *Science* 119 (1954): 887–92.

———, "The Receptors of Human Color Vision," *Science* 145 (1964): 1007–17.

———, and P. K. Brown, "Human Rhodopsin," *Science* 127 (1958): 222–26.

Warren, R. M., and R. P. Warren, *Helmholtz on Perception*. New York: John Wiley & Sons, Inc., 1968.

Wegel, R. L., and C. E. Lane, "The Auditory Masking of One Pure Tone by Another and Its Probable Relation to the Dynamics of the Inner Ear," *Phys. Rev.* 23 (1924): 266–85.

Weintraub, D. J., and E. L. Walker, *Perception*. Belmont, Calif.: Brooks/Cole Publishing Company, 1966.

Weiss, P., *Principles of Development*. New York: Henry Holt and Company, 1939.

Wendt, G. R., "Vestibular Functions," in S. S. Stevens (ed.), *Handbook of Experimental Psychology*. New York: John Wiley & Sons, Inc., 1951.

Wever, E. G., *Theory of Hearing*. New York: John Wiley & Sons, Inc., 1949.

———, and C. W. Bray, "Action Currents in the Auditory Nerve in Response to Acoustical Stimulation," *Proc. Nat. Acad. Sci.* 16 (1930): 344–50.

———, and C. W. Bray, "The Perception of Low Tones and the Resonance-Volley Theory," *J. Psychol.* 3 (1937): 101–14.

———, and M. Lawrence, *Physiological Acoustics*. Princeton, N.J.: Princeton University Press, 1954.

Wilson, M., and the editors of *Life*, *Energy*. New York: Time, Inc., 1963.

Witschi, E., *Development of Vertebrates*, Philadelphia: W. B. Saunders Company, 1956.

Wolsk, D., "Chemical Sensitivity," in M. Alpern, M. Lawrence, and D. Wolsk, *Sensory Processes*. Belmont, Calif.: Brooks/Cole Publishing Company, 1967.

———, "The Internal Environment," in M. Alpern, M. Lawrence, and D. Wolsk, *Sensory Processes*. Belmont, Calif.: Brooks/Cole Publishing Company, 1967.

Wood, A. B., *A Textbook of Sound*. New York: The Macmillan Company, 1955.

Woodrow, H., and B. Karpman, "A New Olfactometric Technique and Some Results," *J. Exptl. Psychol.* 2 (1917): 431–47.

Woodworth, R. S., *Experimental Psychology*. New York: Henry Holt and Company, 1938.

———, and H. Schlossberg, *Experimental Psychology*. Rev. ed. New York: Holt, Reinhart and Winston, Inc., 1954.

Woolridge, D. E., *The Machinery of the Brain*. New York: McGraw-Hill Book Company, 1963.

Wright, W. D., *Researches on Normal and Defective Colour Vision*. London: Henry Kimpton, 1946.

———, "The Characteristics of Tritanopia," *J. Opt. Soc. Am.* 42 (1952): 509–21.

Zigler, M. J., "Pressure Adaptation-Time: a Function of Intensity and Extensity," *Amer. J. Psychol.* 44 (1932): 709–20.

———, and A. H. Holway, "Differential Sensitivity as Determined by the Amount of Olfactory Substance," *J. Gen. Psychol.* 12 (1935): 272–82.

Zotterman, Y. (ed.), *Olfaction and Taste*. New York: The Macmillan Company, 1963.

Zwaardemaker, H., *Die Physiologie des Geruchs*. Leipzig: Engelmann, 1895.

Zwicker, E., G. Flottrop, and S. S. Stevens, "Critical Bandwidth in Loudness Summation," *J. Acoust. Soc. Amer.* 29 (1957): 548–57.

INDEXES

NAME INDEX

SUBJECT INDEX